Why Socks Disappear in the Wash

AND OVER 250 OTHER MOMENTS OF SCIENCE

Don Glass

BARNES & NOBLE

NEW YORK

CONTENTS

PREFACE

The short essays contained in this book are adapted from the scripts for the radio series *A Moment of Science*. The series of two-minute radio programs was conceived by Paul Singh, professor of physics at Indiana University, and produced and distributed by WFIU, the university's public radio station. Dr. Singh served as the science producer, and Don Glass produced the radio programs.

The intent of the programs was to present the relevancy of scientific findings in a manner that was clear, concise, and unintimidating. Unnecessary jargon was avoided, and the material was presented so that it could be understood and appreciated without prior scientific knowledge.

Since its national debut in 1988, listeners to *A Moment of Science* have regularly asked for transcripts of the programs. It seemed that a logical step would be to prepare a selection for publication.

All of the original scripts in this volume were written by Stephen Fentress. He wrote each program so that it would be an enjoyable diversion which would move the listener to think, "Wow, that's neat!" and go tell somebody about it. We have removed some on-the-air business and updated a few items, but otherwise we present this material as it was broadcast.

We purposely have not grouped the scripts by scientific area, because we wanted to maintain that little element of surprise as the reader moves from one to the next. The short format of the radio programs was based on the premise that people have limitless curiosity, but limited time. That applies to this book as well: each selection is self-contained, so you can read one or a dozen at a time, depending on how much time you have.

If after reading these *Moments of Science* you have a little better understanding of the world around you, then our goal has been achieved.

Don Glass and Paul Singh
Bloomington, Indiana

ACKNOWLEDGMENTS

Without the cooperation of the administration and scientific community of Indiana University, neither the radio series nor this book would have been possible.

Funding, of course, is critical to any undertaking, and for that we thank the Dean's Incentive Fund of the College of Arts and Sciences, the Office of Research and Graduate Development, the Office of the Vice-President of the Bloomington campus as well as the Office of the Chancellor, the Office of the President of the University, and the Indiana University Radio and Television Services.

We express our sincere appreciation to the scientists who generously gave of their time by checking the copy for scientific accuracy. Those who helped with this series include Barry Aprison, Biology; Alan Backler, Teaching Resources Center; Tom Blumenthal, Biology; John Castellan, Psychology; James Craig, Psychology; David Easterling, Geography; Guy Emery, Physics; John Ewing, Mathematics; Daniel Knudsen, Geography; Harold Ogren, Physics; David Parkhurst, Public and Environmental Affairs; William Popkin, Law; Robert Port, Linguistics; Elizabeth Raff, Biology; Rudolf Raff, Biology; Steven Russo, Chemistry; and Eugene Weinberg, Medical Sciences and Biology.

Benjamin Franklin and the Swatches on the Snow

In a letter written in 1761, Benjamin Franklin tells how he collected some little squares of broadcloth, tailor's samples of different colors: black, dark blue, light blue, green, purple, red, yellow, and white. He wanted to demonstrate that these colors would absorb different amounts of light from the sun and convert the light to different amounts of heat.

On a bright winter day, when the ground was blanketed with freshly fallen snow, Franklin laid the cloth squares on the snow, in the sun, and left them for a few hours. When he came back, he saw that the black square had sunk deeper into the snow than any of the others. The dark blue cloth had sunk a little less, and the white square not at all. Each of the other squares had melted its way down to some in-between depth.

Even two hundred years ago, people knew that dark-colored things get warmer in the sun than light-colored things. But Franklin's little experiment demonstrated it scientifically by comparing cloth samples that were all the same except for one thing: color.

The dyes in the samples absorbed different amounts of sunlight. The black cloth got the warmest because it absorbed all the colors of the sunlight and reflected almost none—that's why it looked black. The white cloth stayed the coolest; it reflected all the colors of the sunlight and absorbed very little light. The red cloth absorbed some of the sunlight and warmed to a medium temperature, but it reflected red light to the eye and looked red. And so on for the other colors.

Benjamin Franklin did other experiments, especially with electricity, and even speculated about whether flies drowned in wine could be brought back to life. But that's another story.

N. G. Goodman, ed., *The Ingenious Dr. Franklin: Selected Scientific Letters of Benjamin Franklin* (1931; Philadelphia: University of Pennsylvania Press, 1974), p. 181.

Once You've Had It, You Can't Catch It Again

The human body fights infection by recognizing the invader. Suppose the invader is a virus. Viruses are a threat because they take over living cells and use the machinery inside to make more viruses. This wrecks the cells.

But before a virus reaches a cell, it may run into an antibody. Antibodies are giant molecules, shaped a little like twisted coat hangers. Your body has about a million different types of antibodies. An antibody fits its corresponding virus like a key in a lock.

When an antibody attaches to a virus, it may spoil the virus's ability to invade cells. Or the antibody may simply put a chemical tag on the virus that says, in effect, "White blood cells, please destroy me."

Once the invading virus is recognized, mass production of the corresponding antibody begins. It takes a few days, but if the body can make antibodies faster than the virus can make viruses, the viruses lose and the body gets well. The disease AIDS, by the way, represents a failure of this system.

After the body gets well, what's left? White blood cells, mopping up. Unused antibodies. And memory cells that save the recipe for the antibody just used. If the same virus ever returns, it will be defeated much faster the next time. That's why you don't get chicken pox again. "Howdy, viruses," your immune system says. "You're only a stranger here once."

N. K. Jerne, "The Immune System," *Scientific American*, July 1973.
Helena Curtis, *Biology*, 4th ed. (New York: Worth, 1983).

Why is the sky blue?

Why is the sky blue? It can't be that the atmosphere has a blue color like the blue of a tinted windshield. In that case, going outside in the daytime would be like walking around inside a blue glass bottle, with a blue sun shining blue light everywhere, and blue stars and a blue moon at night.

The blue can't be from dust, because the air over gravel parking lots and quarries is whitish, not bluish.

The blue can't be the result of water droplets. Clouds are made of water droplets, and clouds are white. It's not a matter of relative humidity, either; a dry sky over Arizona can be just as blue as a humid sky over Minnesota.

Blue is not the color of outer space. The background of space is black. So, the sky is black at night—it's blue only during the daytime, when the sun is shining on the atmosphere.

The sun shines with all the colors of the rainbow—blue, yellow, red, and all the rest—mixed together to make white light. The reds and yellows pass through air easily, but some of the blue portion of sunlight is scattered in every direction by air molecules. When you look to the sky on a clear day, you see blue light scattered from sunbeams by molecules of nitrogen, oxygen, and carbon dioxide.

The more air, the more scattering. In early morning and late afternoon, the sun's light passes through so much air that most of the blue has been scattered away by the time the light reaches you. The reds and yellows remain and the sun looks reddish.

Marcel Minnaert, *The Nature of Light and Colour in the Open Air* (New York: Dover, 1954).

Richard P. Feynman, *The Feynman Lectures on Physics* (Reading, Mass.: Addison-Wesley, 1964), vol. I, chap. 32.

Static Electricity

Static electricity reveals the nature of the so-called electrical force, one of the basic forces of the universe.

In some ways the electrical force is like the force of gravity. Electrical and gravitational forces get stronger if the interacting particles get closer, and weaker if they get farther apart. Actually, the electrical force is about a billion billion billion billion times stronger than gravity at the same distance.

Unlike gravity, which always pulls things together, the electrical force can pull particles together or push them apart, depending on the so-called charges of the particles. Electrical charges can be positive or negative. Like charges repel; opposites attract. Positive and negative charges attract, but two positives or two negatives repel each other. (Incidentally, some elementary particles, such as neutrons, have no electrical charge.)

Electricity holds atoms together. The nucleus at the center of every atom has a positive charge; the electrons surrounding the nucleus have negative charges, so they stay nearby. In most objects the positive and negative charges are exactly equal in number, so the net charge is zero.

Sometimes, though, everyday objects pick up a few extra electrons or lose a few electrons. When that happens, the object has a net static charge—static in the sense that those displaced electrons stay where they are, rather than flowing as a current. A charged object, like a bed sheet coming out of a clothes dryer, exerts noticeable electrical forces on other objects—like socks in the same load.

Richard P. Feynman, *The Feynman Lectures on Physics* (Reading, Mass.: Addison-Wesley, 1964), vol. II, chap. 1.

A. D. Moore, "Electrostatics," *Scientific American*, March 1972.

WHY ONE ROTTEN APPLE CAN SPOIL THE BARREL

If you buy green, underripe lemons or bananas, you can make them ripen faster by keeping them in a paper bag.

Chinese growers used to ripen fruit by keeping it in a room with burning incense.

In the West, farmers used to "cure" fruit with kerosene stoves.

What's behind all these processes is a gas called ethylene. Ethylene comes from burning fuels like kerosene, and it's made naturally by all parts of a plant at one time or another. Ethylene stimulates germination of the seed, flowering, ripening of fruit, dropping of fruit, and dropping of leaves. The ethylene produced by ripe fruit will stimulate another nearby fruit to ripen. So there's a chemical basis for the proverb about one rotten apple spoiling the whole barrel.

Ethylene is used in commercial agriculture to stimulate the ripening of bananas, tomatoes, and citrus fruits and to help give them the colors people expect.

Fruit shippers usually want to stop the ripening process, so they store fruit in rooms that have ethylene chemically removed from the air.

Incidentally, farmers at one time thought that it was the heat from a kerosene stove that was ripening their fruit. But those who tried modern non-kerosene heaters didn't get the results they wanted. It wasn't 'the heat that was "curing" the fruit—it was the ethylene.

"Ethylene," in *McGraw-Hill Encyclopedia of Science and Technology* (New York: McGraw-Hill, 1987).

Frank B. Salisbury and Cleon W. Ross, *Plant Physiology*, 3rd ed. (Belmont, Calif.: Wadsworth, 1985).

Superconductors

Superconductors are materials that are radically different from ordinary materials. Superconductors conduct electric current with absolutely no resistance. Ordinary materials, including the metals we use to make wires in electrical appliances, offer some resistance to electric current. That's why electrical appliances get warm.

Thousands of metals and alloys and other materials are known to be capable of superconductivity—if the material is chilled to a temperature of about 450 degrees below zero Fahrenheit. That takes a fancy refrigerator. So superconductors have remained in the world of esoteric laboratory experiments since their discovery in 1911.

Until now, that is. In the last couple of years, materials have been found that don't have to be at 450 below to superconduct—they'll do it at 240 below. Still cold, but not nearly as cold as before.

Now the world's laboratories are competing to find some workable material that will superconduct at ordinary room temperature. Room-temperature superconductors could be used to make electric motors that would never overheat, power lines that would transmit 100 percent of the power from utility to customer, magnetic levitated trains, and superfast computers, among other things.

But today, experiment is ahead of theory in superconductivity. No one knows exactly how superconductors work. So no one knows how to discover better superconductors, except by trial and error.

"Superconductivity: The State That Came in from the Cold," *Science* 239:367 (January 22, 1988).

"The 1987 Nobel Prize for Physics," *Science* 238:481 (October 23, 1987).

"More Superconductivity Questions Than Answers," *Science* 237:249 (July 17, 1987).

Does smoking cause lung cancer?

People who smoke tend to die of lung cancer more often than people who don't smoke. Does that mean that smoking causes lung cancer? Government reports on smoking and cancer mention five criteria for judging whether statistics prove a cause-and-effect relationship.

First: were the researchers who came up with the statistics biased, or could they have made some mistake? It takes several different studies, done by different people, at different times, in different places, using different methods, but reaching the same conclusions, to imply that the link between smoking and cancer is real.

Second: is the lung cancer death rate among smokers definitely greater than that among non-smokers, or is the difference so small that it could be a peculiarity of the group selected for the study?

Third: have the researchers figured in the possibility that something other than smoking—maybe heredity or smog—could be causing some of the cancer?

Fourth: does the smoking consistently happen before the lung cancer?

Fifth: does the idea that smoking causes lung cancer seem plausible in light of what's already known about smoking and about cancer?

As you can tell from the Surgeon General's warning on cigarette packs, the Public Health Service has concluded that smoking causes lung cancer. Eight long-term studies and dozens of smaller studies indicate that smokers are about ten times more likely to die of lung cancer than non-smokers—twenty or thirty times more likely in the case of heavy smokers. Lung tissue in people and animals starts to change after exposure to tobacco—and changes back after the tobacco is taken away.

U.S. Department of Health and Human Services, *Health Consequences of Smoking: Report of the Surgeon General—Cancer* (1982).

U.S. Department of Health, Education, and Welfare, *The Health Consequences of Smoking: A Reference Edition* (1976).

What is a gene?

Consider the iris of the eye of a brown-eyed person. The color of the iris is one of the few inherited traits basically unaffected by diet and climate.

A brown iris is made of cells that contain brown pigment. The cells contain brown pigment because the genes in the nucleus of each cell told it to make brown pigment. A cell runs like an automated factory controlled by a computer program. If the computer program tells the factory to make brown pigment, the factory makes brown pigment. If the genes in a cell tell that cell to make brown pigment, the cell makes brown pigment.

Genes are made of a substance in the nucleus of a cell—nucleic acid, deoxyribonucleic acid, the famous DNA. Molecules of DNA take the form of fine strands. Every strand is made of smaller molecules connected end to end. There are millions of these smaller molecules in one strand, but they come in only four varieties. The four varieties of smaller molecules can be assembled in any order, like letters in a four-letter alphabet. A DNA strand is like a book written in a four-letter alphabet, with the text run together in one long line.

This book has different chapters. One chapter—or maybe several—carries the chemical formula for making brown pigment. Those chapters, those small sections of the DNA strand, are the genes for brown eye color.

"Genetics and Heredity," in *Encyclopaedia Britannica*, 15th ed.

"Eye Color," in Victor A. McKusick, *Mendelian Inheritance in Man: Catalogue of Autosomal Dominants, Autosomal Recessives, and X-Linked Phenotypes*, 4th ed. (Baltimore: Johns Hopkins University Press, 1975).

WHY DO CATS' EYES GLOW AT NIGHT?

You're driving along a lonely road at night. Ahead, in the dark, you see a pair of bright, disembodied eyes. You get closer and the eyes slip away into the grass—the eyes of a prowling cat.

The cat's eyes shine because your eyes, your car's headlights, and the cat's eyes are nearly in a straight line. The light from your headlights, or the sound from your engine, attracts the attention of the cat toward your car. The cat focuses its eyes on your headlights. In each of the cat's eyes, the lens brings the light from your headlights to a sharp focus, making a distinct image on the retina like the image on film in a camera.

But the light goes both ways. Some of it is reflected from the cat's retina back out through the lens of the eye. At night, the pupil of the cat's eye is wide open, so a lot of light goes through. The reflected light forms a narrow beam aimed at your car, because that's where the cat is looking. You look into the beam and get the weird impression that the eyes are shining by their own light. The impression is even more weird if you can't see the rest of the cat.

You can see the same glow in the eyes of rabbits that look up from their nighttime grazing to watch your car go by. And you can see it in the eyes of people in snapshots taken at evening parties. Anyone looking at the camera when the flash goes off has red eyes in the picture. The red comes from the color of the human retina. (This is easy to demonstrate with a model of an eye. Put a lens over a hole in a box whose depth is about the same as the focal length of the lens [the focal length should be marked on the metal barrel of the lens, e.g., 50mm]; stand at a distance and shine a flashlight beam on the box.)

But there's more. Cats have a special layer of tissue in their eyes that reflects light something like a metallic surface. It is located just behind the special cells in the retina that convert light to nerve impulses—the rod and cone cells. The apparent function of this reflecting layer is to make the cat's eye more efficient in dim light.

When light enters the cat's eye, some of it is absorbed by the rods and cones. But some light gets past the rods and cones and goes on to the back of the eye. The reflecting layer bounces this leftover light forward again, so it encounters the rods and cones a second time. Light entering a cat's eye has not one, but two chances to be detected by the cat.

Some light misses the rods and cones both times and leaves the cat's eye through the lens. That's the light we see as eyeshine. But because of this reflecting layer in the back of the eye, more light is used by the cat and less is wasted than if the reflecting layer weren't there.

Cats aren't the only animals that have reflective tissue in their eyes. Cattle, oxen, opossums, alligators, and some fishes are among the other animals that have it. We humans don't, and that's part of the reason we're not as good as cats at finding our way in the dark.

Marcel Minnaert, *The Nature of Light and Colour in the Open Air* (New York: Dover, 1954).

"Eye (Vertebrate)," in *McGraw-Hill Encyclopedia of Science and Technology* (New York: McGraw-Hill, 1987).

Stephen L. Polyak, *The Vertebrate Visual System* (Chicago: University of Chicago Press, 1957).

Paul Ehrlich, Dyes, and Drugs

A hundred years ago, clothes weren't available in nearly as many colors as they are now. But things were improving. Among the most exciting new chemical products of the nineteenth century were synthetic dyes, with names like mauve, amaranth, and Congo red.

A German medical student, Paul Ehrlich (1854–1915), was fascinated with what he learned about dyes in his anatomy classes in the 1870s. Just as some dyes stick to cotton but not to wool, some dyes stain only certain kinds of tissue, or certain parts of a cell, but not others. The dye methylene blue, for example, stains nerve cells but not other cells. So methylene blue highlights the nerve cells in a tissue specimen. There was what Ehrlich called a chemical affinity between the methylene blue and the nerve cells.

Now for Ehrlich's great leap of scientific imagination.

Maybe, he thought, a sick person or animal could be cured with a dye that would stick only to the bacteria causing the disease. If the right dye could be found and put into the bloodstream, it would attack the harmful bacteria like a magic bullet, leaving the regular cells untouched.

Ehrlich spent most of his career developing this idea. Early on, he found that the dye trypan red would cure South American horse disease. Later he developed the first safe and effective drug to treat syphilis in people.

Paul Ehrlich's work on the chemical affinity of dyes and his magic-bullet idea led all the way to sulfa drugs and other antibiotics still in use today.

Claude E. Dolman, "Paul Ehrlich," in *Dictionary of Scientific Biography* (New York: Charles Scribner's Sons, 1971).

Aaron J. Ihde, *The Development of Modern Chemistry* (New York: Harper and Row, 1964).

Alexander Findlay, *A Hundred Years of Chemistry* (Atlantic Highlands, N.J.: Humanities, 1965).

Of related interest: Allan M. Brandt, "The Syphilis Epidemic and Its Relation to AIDS," *Science* 239:375 (January 22, 1988).

Why you can never get to the end of the rainbow

It seems that anything as beautiful as a rainbow must lead to a wonderful place where it touches the ground. But if you've ever tried to approach a rainbow, you know that it recedes as you move toward it. The rainbow appears beyond that stand of trees, or over that next hill. When you move, the rainbow moves with you.

Sooner or later you realize that the end of the rainbow is not in any definite place you can mark on the map. No part of a rainbow is in any definite place, except in relation to your eye.

A rainbow is just a total of all the light coming to your eye from certain directions. The light from a rainbow is sunlight, reflected and broken into colors by water drops.

A rainbow always forms part of a circle, and the center of that circle is the point opposite the sun—from your point of view. The rule is that any water drops forty-two degrees of angle away from that point opposite the sun contribute to the rainbow you see.

Whether the water drops are ten feet away or ten miles away, they reflect light at that same angle and contribute to the same rainbow—for you. If you walk toward the end of the rainbow, it stays ahead of you as long as there are water drops in the air ahead of you.

Marcel Minnaert, *The Nature of Light and Colour in the Open Air* (New York: Dover, 1954).

H. Moysés Nussenzweig, "The Theory of the Rainbow," *Scientific American*, April 1977.

Robert Greenler, *Rainbows, Halos, and Glories* (New York: Cambridge University Press, 1980).

The difference between a square and a diamond

On red paper, trace the outline of a record album jacket, cut it out, and tape it to the wall with one side parallel to the floor. Everybody will say you have a square on your wall. The eye-brain combination is saying, in effect, "I see a shape with four equal sides and right angles at the corners. In school we called that a square. So I'm looking at a square."

Now take your red square and hang it by one corner. Bring in some new friends. They'll probably say you have a diamond on your wall. But a diamond also has four equal sides and right angles at the corners. Evidently the eye-brain combination looks at more than sides and angles; it says something like, "I see a four-sided shape with points on the top and bottom and sticking out of the sides. That's a diamond."

Now, with your diamond on the wall, tilt your head forty-five degrees and look. Your retina now has an image on it that's the same as the image of the red paper when you first hung it up. But it's still a diamond, not a square. Your earlier decision about what's top and what's bottom is still in effect, even though your head is still tilted.

So the task of judging a shape has at least two parts to it—the task of seeing sides and angles, and the task of assigning directions, such as top and bottom.

Sketch an outline of the continental United States, and turn the paper so the East Coast is down. If you show it to people without saying anything, how many will see a profile of Abraham Lincoln?

See Irvin Rock, "The Perception of Disoriented Figures," *Scientific American*, January 1974 (also bound in the *Scientific American* book *Recent Progress in Perception* [San Francisco: W. H. Freeman, 1976]).

Sounds over a Lake at Evening

Sometimes, standing by the lake shore or sitting in a rowboat just after sunset, you can hear voices from far away—real voices—with amazing clarity.

A good time to listen is just after sunset when the sky is clear and the wind calm. As night approaches, the water, no longer getting any sunlight, cools off. The cool water cools the air just above it. Meanwhile, a few dozen feet above the lake, the air not in contact with the water stays warmer.

A quarter of a mile away, someone speaks. The voice is carried by sound waves. You can think of a sound wave as an invisible wall of very slightly compressed air, traveling across the lake at the speed of sound.

But the speed of sound varies. Sound travels slightly faster in warm air than in cool air. The part of the invisible wall up in the warm air travels a little faster than the part down in the cool air near the water, so that the top gets ahead of the bottom. The invisible wall bends downward as it goes. Thus the sound of a distant voice is also bent downward. Less sound goes up into the sky at evening than at midday. Because of the cool surface air, evening sounds stay near the water and travel a long way—sounds of human voices, birds, bells, trains, motorboats, tape decks, and radios.

Joe R. Eagleman, *Meteorology: The Atmosphere in Action*, 2nd ed. (Belmont, Calif.: Wadsworth, 1985), chap. 13, "Atmospheric Optics and Acoustics."

Do THE BEST DOGS COME FROM THE POUND?

The best dog for someone else may not be the best dog for you. But there's something to the idea that a mutt from the animal shelter can give you the best of everything, including good health and good disposition. There's a principle of heredity at work.

A mutt is a dog whose parents are completely unrelated—they have no ancestor in common. Whatever undesirable genetic traits the parents may carry are likely to cancel each other out in the offspring.

On the other hand, if two parents are closely related—as brother and sister, for instance—if they have any recent ancestor in common, then each parent might have inherited a copy of the same bad gene from that common ancestor. If two dogs with the same bad gene now breed, some of the puppies will probably inherit two copies of that bad gene—and two copies are usually necessary for a genetic problem to show up. This can happen in puppy mills where incestuous matings are used to produce dogs in quantity for fast cash.

Responsible breeders breed only dogs whose ancestry they've checked out, looking for genetic problems. Responsible breeders also give their puppies individual care so the puppies learn to get along with people.

So some of the best dogs do come from the pound, and some of them come from top-notch breeders. Let the buyer beware of dogs from unscrupulous operators who use inbreeding for the sake of quantity, not quality.

The Monks of New Skete, *How to Be Your Dog's Best Friend* (Boston: Little, Brown, 1978).

Flip a Coin, Beat the Odds

In a hundred tosses of a coin, you expect about fifty heads. Ever tried it? Imagine: a kitchen table, a chance idle moment. Flip a penny. Heads.

Toss again. Heads again? Somewhat unusual. Two heads is only one of four possible results in two throws.

Heads again? There's only a one-in-eight chance of three heads in three tosses.

Heads a fourth time! You've beaten one-in-sixteen odds! Interesting. Keep flipping. Good luck.

Twenty heads in a row! No hidden magnets? The chance of twenty straight heads is about one in a million. Success breeds success, right?

Wrong, in the case of *honest* coin flips. No matter what happened before, your chance for heads next time is always fifty-fifty.

Ninety-nine tosses, ninety-nine heads! The chance of that is about one in six hundred billion billion billion. If you'd only known, you could be rich!

At this point, some people might say you're on a roll. Others, that you're due for a string of tails. Smart ones won't play. The chance of getting heads next time is still fifty-fifty.

Two hundred and ninety-nine heads in a row? The odds against that are about one with ninety zeros. Someone should see this—a TV reporter, a mathematician! Too late. The previous two hundred and ninety-eight throws are in the past—gone.

Happy tossing. But remember: honest coin flips are independent. Past performance has no bearing on future results.

The number of possible outcomes of n tosses of a coin is 2^n. Straight heads is only one of the 2^n possibilities. $2^{20} = 1.049 \times 10^6$; $2^{99} = 6.338 \times 10^{29}$; $2^{299} = 1.109 \times 10^{90}$.

Stroboscopic Stagecoach Wheels

Maybe you've noticed something odd in western movies that show a stagecoach leaving town. Even though the stagecoach is moving forward, sometimes the wheels seem to turn backward. The spokes seem to be going the wrong way.

To understand how this happens, remember that each second of movie film is really twenty-four pictures—or "frames," as they're called in the business—flashing onto the screen one after the other. Suppose that in the first frame there's a spoke on the stagecoach wheel that's in the twelve o'clock position, pointing straight up from the hub. By the next frame, the wheel will have turned a little. Now there may be a spoke in the eleven-fifty-nine position. It doesn't have to be the same spoke. In the third frame there might be a spoke photographed in the eleven-fifty-eight position; in the fourth frame, eleven-fifty-seven, and so on.

Since all the spokes look the same, when the pictures are run as a movie you see what looks like the same spoke moving from the twelve o'clock position, to eleven-fifty-nine, to eleven-fifty-eight, to eleven-fifty-seven, and so on. The wheel appears to turn backward.

There are variations on this as the stagecoach goes faster. The spokes appear to go backward, then forward, then backward, changing speed all the time: faster, then slower, then faster. The effect depends on where the spokes are when the camera catches them, and how each picture relates to the ones before and after. When the stagecoach gets going fast enough, each frame of the movie shows a blur instead of a clear image of spokes, and the illusion disappears.

If you don't like westerns, you can see the same effect in movies of propeller-driven airplanes starting their engines. The prop seems to go one way, then the other, always changing speed, until the effect disappears in a blur.

Marcel Minnaert, *The Nature of Light and Colour in the Open Air* (New York: Dover, 1954).

WHY ARE BELLS MADE OF METAL?

Why are bells made of metal? Or, to ask the question another way, why is metal a good material for bells?

Try a simple home experiment. Hold an ordinary stainless-steel kitchen table knife loosely between two fingers and tap it sharply with another knife. It rings like a bell.

When you tap on the knife, it flexes very slightly away from the place you tapped. Then it springs back. But here's the important part: the knife doesn't just spring back to its original shape. It springs back with so much energy that it overshoots and flexes the other way. And, having flexed the other way, the knife springs back yet again—with enough energy to overshoot the original position again, and flex the other way, again.

This flexing back and forth happens hundreds of times per second, and in a piece of the right kind of metal, it may go on for five or ten seconds or more. That's why metal is a good material for bells.

Each flex compresses the air near the knife. That's a sound wave. The rhythm of the flexing back and forth is regular, so the sound waves are regular and we hear a musical tone. In other words, the metal knife vibrates and makes a sound. A bell is a piece of metal in another shape doing the same thing.

Metal isn't the only kind of material that will ring like a bell. Glass also will do it. Some kinds of wood will ring for a short time—for example, the rosewood in xylophones and marimbas. Since these different materials share the property of ringing when struck, there must be something similar about the way the atoms in each material are held together.

Rodney Cotterrill, *The Cambridge Guide to the Material World* (New York: Cambridge University Press, 1985).

J. Bronowski, *The Ascent of Man*, book and video (Boston: Little, Brown, 1974).

Scientific American, September 1967.

Richard P. Feynman, *The Feynman Lectures on Physics* (Reading, Mass.: Addison-Wesley, 1964), vol. I, chap. 21.

Why RIVERS DON'T FLOW IN A STRAIGHT LINE

If a river has a chance, it will meander, winding over the land in a series of loops. Geologists even call the loops meanders.

You can see meanders on a map—along the lower Mississippi, the Alabama River near Selma, the Arkansas near Tulsa, the Ohio near Evansville, and on thousands of smaller streams, wherever there's a steady flow of water over nearly flat land of fine-textured soils.

Rivers meander because any small bend in a river tends to grow.

Water flowing around a bend in a river is a little like a car speeding around a bend in a road. The water is thrown toward the outside of the turn. That fast-moving water erodes the riverbank on the outside of the bend.

Meanwhile, on the inside of the bend, the water flows more slowly. Sediment held by the water can settle out and accumulate along the inside bank.

So the water eats away the outside of the bend while it builds up the inside of the bend. The bend in the river grows into a big loop.

When the loop gets big enough, the water cuts across the narrowest part of it and starts the meandering process all over again. The cut-off loop becomes an oxbow lake.

A meandering river often alters its course. Mark Twain, in his book *Life on the Mississippi,* says that steamboat pilots of his day traveled up and down the river even when they weren't working, just to keep track of the latest changes in the course of the water.

See Luna Leopold and W. B. Langbein, "River Meanders," *Scientific American,* June 1966.

John S. Shelton, *Geology Illustrated* (San Francisco: W. H. Freeman, 1966).

Wʜᴀᴛ's ʏᴏᴜʀ ᴀᴠᴇʀᴀɢᴇ sᴘᴇᴇᴅ?

Strange noises are coming from your car. You are five hundred miles from home, at your favorite vacation spot. The drive out here took eight hours, for an average speed of sixty-two and a half miles an hour—fast, but probably illegal.

Anyway, you get a mechanic to look your car over before you start for home. The mechanic announces, "You have a worn clutch, bad piston rings, and a dirty carburetor, among other problems. Your car has only five hundred miles left on it!

"Furthermore, you'll be able to leave my garage at sixty-two and a half miles an hour, but your car will slow down steadily. Your speed will decrease to zero just as you crawl into your driveway. Your trip home will take you sixteen hours. Your speed will average out to thirty-one and a quarter miles per hour."

This mechanic remembers his math from school.

"During the first eight hours of your sixteen-hour trip, you'll cover three hundred and seventy-five miles," he says. "During the last eight hours, you'll go only one-fourth as far—a hundred and twenty-five miles. During the last four hours, you'll go about thirty-one miles. During your last half-hour you'll have plenty of time to wave hello to the neighbors, because you'll go only half a mile!"

"Hmm—maybe I should fly home. There's a commuter flight that takes two hours."

"Better count on three hours at the airport here, and another three hours to get your luggage at the other end," the mechanic says.

"Gee, that's a total of eight hours—if I fly home, my average speed will be the same as if I had a good car! Maybe I can sell this one for scrap and get enough cash to buy a plane ticket."

THE BASIC UNIT OF LIFE

One of the most important unifying ideas in modern biology is that the cell is the basic unit of life. All living things are composed of one or more cells.

The basic role of cells has gradually become apparent since the invention of the microscope nearly four hundred years ago. Cells were seen first in plants; then the basic similarity between plant and animal cells was noticed; still later it became clear that new cells come only from other cells.

Biologists have been impressed by the similarity of cells, whether those cells come from oak trees or human beings. All cells are surrounded by a membrane that controls what gets into and out of the cell. All cells are chemical factories, taking in nutrients, making new substances, changing energy from one form into another, and eliminating wastes. All cells contain genetic information, coded in the form of molecules of deoxyribonucleic acid, the famous DNA.

Cells also contain strange relics of the distant past. Within the cells of algae, plants, and animals, there are little bodies that have their own DNA, their own genetic system, their own line of inheritance separate from the rest of the cell. These little objects go by the names of mitochondria and chloroplasts. Algae, plants, and animals, including us, have mitochondria in their cells; only algae and plants have chloroplasts. Mitochondria and chloroplasts are indispensable—they supply chemical energy to the rest of the cell. But in many ways they resemble bacteria living in the cell as guests. Evidence now indicates that those mitochondria and chloroplasts are, in fact, descendants of bacteria that lived independently a billion years ago.

C. P. Swanson and P. L. Webster, *The Cell*, 5th ed. (Englewood Cliffs, N.J.: Prentice-Hall, 1985).

Helena Curtis, *Biology*, 4th ed. (New York: Worth, 1983).

How Aspirin Got Its Name

The word "aspirin" was invented in Germany just before the turn of the century, at the chemical firm founded by Friedrich Bayer.

Felix Hoffmann, a staff chemist at Bayer, was studying the usefulness of salicylic acid, a substance that had been on the market for years as a food preservative. Hoffmann wondered whether it could be used as a drug. Chemicals related to salicylic acid were present in willow bark and oil of wintergreen, which had been used as traditional pain relievers.

Hoffmann tried giving pure salicylic acid to sick people. It relieved pain and reduced fever, but it was hard on the stomach. Hoffmann modified the pure acid by a process called acetylation, hoping that acetylated salicylic acid would be less upsetting but still effective. It was. Hoffmann had created a potential best-seller among drugs. But would the public swallow the name—acetylsalicylic acid?

One of Hoffmann's superiors at Bayer, Heinrich Dreser, had an idea. Dreser remembered that salicylic acid was also found in plants of the type known as spirea; in that form, the stuff was called spiric acid. Dreser combined "a" for "acetylated" with "spirin" for spiric acid to create the now-famous word "aspirin." That was in 1899, and that's how aspirin got its name.

Who knows what hard-to-pronounce scientific terms of today will be streamlined to become household words of tomorrow?

Carrie Dolan, "What Soothes Aches, Makes Flowers Last, and Grows Hairs? Aspirin, the Model-T of Drugs, Does All This and More; Fire Ants and Willow Bark," *Wall Street Journal*, February 19, 1988.

Carroll Hochwalt, "The Story of Aspirin," *Chemistry* 30(6):10 (1957).
Aaron J. Ihde, *The Development of Modern Chemistry* (New York: Harper and Row, 1964).

COLD WATER AT THE BOTTOM OF A LAKE

It's a warm summer morning, and you're standing in a freshwater lake with water up to your neck. You notice that your feet are colder than your shoulders. Cold water sinks, of course. But how much colder could the water be on the very bottom of the lake?

It depends on the lake—where it is, and how deep it is. But in a freshwater lake the coldest water at the bottom will not be colder than 39 degrees Fahrenheit.

Fresh water is denser at a temperature of 39 degrees than at any other temperature. Any 39–degree water in a lake will go to the bottom. Water that's warmer or colder than 39 degrees will float on top and be exposed to the weather.

So the water in a lake usually divides into layers according to temperature—except for two brief periods each year when the surface water temperature matches the deep water temperature. The temperatures match for a few days in spring as cold surface water is warmed up by the sun, and in fall when warm surface water cools off with the approach of winter. During those special times, called the spring turnover and the fall turnover, all the water in the lake has the same temperature.

Then, wind stirs the water, mixing oxygen and nutrients through the whole lake. For fish and other things living in a lake, those turnovers are among the year's biggest events.

Robert Leo Smith, *Ecology and Field Biology* (New York: Harper and Row, 1974).
George K. Reid, *Pond Life* (New York: Golden Press, 1987).

WHY DO WOMEN LIVE LONGER THAN MEN?

In the industrialized world, women live longer than men, on the average. And women live longer even though the game of life, if you want to call it that, starts with men in the lead.

It's estimated that at conception males outnumber females by about

115 to 100. In the months before birth, the male lead is reduced by miscarriages and stillbirths. At birth, males outnumber females by about 105 to 100.

By age thirty, males and females are about equal in number. After thirty, women pull ahead in the survival game. By age sixty-five, women outnumber men by about 120 to 100.

The complex reasons for this are just beginning to be figured out.

Men are more likely to die of heart disease, stroke, lung cancer, accidents, and homicide. Women tend to be sicker, but their diseases are less likely to be fatal—diseases like arthritis, lupus, and sinusitis.

Women seem to be protected from heart disease by their sex hormones, known as estrogens. Estrogens somehow keep the level of harmful blood cholesterol down. On the other hand, men's sex hormones, the androgens, tend to raise their harmful cholesterol levels. This jibes with the observation that while men have a big increase in their chance of heart disease during their forties, the increase doesn't hit women till after menopause.

All this is changing, though—in particular, more women are smoking now than decades ago. Maybe women won't outlive men so often in the future.

"Why Do Women Live Longer Than Men?" *Science* 238:158–160 (October 9, 1987).

A THIRTY PERCENT CHANCE OF RAIN

If a weather forecast includes a thirty percent chance of rain, what are we supposed to do—carry thirty percent of an umbrella?

A thirty percent chance of rain means that the weather forecasters have combined all their knowledge of the history and present state of the atmosphere and have concluded that out of a hundred days like this one, about thirty will have rain.

You'll notice that whether or not it actually rains today, the forecasters may still be right. Have they evaded responsibility by refusing to give a yes-or-no answer?

Not exactly. The forecasters have used the thirty percent figure to describe the imperfection of their knowledge as accurately as they can.

Whether we take an umbrella depends on how much we care about getting wet. We ask ourselves questions that only we can answer:

"How many hours do I expect to spend outdoors today?"

"If I leave my umbrella home and it rains, will I be extremely annoyed, only slightly inconvenienced, or just amused?"

"If I take my umbrella and it doesn't rain, will I leave the umbrella somewhere by mistake and lose it?"

"Am I carrying anything today that must not be allowed to get wet, like a watercolor painting or a cat?"

The forecasters have done their part; they've given their best estimate of the chance of rain. We have to decide for ourselves, based on our own values, whether or not to take a hundred percent of an umbrella. If rain does fall, thirty percent of an umbrella won't keep us dry.

For more information on scientific risk assessment, see Richard Wilson and E. A. C. Crouch, "Risk Assessment and Comparisons: An Introduction," *Science* 236:267–270 (April 17, 1987).

Limeys

The derogatory slang epithet "limey" is short for "lime-juicer."

The original lime-juicers were British sailors of the 1800s who got lemon or lime juice with their food in order to prevent scurvy, a condition characterized by rotten gums, weak knees, and fatigue. During the late 1700s, about one-seventh of the sailors of the British navy were disabled by this disease.

A Scottish naval surgeon, James Lind, collected information about scurvy and learned that it had often been cured by a diet of fresh fruits and vegetables—which the gruel-eating sailors certainly weren't getting. Lind understood that it was impractical to carry a lot of fresh produce on a ship in those days. But he experimented and found that the juice alone from lemons and limes and oranges could cure and prevent scurvy. Thus he recommended that sailors drink lemon juice at sea. The navy eventually took Lind's advice and put lemon juice aboard British ships starting in the 1790s. By the mid-1800s limes were cheaper than lemons, so lime juice was used instead. The British sailors became "lime-juicers," then "limeys."

Today we'd say that what the British sailors were getting from the fruit juice was vitamin C. For a while vitamin C was called the antiscorbutic substance because it prevented scurvy. The streamlined generic name ascorbic acid was invented in 1933.

Eric Partridge, *A Dictionary of Slang and Unconventional English*, ed. Paul Beale (London: Routledge and Kegan Paul, 1984).

"James Lind," in *Dictionary of Scientific Biography* (New York: Charles Scribner's Sons, 1973).

"Biochemical Components of Organisms" and "Medicine," in *Encyclopaedia Britannica*, 15th ed. (1986).

How does lung cancer start?

Exactly how does lung cancer start? There's evidence that it happens something like this:

Your lungs are made of cells. When you're growing up, your lung cells often divide to make new lung cells. Normally this process is magnificently controlled and coordinated to produce a growing, healthy lung.

Once you've grown up, your lung cells don't divide nearly so often. They don't divide because there are genes in each cell that keep the cell from dividing—genes whose purpose is to say to the cell, "Don't divide."

Now, suppose some of the genes in a lung cell are damaged, maybe by something you inhale—something in tobacco smoke, for instance. Suppose the "don't divide" genes are the ones that get damaged. Then the cell will go ahead and divide. There's nothing stopping it. It will divide into two new lung cells, each of which has damaged "don't divide" genes, just like the original. Each of those will, in turn, divide into two cells—with damaged "don't divide" genes—and so on, to uncontrolled copying of the original bad cell. That's lung cancer.

This connection between a gene not doing its job and cancer has been seen with particular clarity in the case of lung cancer, but it may be the central process in other kinds of cancer as well.

J. Michael Bishop, "Oncogenes," *Scientific American*, March 1982.

"Single Gene Deficiency Linked to Lung Cancer," *New York Times*, December 11, 1987, p. 17 (national ed.).

K. Kok et al., "Deletion of a DNA Sequence at the Chromosomal Region 3p21 in All Major Types of Lung Cancer," *Nature* 330:578 (December 10, 1987).

H. Brauch et al., "Molecular Analysis of the Short Arm of Chromosome 3 in Small-Cell and Non-Small-Cell Carcinoma of the Lung," *New England Journal of Medicine* 317:1109–1113 (October 29, 1987).

THE LIGHT OF SPRING

When people talk about springtime, they usually talk about warm weather or melting snow. But for most living things, the real sign of spring is increasing sunlight.

The sun is higher in the sky at noontime on a spring day than at noon on a winter day. And the sun is up for more hours each day as winter turns into spring and then summer.

Green plants use sunlight to make their food. Each plant has a strategy for getting the light it needs.

In a deciduous forest, the major consumers of sunlight are the big trees—oaks, maples, hickories, and so on. By summertime, these trees make a canopy of leaves that intercepts most of the sunlight reaching the forest. How do other plants survive?

Beneath that canopy, plants have to get by on a tiny fraction of the intensity of full sunlight. Some of these shade plants are the Jack-in-the-pulpit, wild ginger, and trilliums.

Other plants survive on the forest floor by taking advantage of the full sunlight of springtime, when the sun is high in the sky but not yet blocked out by the leaves of the big trees. The so-called ephemeral wild-flowers, including the trout lilies, Dutchman's breeches, and spring-beauty, bloom and die back before the tree leaves are fully expanded. These ephemeral wildflowers have to make enough food during their short growing season to last the rest of the year, storing it in a bulb or some other underground organ.

So ephemeral wildflowers, shade plants, and big trees have a schedule for sharing sunlight. That pattern of coexistence must have taken a long time to develop.

John Mitchell and the Massachusetts Audubon Society, *The Curious Naturalist* (Englewood Cliffs, N.J.: Prentice-Hall, 1980).

Peter Farb, ed., *The Forest* (New York: Time, 1961).

Robert Leo Smith, *Ecology and Field Biology* (New York: Harper and Row, 1974).

Vitamines and Vitamins

In 1912 a Polish biochemist, Casimir Funk, published an article about food substances that could prevent diseases like beriberi and scurvy. Funk's analysis showed that these disease-preventing food substances might be members of a family of chemicals called amines. These substances were vital for a healthy diet, so Funk called them vital amines, or vitamines—spelled like "vitamins," but with an "e" at the end.

By 1916 there was evidence that these disease-preventing food substances might not actually be what chemists call amines. The name "vitamine" was thrown out in favor of the names "fat-soluble A" and "water-soluble B." (Only those two types were known at the time.)

In 1920 another chemist wrote that the names "fat-soluble A" and "water-soluble B" were unwieldy. He suggested dropping the "e" from the old word "vitamine" and calling the substances vitamins. Whatever the substances might turn out to be, the name "vitamin" would be chemically permissible. As new types were discovered, they could be given letters—vitamin A, vitamin B, vitamin C, and so on.

See "Vitamin," in *Supplement to the Oxford English Dictionary*, and "-in" in the *OED*.
Aaron J. Ihde, *The Development of Modern Chemistry* (New York: Harper and Row, 1964).
Elmer V. McCollum, *A History of Nutrition: The Sequence of Ideas in Nutrition Investigations* (Boston: Houghton-Mifflin, 1957).

Colors and Their Opposites

Let's begin with some thoughts about paint.

We usually think of paint as a substance that adds color to things. But from a physical point of view, paint works by taking colors away—from white light.

Take the example of a red car parked in the sun. The sunlight already contains all the colors of the rainbow. The red paint on the car absorbs the non-red colors from sunlight and reflects only red to our eyes. Red paint absorbs, or subtracts, non-red from white.

What happens to those non-red colors absorbed by the paint? Actually, the absorbed light is converted to heat. But here's an almost philosophical question. If somehow we could see the light that red paint absorbs, what would we see? That is, what does non-red look like?

In fact, it's a bluish-green color called cyan. People who work with color professionally say that cyan is the complement of red.

Cyan is the color that red paint takes away from white light. Now, what if you put cyan and red back together? When you add cyan light to red light, you get white light—you're reassembling the colors of sunlight. Whatever colors are not supplied by the cyan are supplied by the red.

With paint it's different. Cyan paint added to red paint makes black paint, because whatever colors the cyan doesn't absorb, the red does. Nothing is reflected, so the paint looks black.

The mixture of any color and its complement makes white if you're mixing *light*, and black if you're mixing *paint*. This is one of the basic secrets in any business involving color—from painting to color television.

See "Colour" and related entries in *Encyclopaedia Britannica.*
Matthew Luckiesh, *Color and Its Applications* (New York: D. Van Nostrand, 1915).

HOW DOES THE WORLD LOOK TO A BEE?

To describe light in a general way, you need to specify at least three qualities: its brightness or intensity, its color, and its polarization.

Polarization is a quality our eyes don't detect. We have no everyday words to describe polarization, so we have to resort to a more or less scientific description of it.

If we think of light as a wave traveling through space something like a ripple crossing a pond, then we can think of polarization as describing the direction in which the wave vibrates. The vibration in a light wave is always perpendicular to the direction the wave is traveling. But the vibration of light can be up and down, sideways, or any combination of the two.

If the vibrations are in random directions, the light is said to be unpolarized; if all the vibrations are in the same direction, it's completely polarized; in-between amounts of polarization are most common.

To our eyes, polarization makes no difference. But it has been known for decades now that insects in general, and bees in particular, can detect the direction a light wave is vibrating. Bees navigate by referring to the direction of the sun. But they don't have to see the sun directly; all they need is a clear view of a small piece of the sky. The blue glow of the sky is polarized, and the direction and the amount of polarization are different in every part of the sky, depending on where the sun is. A bee can tell where the sun is by looking at the polarization of any small piece of the sky.

So bees have a dimension to their vision that we lack. In addition to color and brightness, bees see polarization. What does that sensation feel like? How does the world look to a bee? We can only wonder.

G. P. Können, *Polarized Light in Nature* (New York: Cambridge University Press, 1985).

Knut Schmidt-Nielsen, *Animal Physiology: Adaptation and Environment,* 3rd ed. (New York: Cambridge University Press, 1983).

Marcel Minnaert, *The Nature of Light and Colour in the Open Air* (New York: Dover, 1954).

DEATH OF THE DINOSAURS: A QUICK REVIEW

The fossil record indicates that about 65 million years ago, more than half of all living species, including the last of the dinosaurs, suddenly became extinct. What happened? This mystery is one of the best-known in all science.

The modern controversy began in 1980 with the discovery of a layer of clay, enriched in the element iridium, at a depth in the rocks corresponding to the time of the extinction. The layer was found at several places around the world. Iridium occurs in greater concentrations in meteorites than in earth rocks, so Luis Alvarez at the Lawrence Berkeley Laboratory in California suggested that Earth might have been struck by a giant meteorite or a small comet 65 million years ago. The impact would have raised a worldwide dust cloud, blocking the sun, leading to the death of green plants and of animals who ate them. More recent evidence in favor of the impact idea includes the discovery of quartz grains from the period showing signs of shock.

But some geologists argue that the iridium enrichment and the shocked quartz could be explained by volcanic eruptions instead of an impact. And some paleontologists say that the extinctions 65 million years ago may not have happened at exactly the same time. Also, there were many survivors of the extinction event, including the ancestors of all organisms now living.

Maybe, a more recent argument goes, there were many smaller impacts over a period of several hundred thousand years, spreading the extinctions out over time. Maybe Earth was hit by a swarm of comets thrown into the inner solar system by an encounter with a nearby star!

These are just a few highlights of the dinosaur-extinction controversy. No resolution is in sight.

"Star-Struck? Impacts' Role in the History of Life Remains Contentious," *Scientific American*, April 1988, p. 37.

Why do we put cut flowers in water?

Water keeps cut flowers and other plants crisp because of one of the most important and all-pervasive natural processes operating on the face of planet Earth: osmosis. Osmosis is the process in which liquid water tends to move toward regions with a higher concentration of dissolved substances. The dissolved substances might be minerals, sugars, anything— water will usually move to where there's more dissolved material.

Each cell of a plant has a sort of skin—a membrane. Water can pass through the membrane easily, but other materials can't. Each plant cell maintains a relatively high internal concentration of dissolved materials. Water therefore tends to move into the cell.

As long as the concentration of dissolved substances is higher inside the cell than outside, water will usually push its way in. The water pressure that builds up inside the cell is what gives a healthy plant its crisp texture. Often that pressure will make cells expand; that's one way plants grow. And from this you can see why plants wilt if they don't get enough water: the cells lose internal water pressure.

So plants in general, and cut flowers in particular, stay crisp because dissolved materials in effect draw water through the cell membranes into the plant cells by the process of osmosis. There are other ways living things move water from one place to another, but osmosis is one of the most important.

Frank B. Salisbury and Cleon W. Ross, *Plant Physiology*, 3rd ed. (Belmont, Calif.: Wadsworth, 1985).
Helena Curtis, *Biology*, 4th ed. (New York: Worth, 1983).

Life without zero

Zero is one of humanity's greatest inventions, a symbol that stands for nothing in a very definite way.

The ancient Greeks and Egyptians had no zero. They used completely different symbols for 9, 90, 900, and so on. This system has a couple of big disadvantages. First, it has symbols only for numbers people have already thought of. If you want to talk about, say, 900 billion, you will have to invent a symbol for it. The old Greek and Egyptian systems also make arithmetic hard. Without zero, multiplying 3 times 90 is a whole different problem from multiplying 3 times 9.

The first known zero symbols appear in Babylonian clay tablets of about 500 B.C.; there, the zero was used to clarify the symbols for large numbers.

The idea that zero can be treated in arithmetic problems as a number, like any other number, came from a Hindu astronomer of the seventh century A.D., Brahmagupta. He was the first to write down the rules for arithmetic with zeros. Western civilization didn't adopt arithmetic with zeros until about seven hundred years later, based on the work of the thirteenth-century Italian mathematician Leonardo Fibonacci.

Thanks to zero, we have to learn multiplication tables only up to ten times ten. Thanks to zero, we can punch any number into our calculators using just ten keys. And if we want to imagine some gigantic number, we can do it easily—just by adding more zeros.

"Zero," in *McGraw-Hill Encyclopedia of Science and Technology* (New York: McGraw-Hill, 1987).
"Numerals and Numeral Systems," in *Encyclopaedia Britannica*.
O. Neugebauer, *The Exact Sciences in Antiquity* (New York: Dover, 1968).
"Brahmagupta," in *Dictionary of Scientific Biography* (New York: Charles Scribner's Sons, 1970).

Prostaglandins

Prostaglandins are a family of chemical messengers in the body. In that respect they're like hormones. But unlike the familiar hormones, prostaglandins don't come from special glands—apparently they can be made by cell membranes in just about any part of the body.

Prostaglandins are found, among other places, in human semen. A remarkable early discovery was that prostaglandins in semen induce muscle contractions in the uterus, helping sperm to be carried into the female reproductive system. So in this case, prostaglandins from one individual seem to have their function in another individual.

Other prostaglandins have other functions. Some influence the secretion of digestive juices. Some cause blood vessels to constrict, others cause them to dilate; some help to promote blood clotting, others help to prevent it.

A byproduct of the study of prostaglandins was an answer to the decades-old mystery of how aspirin works. Various prostaglandins in large amounts can cause tissue inflammation, headache, and fever, as well as muscle contractions. About 1970 it was found that aspirin inactivates an enzyme necessary for the production of prostaglandins. Apparently that's why aspirin relieves inflammation, headaches, fever—and menstrual cramps. (That research led to a Nobel Prize in 1982.)

Prostaglandins were discovered in 1930, but not much could be learned about them because they're made by the body in only tiny amounts and are broken down by enzymes in a matter of minutes. Progress in our knowledge about them came more rapidly with new techniques for sensitive chemical analysis developed in the 1960s and beyond. But much about prostaglandins is still unknown.

Helena Curtis, *Biology,* 4th ed. (New York: Worth, 1985).

J. R. Vane, "Inhibition of Prostaglandin Synthesis as a Mechanism for the Action of Aspirin-Like Drugs," *Nature: New Biology* 231:232–235 (1971).

J. B. Smith and A. L. Willis, "Aspirin Selectively Inhibits Prostaglandin Production in Human Platelets," *Nature: New Biology* 231:235–237 (1971).

Sweetened Condensed Milk

Sweetened condensed milk is a good ingredient for sweet recipes because of all the added sugar—about 25 percent by weight. But when sweetened condensed milk was invented in the 1800s, the original reason for adding sugar to the milk was not for flavor, but for protection against spoilage. And it works—even after you open the can, sweetened condensed milk keeps longer than fresh milk.

That added sugar kills bacteria that otherwise would digest the milk and spoil it. The sugar kills not by poisoning the bacteria, but by a more direct physical process. It draws water out of the bacteria so the bacterial cells shrivel and die.

Each bacterial cell has a sort of skin—technically, a membrane. Water can pass through this membrane pretty easily, but substances dissolved in the water can't. Water has a natural tendency to move toward any region where there's a high concentration of dissolved substances. A bacterial cell in a can of sweetened condensed milk finds itself immersed in an extremely concentrated solution of sugar. Water inside the cell will therefore pass out through the cell membrane into the sugar solution. The bacterial cell dehydrates and dies in a sea of sugary water.

Sugar added to fruit has the same effect—that's the idea behind fruit preserves. Other foods are preserved with salt, exploiting the same principle.

That tendency of water to move toward a region where there's a high concentration of dissolved substances goes by the technical name of osmosis. In living things osmosis is one of the most important ways water gets from one place to another.

Harold McGee, *On Food and Cooking: The Science and Lore of the Kitchen* (New York: Macmillan, 1974).

Irma S. Rombauer and Marion Rombauer Becker, *The Joy of Cooking* (Indianapolis: Bobbs Merrill, 1974).

WHAT THE WEATHER REPORT DOESN'T TELL YOU

When we hear a report that the temperature outside is, say, 70 degrees, we're usually hearing a measurement made with a thermometer at least six feet off the ground. But there can be big variations in temperature closer to the ground. On a sunny day, it may be five or ten degrees warmer at ankle level than at eye level. A cool day for us can be a warm day for rabbits and squirrels.

Sunshine warms both the ground and the air, but it warms the ground better than it warms the air. Soil and green plants absorb sunlight and convert it to heat better than air does. So a field of grass and clover and dandelions feels warm to the touch on a cool, sunny afternoon.

The warm ground heats the air a few inches above the ground. That surface air doesn't move much—it's not affected by breezes—so it gets warm and stays warm.

Where there's vegetation, the level of warmest temperature tends to follow the height of the leaves. The warmest place in a field of clover may be about half an inch above the ground; in a field of mature corn, four or five feet up; in a forest of oaks and maples, the hottest place is at the top of the canopy of leaves—maybe a hundred feet up.

This principle applies even if the vegetation is plastic. At a daytime major-league baseball game, the temperature might be 90 in the stands and 110 on the field, partly because artificial grass is so good at changing sunlight to heat.

Robert Leo Smith, *Ecology and Field Biology* (New York: Harper and Row, 1974).

Food and Agriculture Organization of the United Nations, *Forest Influences: An Introduction to Ecological Forestry*, Forestry and Forest Products Studies no. 15 (New York: Unipub, 1962).

WHY MOWING THE LAWN DOESN'T KILL THE GRASS

If you cut down an oak tree, the stump dies. But if you cut grass, you don't hurt it at all. That's because new growth on an oak tree is at the tips of the branches; new growth in grass happens at ground level. Also, grasses, unlike other plants, can replenish their leaves.

A blade of grass is the end of a long, narrow leaf. If you trace a grass blade back to the stem on a tall grass plant, you see that the blade comes from a sheath wrapped around the stem. At the base of that sheath is a node, a place where the stems of some grasses have a slight bulge. Nodes are where new growth happens in a grass plant. A short grass plant has at least one node near ground level, out of reach of the lawn mower; a tall grass plant may have several more nodes farther up along the stem.

When a grass blade is cut off by a lawn mower or a grazing animal, some as-yet-unknown signal is sent down to the node, stimulating it to produce more leaf. Grazing animals take particular advantage of this; eating the grass causes more to grow in its place.

The capacity to add new material to old leaves is characteristic of grasses. Other plants generally don't have this ability. An oak tree grows new leaves every year, but it can't replace part of an existing leaf. An oak leaf grows to a certain mature size and stops. If part of an oak leaf is cut away, it doesn't grow back.

The ultimate fate of an oak leaf is old age and death; leaves of grass remain youthful all summer long.

Frank B. Salisbury and Cleon W. Ross, *Plant Physiology*, 3rd ed. (Belmont, Calif.: Wadsworth, 1985).

Helena Curtis, *Biology*, 4th ed. (New York: Worth, 1985).

A MIRROR RIDDLE

Exactly what is the difference between the appearance of a real object and its reflection in a mirror?

Obviously, a mirror reverses the image of an object in some way. For instance, when you look into a bathroom mirror, you see an image with left and right switched. If you hold up a toothpaste tube, the letters on the reflected tube are backward. Evidently, reflection in a bathroom mirror reverses left and right.

But not all reflections reverse left and right. Some switch top and bottom. Think of trees on the far side of a lake, and how they're reflected in the water. The reflected trees have top and bottom switched, but left and right remain the same for the reflected trees and the real trees.

It seems like a contradiction: a bathroom mirror switches left and right, and the surface of a lake switches top and bottom. How can that be? (The explanation, by the way, has nothing to do with the difference between glass and water. If you put a mirror flat on a table, the reflections will be oriented the same way as in the surface of a lake.) Is there some precise way of describing the essential difference between a real object and its mirror image—some rule that will work in every situation?

Here's a hint: look at the reflection of a clock in a mirror—the old-fashioned kind of clock, with hour and minute hands. A second hand is even better. What's the essential difference between the real clock and its reflection?

Think about what you saw when you looked at the reflection of the clock. While the hands on a real clock run forward, or clockwise, the hands on the reflected clock run backward, or counterclockwise. Therein lies the answer to our riddle: a mirror switches the clockwise and counterclockwise directions. Whether the reflection is right side up, upside down, or sideways simply depends on where you put the mirror. But the essential difference between reality and reflection is the reversal of clockwise and counterclockwise.

Look at the letter "p," as in "toothpaste" on your toothpaste tube. The shortest trip from the top of that letter "p" around the loop is clockwise on the real tube and counterclockwise in the upside-down reflection in the water. On the face of your clock, the shortest trip from the 12 to the 3 is clockwise in reality and counterclockwise in the mirror.

A mirror switches clockwise and counterclockwise. That surprisingly subtle rule is the only one that always works, regardless of the position of the mirror, or the person looking, for any reflected image.

GALILEO'S JOB APPLICATION

Here's a story about patronage through flattery: how a seventeenth-century scientist made his living.

Galileo Galilei wanted a court appointment with those well-known patrons of the arts, the Medici family of Florence. In 1607 word came that Prince Cosimo de Medici was interested in magnetism. Galileo responded with a flattering and educational gift: a lodestone, a natural magnet, on a handsome base inscribed with the Latin words *vim facit amor*, "love produces strength." The lodestone's strength was demonstrated by two little iron anchors stuck to its poles—anchors made under Galileo's personal supervision by artisans in Venice.

Galileo's pressing concern now was to deliver this lodestone to the Medici courier, whose address he had been given, in time for the last Sunday night dispatch from Venice to Florence. His own letters give us a picture of Galileo quite different from those serene museum portraits: the great astronomer, plying the canals of Venice on a rainy Sunday night with a surly gondolier, knocking on one door after another in the dark, looking for the Medici courier.

The lodestone eventually made it to Florence, and Galileo got his appointment, not so much because of the lodestone but because he named the four large moons of Jupiter (which he discovered) the Medicean stars. The name didn't stick, however. Today we call Jupiter's four largest moons the Galilean satellites.

Richard S. Westfall, "Science and Patronage: Galileo and the Telescope," *ISIS* 76:11–30 (1985).

THE CONSEQUENCES OF SMALLNESS

Put a teaspoonful of granulated sugar in a glass of water and stir. The sugar dissolves in a few seconds. Do the same thing with a single lump of very hard candy, and two or three minutes later some of the candy will still be undissolved. The amount of sugar is about the same in both cases. The difference is that the small size of the grains of granulated sugar give the sugar and water more opportunity to interact.

Dissolving happens only where sugar meets water. The more square inches of sugar exposed to water, the faster the sugar dissolves. In general, thousands of small grains have more surface area than one big lump of the same volume. It's amazing how much surface area you can get by grinding a solid lump into a fine powder. One cubic inch of material, divided into particles a hundred-thousandth of an inch wide, has a surface area of several hundred square yards.

This has many implications—in biology, for instance. Large living things are made of many tiny cells. Each cell must constantly adjust its internal balance of water, nutrients, and waste products to function properly. These substances get into and out of cells through their surfaces. The more square inches of cell surface a living organism has, the faster it can adjust its chemical balance. So it's advantageous to be made of small cells.

William A. Kieffer, *Chemistry: A Cultural Approach* (New York: Harper and Row, 1971).
Helena Curtis, *Biology,* 4th ed. (New York: Worth, 1983), p. 98.

Ozone and Ice

Ozone is a natural component of the Earth's upper atmosphere. A molecule of ozone is made of three oxygen atoms bound together; a molecule of the oxygen we breathe has two oxygen atoms. That's an important difference. The three-oxygen molecule blocks the sun's ultraviolet light, which would disrupt life on Earth if it reached the ground in large amounts.

Ozone in the upper atmosphere has been disappearing at an alarming rate in the last twenty years, especially over Antarctica. The culprit seems to be chlorine from chlorofluorocarbons, man-made chemicals once used in spray cans and still used in air conditioners and foam cushions. Chlorine destroys ozone by pulling loose one of its three oxygen atoms.

There's a natural process that was once thought adequate to protect ozone from attack by chlorine. In this process, the harmful chlorine is trapped by chemical reactions with naturally occurring compounds containing nitrogen. But there's yet another factor in the process: ice crystals in high-altitude clouds that form during the long, cold Antarctic winter night. Apparently these crystals trap the helpful nitrogen compounds.

So, chlorine from chlorofluorocarbons destroys ozone. Natural nitrogen compounds can prevent that destruction, but not if those nitrogen compounds are trapped in ice clouds. And that may be only part of the story. A cloud of tiny ice crystals has an immense amount of surface area where unknown chemical reactions might happen. Chemistry on the surface of a solid particle is different from chemistry in a test tube, and less is known about it. More needs to be learned about the chemistry of ice clouds.

Richard A. Kerr, "Stratospheric Ozone Is Decreasing," *Science* 239:1489–1491 (March 25, 1988).
Richard Monastersky, "Decline of the CFC Empire," *Science News* 133 (April 9, 1988).
Richard A. Stolarski, "The Antarctic Ozone Hole," *Scientific American,* January 1988.

Benjamin Franklin's Madeira Wine Surprise

Benjamin Franklin, who discovered that lightning is electricity as well as helped to write the Constitution, also speculated about the boundary between life and death. It was a great mystery in his day, as it is in ours.

One day when Franklin went to dinner at the home of some friends in London, he took along a bottle of Madeira wine from Virginia. At the table the bottle was opened and, as Franklin tells it, "three drowned flies fell into the first glass that had been poured."

Franklin doesn't say how his friends reacted—maybe finding flies in your drink was common in those days. Franklin, however, saw this as an opportunity to test an idea he'd heard—the idea that drowned flies could be revived by sunlight.

He strained the flies out with a sieve and put them in the sun. After three hours, according to Franklin, two of the three flies revived and flew away, "finding themselves in Old England," he wrote, "without knowing how they came thither."

"I wish it were possible," he went on, "from this instance, to invent a method of embalming drowned persons, in such a manner that they may be recalled to life at any period, however distant; for having a very ardent desire to see the state of America a hundred years hence, I should prefer to any ordinary death the being immersed in a cask of Madeira wine, with a few friends, till that time, to be then recalled to life by the solar warmth of my dear country!"

Benjamin Franklin, writing in 1773. We don't know exactly what happened to those flies, but we can marvel at Franklin's anticipation of speculative fiction of the twentieth century.

From a letter from Franklin to Barbeu Dubourg, published in N. G. Goodman, ed., *The Ingenious Dr. Franklin: Selected Scientific Letters of Benjamin Franklin* (1931; Philadelphia: University of Pennsylvania Press, 1956), pp. 150–152.

Viruses Attack Bacteria

Biologists have learned a lot about how viruses operate by watching those whose preferred targets are bacteria.

A particularly well-known bacteria-attacking virus is the one biologists call T2. Like most viruses, T2 is simple. It has a strand of DNA—the molecule that carries hereditary information—enclosed in a coat of protein that looks like a dome-shaped hollow shell with a tube coming out of one side. When a T2 virus attacks a bacterial cell, it uses that tube to punch through the surface of the cell and inject its DNA.

Once injected into the bacterial cell, the virus's DNA takes charge of the cell's chemical processes. Raw materials in the cell are no longer used for the bacteria's own purposes, but are diverted to build new viruses. Around twenty-five minutes after the initial virus attack, the disabled bacterial cell breaks open and releases about a hundred brand-new T2 viruses.

Not all viruses operate exactly like T2. Some spend a long time inside a cell doing nothing—a latent period—until the copying process is triggered by something outside. This is true of a familiar virus that attacks not bacteria but human beings. The herpes simplex virus that causes cold sores in humans has a latent period that can last weeks or months.

Different viruses attack different kinds of cells, and take different amounts of time to act. But no virus can reproduce except by taking over a living cell and using the materials inside to its own advantage.

André Lwoff, "Interaction among Virus, Cell, and Organism," Nobel Lecture, 1965, in *Nobel Lectures in Molecular Biology, 1933–1975* (New York: Elsevier–North Holland, 1977).

THE BIRTH OF THE ATOMIC AGE

In 1895, physicists were excited about a recent discovery: X-rays. Henri Becquerel of Paris wondered whether X-rays would be emitted by certain substances when they were exposed to sunlight.

Becquerel experimented with crystals of a salt containing uranium. He wrapped a photographic plate in black paper, put a few grains of uranium salt on the paper, left the whole arrangement in the sun all day, then developed the plate. An image of the uranium salt grains appeared. Becquerel cautiously concluded that uranium salts, exposed to sunlight, gave off rays capable of penetrating black paper.

One day Becquerel went outside with another wrapped photographic plate topped with uranium salts, planning to leave it outside as before. But the sky was partly cloudy, so he took the plate back indoors and put it in a drawer.

After a couple of days, he developed the plate anyway. To his surprise, Becquerel found an image just as strong as those on plates that had lain in the sun. Without sunlight, this uranium salt had made rays that would go through black paper! Nineteenth-century physics couldn't explain it. Becquerel had discovered a new property of matter: radioactivity.

In his 1903 Nobel Prize lecture, Henri Becquerel anticipated the whole era of atomic energy by guessing that "the emission of energy is the result of a slow modification of the atoms of the radioactive substances. Such a modification . . . could certainly release energy in sufficiently large quantities to produce the observed effects, without the changes in matter being large enough to be detectable by our methods of investigation."

Henri Becquerel, lecture quoted in *Moments of Discovery: The Development of Modern Science,* ed. George Schwartz and Philip W. Bishop (New York: Basic Books, 1958).

"On Radioactivity, a New Property of Matter," Nobel Lecture, 1903, in *Nobel Lectures: Physics, 1901–1921* (New York: Elsevier, 1967).

Honest Answers to Personal Questions

A stranger knocks on your door and says he's taking a poll about tax-law compliance. He asks you whether you've ever cheated on your taxes.

Suppose, for the sake of argument, that you have. You'll probably say no, especially if you have any suspicion that this poll-taker actually works for the IRS.

But suppose the poll is legitimate—the pollsters don't care about your taxes in particular; they actually want to find out what percentage of people cheat on their taxes. You, as a citizen, see value in finding this out, but you don't want your privacy compromised.

A solution is this: the poll-taker gives you a spinner, like the ones that come with children's board games. The circle on the spinner is divided into four equal parts. One of the parts is marked "yes"; the other three parts are marked "no." The poll-taker asks, "Have you ever cheated on your taxes? Don't tell me the answer," he says. "Spin the spinner where I can't see it and just tell me whether the answer is right or wrong for you."

From your answer—"right" or "wrong"—the poll-taker cannot find out whether you personally cheated. But your answer, along with many others, allows him to calculate what percentage of people cheated on their taxes. For example, if everyone cheated, about one-fourth of the respondents would say the spinner was right; if no one cheated, about three-fourths would say it was right.

Spinners and other randomizing devices provide a way to get honest answers to personal questions without violating anyone's privacy. Randomized surveys have already been used to find out about drugs, abortion, and even shady practices in selling cars. Future applications may include finding out more about the connection between sexual behavior and AIDS.

Gina Kolata, "How to Ask about Sex and Get Honest Answers," *Science* 236:382 (April 24, 1987).

Risk Assessment

In modern times, we often find ourselves evaluating risks in order to make decisions about new technologies and new chemicals. Estimates of risk come to us—from scientists, engineers, and doctors—in the form of statistics that are sometimes hard to grasp, even for experts.

Specialists in the relatively new field of risk assessment offer some suggestions about judging statistics:

We can be critical about data. Is a risk assessment based on historical statistics? Laboratory experiments? How closely do those situations resemble our own?

We can observe how a risk is expressed. Saying there's a .1 percent chance of catastrophe in a certain situation may have a different psychological effect from saying there's a 99.9 percent chance nothing will go wrong.

We can compare the new to the old, the unfamiliar to the familiar: flying versus driving, a nuclear accident versus a dam collapse.

We can compare the risks of two alternatives. We already do this when we balance the risk of getting cancer from bacon treated with sodium nitrite against the risk of getting botulism from bacon not treated with it.

Better decisions require good information, presented in as many ways as possible. Comparing the familiar to the unfamiliar is especially helpful. That's the job of scientists.

Once the scientific part is done, the social part begins. We citizens must interpret the risks in terms of our own values. Sometimes we have to search for the right balance between the interest of the individual and the interest of society. Then we must judge, decide, act, and live with the consequences.

See articles on risk assessment in *Science* 236 (April 17, 1987).

Broken symmetry: cosmetic or cosmic?

Mirrors do funny things to reality. Clocks run counterclockwise. Writing is backward. (See "A Mirror Riddle.")

But processes of nature, in which decisions by living organisms are not involved, look perfectly all right in a mirror. If you look at the bathroom faucet in a mirror, you see water going down the drain, not up to the sky. You can't tell, unless the mirror is dirty, whether you're looking at reality or its reflection. In the mirror, no laws of physics are broken—except in a few esoteric physics experiments of the last thirty years, involving particles smaller than the nucleus of an atom: the so-called neutral K mesons.

Flying through a particle accelerator, neutral K mesons change into other particles which fly off in predictable directions. If you're a physicist familiar with neutral K mesons, you can tell from the directions in which these particles fly off whether you're seeing reality or a mirror reflection. Everything else may look perfectly all right, but the behavior of neutral K mesons will look wrong in a mirror.

This is a mystery. What force, or process, causes this tiny exception to the rule that nature and its mirror image are essentially indistinguishable? Physicists have come to suspect that this flaw in the symmetry of nature may be not just cosmetic, but cosmic.

Richard P. Feynman, *The Feynman Lectures on Physics* (Reading, Mass.: Addison-Wesley, 1964), vol. I, chap. 52.

Robert K. Adair, "A Flaw in a Universal Mirror," *Scientific American*, February 1988.

#

Antimatter is not just the stuff of science fiction; it's real. Antimatter is made of particles complementary, in a way, to matter particles. For instance, the electron, a familiar matter particle, has a negative electrical charge. Its corresponding antiparticle, the positron, has a positive charge. When an electron and a positron meet, they annihilate each other. Both particles disappear in a flash of light—a spectacular case of matter changing to energy. The same thing happens in any encounter of an equal amount of matter and antimatter.

Antiparticles are created in nuclear reactions in stars and in space, but they soon meet matter particles and annihilate. So you're unlikely ever to see antimatter, even in a museum.

A great mystery about antimatter was discovered by the physicist Paul Dirac in 1930. Dirac found that, according to the known laws of physics, antimatter has just as much right to exist as matter. So why does so little antimatter exist today?

One guess says that the very early universe—15 or 20 billion years ago—was made of almost exactly equal amounts of matter and antimatter. But, for some reason, there was just slightly more matter—by about one part in a billion. Annihilation eliminated most of it. But some unannihilated antimatter was left over to become our universe.

Whatever force or process it was that upset the symmetry between matter and antimatter in the early universe may still be at work today. That force or process may be the cause of unexpected behavior among subatomic particles like K mesons. (See "Broken Symmetry.")

Clues about the whole universe in the distant past may be lurking among tiny particles in the present.

Richard P. Feynman, *The Feynman Lectures on Physics* (Reading, Mass.: Addison-Wesley, 1964), vol. I, chap. 52.

Robert K. Adair, "A Flaw in a Universal Mirror," *Scientific American*, February 1988.

THE SECRET OF CLEAR ICE CUBES

The problem: cloudy ice cubes, with unsightly bubbles in the center, even though you started with clear water and a clean ice tray.

The answer: start with hot water, not cold.

The reason: hot water holds less dissolved air than cold water. Those bubbles in the center of an ice cube come from air dissolved in the water.

Bubbles usually form at the center because ice cubes usually freeze from the outside. The top, bottom, and sides of the cube freeze first, leaving a liquid water center. As the cube continues to freeze, dissolved air is forced into the liquid center. Air can't freeze at these temperatures, so when the liquid center of the ice cube finally freezes, the air comes out of solution and forms bubbles in the ice. Hot water has less dissolved air to begin with, so it makes fewer bubbles when it freezes.

To convince yourself that hot water holds less dissolved air than cold water, think of what happens when you heat water in a saucepan on the stove. Long before the water gets hot enough to boil, tiny bubbles form on the bottom of the pan. Those tiny bubbles are air coming out of solution as the water warms up. The same thing happens in your water heater.

Or, think of an aquarium: if the temperature is too warm, fish die—partly because the warm water holds too little oxygen.

Getting back to ice cubes: if some dissolved air has already been removed from water by heating, less air will be left to emerge as bubbles when you freeze the water in an ice tray. So, the secret to making clear ice cubes is to start with hot water.

Ronald A. Delorenzo, *Problem Solving in General Chemistry* (Lexington, Mass.: D. C. Heath, 1981), p. 240.

BROKEN CUPS AND ATOMS

You can gather the pieces of a broken coffee cup and fit them together, but they won't stick. The fit may be good, but you can't make it good enough.

"Good enough" means getting the pieces so close that atoms interact.

Atoms separated by more than a few times their own diameter won't interact—they're basically indifferent to each other. The reason has to do with the inner structure of atoms, which is apparent only at very close range.

Every atom has a nucleus with a positive electrical charge surrounded by electrons with a negative electrical charge. Electrical opposites attract, so the nucleus and electrons attract each other.

Seen at a distance, though, an atom shows no obvious sign of positively and negatively charged parts. At a distance, electrical effects of the nucleus and electrons are canceled out. Only at close range—less than a few times the diameter of one atom—do the nucleus and electrons have distinct electrical effects.

In the same way, at a distance of a quarter-mile, a red-and-white-check tablecloth shows no obvious sign of colored squares—it looks pink. Only at close range do the red and white squares look distinct.

If two atoms are brought close enough—in the ballpark of a ten-millionth of an inch—the nucleus of one may attract electrons of the other. The atoms interact; a bond forms.

When a coffee cup breaks, the atoms are pulled apart so their relationship changes from interaction and bonding to indifference. The inner structure of an atom on one side is no longer apparent to an atom on the other side.

If you want the broken pieces of the cup to stick, you will have to fill the gap with something that will get close enough to the atoms on each piece to interact with them: glue.

Rodney Cotterill, *The Cambridge Guide to the Material World* (New York: Cambridge University Press, 1985).

TRAPDOOR CODES

You're going on a trip, and you pack all the items you need into one suitcase. You're very clever in arranging everything so that it just fits. The first night of your trip, you unpack. But the next morning you can't remember how you got all that stuff into the suitcase. Unpacking was easy; repacking is hard, because you have to reconstruct that perfect arrangement that allowed everything to fit in the suitcase.

Mathematicians have discovered new ways of transforming messages that work in a similar way. With these mathematical procedures, changing a secret message into code is very easy. But changing the coded message back into readable form is nearly impossible unless you know the secret decoding program.

These are called trapdoor codes, after the one-way trapdoors in mystery stories and horror movies. Going through the trapdoor one way is easy, but you can't go the other way unless you know where the secret button is.

What's new about trapdoor codes is that you need one key to put the message into code, and a different key to translate the message out of code. It's perfectly safe for anyone to know the key for coding a message—because that key won't work for decoding the same message.

To send a message by trapdoor code is easy, like unpacking a suitcase. But to read the coded message is hard, like repacking the suitcase.

Trapdoor codes are already being used by some banks. Suppose you want to send an electronic message in confidence to a bank that doesn't know you. You put the message into the bank's code using a key that the bank publishes in the phone book. But only the bank has the decoding key, so only the bank can read your message. Furthermore, you can use your personal trapdoor decoding key to put a signature in the message, proving that you sent it.

Martin E. Hellman, "Mathematics of Public-Key Cryptography," *Scientific American*, August 1979.
Martin Gardner's "Mathematical Games" column in *Scientific American*, August 1977.

LATE-NIGHT RADIO

Why do distant AM radio stations come in better at night?

The story begins in the rarefied atmosphere high above our heads, where ultraviolet light and X-rays from the sun strip electrons off atoms. The result is a gas made partly of electrons and partly of atoms from which electrons have been stripped. The stripped atoms are known as ions, and the part of the atmosphere where sunlight makes ions is known as the ionosphere.

When radio waves encounter the ionosphere, interesting things happen; ions and electrons have electrical charges that affect radio waves in many complex ways.

A radio wave of the right frequency, coming up from the ground, will be turned around and sent back down by the upper layers of the ionosphere—a hundred or two hundred miles up. The upper ionosphere acts like a mirror, reflecting radio waves around the curve of the Earth to distant receivers. That's why you can pick up a baseball game from a station hundreds of miles away.

But why is nighttime the right time for long-distance AM radio?

The reason is that during the day, the radio waves don't even get a chance to reach those reflecting layers of the ionosphere. The waves are blocked by a low-altitude layer, about fifty miles up, that exists only in the daytime. As long as the sun is up, this low layer prevents AM radio signals from reaching the upper ionosphere. But the low-altitude layer of the ionosphere can't exist without continual sunlight. As soon as the sun goes down, the ions and electrons in this low layer get back together to form ordinary air. The obstruction disappears, and radio waves have a clear shot at the upper atmosphere, a hundred miles up in the night sky.

See entries under "Radio," "Radio Broadcasting," "Ionosphere," etc., in *McGraw-Hill Encyclopedia of Science and Technology* (New York: McGraw-Hill, 1987) and *Encyclopaedia Britannica*.

DOES NATURE ABHOR A VACUUM?

"Nature abhors a vacuum"—or does it?

Abhorrence of a vacuum once had the status of a scientific principle. Then along came seventeenth-century Italian physicist Evangelista Torricelli. In his most famous experiment, Torricelli got skilled Italian glassblowers to make a long glass tube, closed at one end—basically a four-foot-long test tube. He filled the tube with mercury, put his finger over the open end, turned the tube over, immersed the open end in a bowl of mercury, and removed his finger. The mercury in the tube didn't all run out; it fell to about thirty inches above the bowl and stopped. Between the sealed top end of the tube and the top end of the mercury was empty space—a vacuum.

The old idea was that this vacuum pulled the mercury and held it up in the tube. Torricelli tested that idea by repeating his experiment with another tube that had a big bulb at the sealed end. The mercury fell to the same level as before, even though there was now more vacuum at the top of the tube. Torricelli concluded that the vacuum in the tube was not pulling the mercury from above; instead, the weight of the atmosphere was pushing the mercury from below—by pushing down on the mercury in the bowl.

We would now call Torricelli's device a mercury barometer. We still express atmospheric pressure in inches of mercury.

It's possible to build a water barometer on the same principle. But since water is less dense than mercury, atmospheric pressure will push water higher—up to a maximum of about thirty-four feet.

Based on a letter by Torricelli, translated in the anthology *Moments of Discovery*, ed. George Schwartz and Philip W. Bishop (New York: Basic Books, 1958).

How does water get to the top of a tree?

After water enters a tree through the roots, it rises through vessels in the tree all the way to leaves at the top. Some trees are as much as three hundred feet tall. How does water climb three hundred feet? An explanation that's pretty widely accepted among botanists is that the process is driven by evaporation from the leaves.

Whenever a water molecule evaporates from the end of a vein in a leaf, that departing molecule pulls a train of other water molecules lined up in the vein behind it. Those water molecules, in turn, pull the ones behind them, and so on, through the twig and the branch, down the trunk, all the way to the ground, where water is pulled from the soil into the roots. It's as if there were an unbroken thread of water extending through the tree, being pulled at the top end by evaporation.

It sounds strange—this idea that water can be pulled like a thread. But it's possible because the water is confined in a strong airtight tube, like one of those vessels. So this thread of water doesn't break because water molecules have a strong attraction for each other.

We see that same attraction at work whenever we spill water on the kitchen table. The water pulls itself together into drops—it doesn't just scatter and disappear.

So, because of the mutual attraction of water molecules, evaporation from leaves pulls water out the top of a tree. And that, in turn, pulls fresh water—and nutrients—in through the roots. Water gets to the top of the tree because it's pulled up by evaporation.

Frank B. Salisbury and Cleon W. Ross, *Plant Physiology*, 3rd ed. (Belmont, Calif.: Wadsworth, 1985).

Richard P. Feynman, *The Feynman Lectures on Physics* (Reading, Mass.: Addison-Wesley, 1964), vol. I, chap. 1.

ADDING AND SUBTRACTING COLORS

Red plus blue plus green makes white when you mix light, and black when you mix paint. Mixing colored light and mixing colored paint are different processes.

You can see mixing of colored light in a color television picture. All the colors we see in the picture from a distance are made of glowing dots of red, green, and blue light on the screen. These dots glow with different intensities to make different colors. If only the red dots glow, the TV picture is red. If the red dots and the green dots glow, the picture looks yellow, because red light added to green light makes yellow light. If all the colored dots glow at full strength, the picture looks white. Other colors are made by adding the three basic colors in various proportions.

Paint, on the other hand, doesn't make light. It absorbs light. Take the example of a red car parked in the sun. Sunlight already contains all the colors of the rainbow. The red paint on the car absorbs non-red colors. In other words, red paint subtracts just about every color from white light, so it looks nearly black.

When you mix paint, you're subtracting colors. When you mix light, you're adding colors. So you have to think of adding and subtracting color when you try to guess, for instance, the color of a light-blue wall illuminated by a yellow-orange light bulb.

See "Colour" and related entries in *Encyclopaedia Britannica*; "Color Television" and related entries in *McGraw-Hill Encyclopedia of Science and Technology* (New York: McGraw-Hill, 1987).

WHAT COULD CHANGE EARTH'S CLIMATE?

What could change Earth's climate? Theoretical possibilities are almost endless. Here's an example of a natural climate cycle that would tend to make cold periods of geological time even colder. The key to this theory is the presence of a continent at one of the Earth's poles—namely, Antarctica at the south pole.

A continent can hold fallen snow; an ocean can't. A continent at a pole, like Antarctica, can stay cold enough to retain winter snow through the summer. A continent covered with snow is white; it reflects a lot of sunlight back into space. A snow-white continent tends to cool the climate by reflecting (rather than absorbing) sunlight.

A cooler climate makes still more snow, which accumulates on the polar continent—Antarctica—eventually forming a sheet of ice that could spread beyond the boundaries of that continent. The growing ice sheet makes a bigger white area on the Earth, which reflects even more sunlight. That cools the climate more, causing more snowfall—and so the cycle continues.

This cycle is plausible. But is it really happening? Is it important? No one knows for sure.

This is a cycle that would tend to magnify small changes in climate—making a cold period colder. A snow-white continent tends to cool the climate by reflecting sunlight. But, since the world is not covered with ice, this can't be the only process influencing our climate.

There are other plausible cycles that would tend to counteract small changes in climate, helping to keep it the same.

"Glacial Epoch," in *McGraw-Hill Encyclopedia of Science and Technology* (New York: McGraw-Hill, 1987).

POLARIZED LIGHT AND A QUIET LAKE

Look at the water. What's that dark patch in the reflection of the sky?

It's a polarized-light effect. To see it, you need patience, luck, a clear twilight sky, and a quiet lake. The sun has to be on the horizon—just rising or setting. The water has to be like glass. The sky has to be clear blue; a few small clouds are okay, but no haze.

Stand right at the edge of the water, with the sun on your left or right—not in front of or behind you. Look at the surface of the water about four feet in front of you. Examine the reflection of the blue sky. What you're looking for is a dark patch in the reflected sky that you don't see when you look up at the real sky. If you see it, here's the explanation: polarization of light, a quality of light the human eye is not sensitive to.

We can think of light as a vibration, something like a vibration traveling along a stretched rope. Light that vibrates in some clearly defined direction is said to be polarized.

The blue light of the sky is polarized. When the sun is low to your left or right, as it is in this experiment, the blue light of the sky right in front of you is polarized vertically—the vibrations are up and down.

But the lake doesn't reflect that light very well. Horizontal surfaces in general don't reflect vertically polarized light very well. You see a dark patch in the lake four feet in front of you because at that angle, the lake doesn't get much light it can reflect.

The blue sky supplies vertically polarized light; the lake, being horizontal, can't reflect it—and that's why there's a mysterious dark patch in the reflection of the sky.

Marcel Minnaert, *The Nature of Light and Colour in the Open Air* (New York: Dover, 1954), p. 253.

G. P. Können, *Polarized Light in Nature* (New York: Cambridge University Press, 1985).

ARE FOREST FIRES ALWAYS BAD?

In nature, fire can be beneficial. Some forests and other natural communities are accustomed to occasional fires. Fire is a normal part of the life cycle of the grasslands of the Midwest, the chaparral and ponderosa pine forests of the Southwest, and some pinelands of the South.

Fire stimulates the germination of some seeds. It reduces dead plants to ash, releasing nutrients that dissolve in the next rain and quickly return to the soil. Fire can help animals by clearing dead stems that get in the way of grazing. After a fire, new seeds can be carried in by wind or animals; that leads to greater diversity of vegetation.

Fire rejuvenates some forests. If you see a natural stand of firs or pines in which all the trees are the same age, you can usually assume that the trees grew from a seedbed prepared by fire.

There are disadvantages to preventing forest fires completely. If a forest grows for too many years without a fire, dead and decaying plant matter piles up on the ground. Then if a fire does start, it'll be hotter and more destructive than cooler fires that otherwise would happen more often.

But we're not suggesting that it's okay for human beings to be careless with fire in the forest. Natural fires happen in random locations, usually in summer, the time of lightning storms. A forest or grassland that's accustomed to fire can recover and even benefit from an occasional fire of moderate intensity. Unnatural fires—those caused by people—happen at times and places that may make it impossible for the forest to recover.

Robert Leo Smith, *Ecology and Field Biology*, 3rd ed. (New York: Harper and Row, 1980).

Death of the Dinosaurs Revisited

Were the last generation of dinosaurs all of the same sex? Here's another theory about that well-known mystery of life on Earth, the disappearance of the dinosaurs 65 million years ago.

According to this theory, the dinosaurs may have become extinct because small variations in the temperature of the climate would cause their eggs to produce all males or all females. The idea came from observations of modern reptiles. The gender of most turtles, alligators, and crocodiles is determined by the temperature at which the eggs are incubated. There is only a small range of temperatures that will produce both males and females from the same brood of eggs. Eggs cooler than that narrow range produce one sex exclusively; warmer eggs produce the other sex.

Mississippi alligators are a case in point. If their eggs are incubated below about 86 degrees Fahrenheit, the babies are all female; above about 93 degrees, all male. Mother alligators ensure a mix of male and female in the next generation by building some nests on hot levees and others in cooler marshes.

If the ancient dinosaurs were like some of their modern relatives, a small change in climate could have produced a whole generation of dinosaurs of one sex. Obviously, if all the newborn dinosaurs were of the same sex, mating soon would have become impossible. Result: extinction.

Scott F. Gilbert, *Developmental Biology* (Sunderland, Mass.: Sinauer Associates, 1985).
M. W. J. Ferguson and T. Joanen, "Temperature of Egg Incubation Determines Sex in *Alligator mississippiensis*," *Nature* 296:850 (April 29, 1982).

Breaking a Coffee Cup

Why is it so easy to break a coffee cup if it's already cracked?

To break a coffee cup, you have to pull atoms far enough apart—maybe a millionth of an inch—so they no longer bond to each other.

All along the crack, atoms have already been separated. The point of interest is at the tip of the crack—where it ends in solid material. To make the crack just a little longer, all you have to do is separate a few more atoms.

The important principle here is leverage.

Leverage is the principle that allows you to pull a nail out of hard wood with a crowbar. A small force at the end of a long crowbar becomes an immense force pulling on the nail. The crowbar has the effect of magnifying the force you apply to it.

Usually, a cracked coffee cup breaks because something hits it or presses on it with a force. The two sides of the crack act as levers, transmitting that force to the tip of the crack like little crowbars, pulling atoms apart. As the crack proceeds through the cup, these levers get longer, so they pull atoms apart with even greater force. The longer the crack becomes, the easier it is to make it just a little longer.

To break a coffee cup, you don't really have to pull billions and billions of atoms apart all at once—you only have to separate a few atoms at the tip of the crack, then a few more after that, and a few more after that, and so on all the way to the other side of the cup.

In real life all this happens in a split second as the cup hits the floor. High-speed photographs show that cracks travel through brittle materials like ceramics and glass at thousands of miles per hour.

A split second is all it takes to break a coffee cup.

J. J. Gilman, "Fracture in Solids," *Scientific American*, February 1960.
J. E. Field, "Fracture of Solids," *Physics Teacher* 2:215 (1964).

How Bacteria Resist Antibiotics

Here's how it happens in a typical laboratory situation: the case of intestinal bacteria and the antibiotic drug streptomycin. Intestinal bacteria are a well-known and well-studied type, easy to grow in a laboratory; they'll thrive on simple nutrient broth in a flask. That's one reason biologists use them so often for experiments. Intestinal bacteria also multiply fast; one cell can leave a billion descendants in a day.

Most intestinal bacteria are easy to kill. A tiny dose of the antibiotic drug streptomycin kills all the intestinal bacteria in a flask—all except about one in a billion, that is. That one intestinal bacterium in a billion is different from the others in that it cannot be killed by streptomycin. A spontaneous change—a so-called mutation—has taken place in that bacterial cell.

Under normal conditions this mutation is of no use to the bacterium. But if the environment changes, that mutation becomes an advantage. The mutant cell can survive in streptomycin. If streptomycin is in the flask, all the normal bacteria are killed, but a new culture springs from that one-in-a-billion bacterial cell that happens to be resistant.

The individual bacterial cells don't change during their lifetimes. It's the bacterial population as a whole that adapts to changing conditions.

So, bacteria can become resistant to an antibiotic because each new generation produces a few different individuals—mutants. Those mutants are a kind of insurance for the future of the whole bacterial population. If conditions change, maybe one of those different individuals will be able to cope and propagate the bacterial culture.

T. Dobzhansky, "The Genetic Basis of Evolution," *Scientific American*, January 1950; reprinted in *Facets of Genetics: Readings from Scientific American*, ed. A. Srb (San Francisco: W. H. Freeman, 1970).

Cool Wind before a Thunderstorm

A blast of cool air from a threatening cloud signifies that the engine that runs a thunderstorm has started. The simplest isolated thunderstorm begins with hot afternoon sunshine baking the ground. Air near the ground becomes warm, moist, buoyant.

At some point, a mass of this buoyant air cuts loose from ground level and rises to create a warm, moist updraft. That warm, moist air expands in the low atmospheric pressure thousands of feet up. Expansion cools the air, just as it does when air escapes from a pressure nozzle; the moisture condenses. In early afternoon that condensation makes fluffy cumulus clouds; later, it makes towering storm clouds with ice crystals and tiny raindrops.

After a while, raindrops grow big and heavy enough to fall through the updraft, dragging cool high-altitude air down with them to make a cool downdraft in the cloud. Some raindrops evaporate as they fall. That takes heat from the air and makes the downdraft even cooler and stronger. Soon, cool air pours from the base of the cloud and makes a gusty wind ahead of the storm. This is an indication that, somewhere in the cloud, rain has begun to fall—along with snow and ice higher up. The thunderstorm's engine is running: warm air and moisture going up, cool air and rain coming down.

Somehow that engine also electrifies the storm cloud to make lightning, which in turn makes thunder.

After fifteen or twenty minutes, the cool downdraft has grown to cover the whole base of the storm cloud. That cuts off the supply of warm air and moisture from the cloud, and the storm dies.

"Thunderstorm," in *Encyclopaedia Britannica*, 15th ed.

C. Donald Ahrens, *Meteorology Today*, 2nd ed. (St. Paul: West, 1985).

Richard P. Feynman, *The Feynman Lectures on Physics* (Reading, Mass.: Addison-Wesley, 1964), vol. II, chap. 9.

Lightning

When lightning strikes the ground, there's an opening act followed by the main event.

The opening act is a stream of negative electrical charge coming down from the storm cloud in steps. This so-called step leader travels about a hundred and fifty feet at about a sixth of the speed of light, then stops for about fifty-millionths of a second; it then moves on another hundred and fifty feet and stops—and so on toward the ground.

That step leader establishes an electrical connection, a path of least resistance, between cloud and ground. The step leader sets the stage for the main event, the bright flash we see as lightning. That bright flash is the "return stroke": positive electrical charge traveling up from ground to cloud at about a million miles an hour along the path established by the step leader.

That's your basic lightning flash: a faint step leader going down, then a bright return stroke going up, all in a tiny fraction of a second.

The leader-and-stroke cycle usually repeats several times along the same channel. High-speed cameras have recorded dozens of individual lightning discharges along the same path in less than a second.

Plenty about lightning is still unknown. For instance, how does the storm cloud get electrified in the first place? Cloud and ground are like terminals of a ten-million-volt battery. What charges the battery in the first place? Updrafts, downdrafts, ice crystals, and raindrops are probably responsible—somehow. Electrification of storm clouds is one of the unsolved mysteries of weather.

C. Donald Ahrens, *Meteorology Today*, 2nd ed. (St. Paul: West, 1985).
Richard P. Feynman, *The Feynman Lectures on Physics* (Reading, Mass.: Addison-Wesley, 1964), vol. II, chap. 9.

THUNDER

What can the sound of thunder tell you?

Lightning is quick; thunder is slow. The electrical discharge of lightning takes only a fraction of a second, even if the lightning stroke is many miles long. But thunder from that lightning stroke, like other sounds, takes about five seconds to go just one mile.

Another interesting fact about sound in air is that low-pitched sounds travel farther than high-pitched sounds before they die out.

With those ideas in mind, you can interpret thunder.

After a lightning stroke, the first thunder you hear will be from the part of the lightning stroke nearest you. Thunder from more distant parts of the same stroke reaches you later. Lightning is almost instantaneous; thunder is spread out in time.

Thunder from nearby lightning still contains most of its original mix of high and low pitches, so it sounds like ripping or cracking. Thunder from far away has lost its high pitches. What's left is a deep rumble—low pitches of the original thunder, mixed with echoes from the ground.

Lightning may have branches in addition to its main channel, like branches from the trunk of a tree. A ripping sound from nearby branches reaches you first; then, a loud crack from the main channel; finally, a deep rumble from distant branches.

So thunder can tell you something about the shape of the lightning stroke that caused it. Scientists have used stereo recordings of thunder to deduce the shape of lightning strokes hidden in clouds.

While you're listening to thunder, please don't get hit by lightning. Don't stand in the middle of an open field; don't sit under the apple tree; bring the sailboat to shore; get inside a car or a building. Survive to listen to another thunderstorm.

Arthur A. Few, "Thunder," *Scientific American*, July 1975.

Heat lightning

One of the more mysterious pleasures of a warm summer evening is the spectacle of lightning from distant thunderstorms, flickering silently on the horizon while stars shine overhead. People usually call it heat lightning.

Lightning is easy to see at great distances, especially when it illuminates high, thin clouds visible for many miles. But thunder usually doesn't carry more than about ten or fifteen miles from the storm, because turbulent air around a storm acts as a damper on sound waves.

Another reason thunder doesn't carry very far has to do with differences in temperature between air at ground level and higher up. Early on a summer evening, the ground is still warm from afternoon sunshine, so the air at ground level is also warm. A few thousand feet up, the air is cooler. This temperature difference bends the sound of thunder upward. Here's how it happens.

We can think of a sound wave as an invisible wall of slightly compressed air, traveling at the speed of sound. Sound travels slightly faster in warm air than in cool air. So the part of that invisible wall down in the warm air travels a little faster than the part in the cool air higher up. The bottom of this invisible wall gets ahead of the top as it travels. The invisible wall of sound bends upward as it goes.

The common term "heat lightning" actually describes an essential feature of the situation. Because of a layer of warm air near the ground, the sound of thunder is bent upward, into the night sky. The result is that you see lightning on the horizon but you don't hear thunder.

C. Donald Ahrens, *Meteorology Today*, 2nd ed. (St. Paul: West, 1985).

HOW MANY GIRLS, HOW MANY BOYS?

Suppose someone marries and has four children. How many will be girls and how many boys? In this example we're neglecting the possibility of twins. If each of the four children has an equal chance of being a boy or a girl, what combination of boys and girls is most likely?

It seems obvious that the most likely combination would be two boys and two girls. But it's not. To find the answer, all you have to do is list all the possibilities.

There could be a girl, then a boy, then two girls; a boy, then two girls, then a boy; four girls and no boys, and so on. There are a total of sixteen possible combinations.

Out of those sixteen combinations, eight have three children of one sex and one of the other. Only six of the sixteen combinations involve two girls and two boys. So, if a couple has four children, it's most likely that they will have three children of one sex and one of the other. If each child has an equal chance of being male or female, and if there are no twins, that outcome is more likely than two boys and two girls.

You can check your list of the sixteen possibilities and also see that there are only two in which all the children are of the same sex; in other words, there's a two-out-of-sixteen or one-out-of-eight chance of having four children of the same sex.

Martin Gardner, *Entertaining Science Experiments with Everyday Objects* (New York: Dover, 1981).

Modern biology in a monastery garden

What do you get when you cross a one-foot pea plant with white flowers and a six-foot pea plant with purple flowers? There have always been superstitions and off-color jokes about questions like that. But Gregor Mendel, one of the most important figures in the history of biology, wanted to find out what really happens—by crossing real pea plants.

Mendel lived in a monastery more than a hundred years ago. He experimented with plant breeding in the monastery garden. Mendel had a hunch that heredity proceeded according to rules; he wanted to find the simplest form of those rules. Here's some of what his experiments revealed:

If you cross a one-foot pea plant with a six-foot pea plant, you get plants that are either one foot tall or six feet tall—not in-between, three-and-a-half-foot plants. If you cross purple flowers with white flowers, you get either purple or white flowers—not in-between, lavender flowers. At least not with pea plants.

On top of that, Mendel discovered that if you know the ancestry of the parent plants, you can predict, using a mathematical formula, what percentage of plants in the next generation will have purple flowers as opposed to white.

Actually, heredity is rarely so simple. But Mendel kept his plant-breeding experiments as simple as possible so that he would get clear results. His results showed that some easy-to-see traits like height and flower color were passed from generation to generation in a strict pattern.

Gregor Mendel was a pioneer in what is now called genetics. His garden experiments of over a century ago revealed heredity operating with almost computer-like precision to help make the luxuriant variety of living plants.

G. Mendel, "Experiments in Plant Hybridization" (1865), trans. and reprinted in *Classic Papers in Genetics*, ed. J. A. Peters (Englewood Cliffs, N.J.: Prentice-Hall, 1959), and in

Genetics: Readings from Scientific American, intro. by C. I. Davern (San Francisco: W. H. Freeman, 1981).

SEE YOURSELF AS OTHERS SEE YOU

One mirror is not enough to see yourself as others see you. When you look at a bathroom mirror, you see an image of yourself with left and right reversed. If you don't believe it, extend your right hand to shake hands with yourself. The "person" in the mirror extends his or her left hand.

A bathroom mirror switches left and right in any image it reflects. To see yourself as others do, you need a second mirror to undo the effect of the first mirror and switch the directions back again.

Hold two hand mirrors in front of you with their edges touching and a right angle between them—like the two covers of a book when you're reading. With a little adjustment you can get a complete reflection of your face as others see it. Wink your right eye—the person in the mirror winks his or her right eye. This may seem strange after a lifetime of looking at bathroom mirrors.

When you look at two mirrors held at right angles like the covers of an open book, you see left and right restored to their original relationship. The reason is that the image you see has been reflected twice before reaching you. When you look at the right-hand mirror, you see a reflection of the left-hand mirror, which in turn gives a reflection of the left-hand side of your face, and vice versa. Two reflections are involved.

This seems complicated, but it's easy to see when you try it.

Martin Gardner, *Entertaining Science Experiments with Everyday Objects* (New York: Dover, 1981).

NEUTRINOS AND THE END OF THE UNIVERSE

The universe is expanding; galaxies are getting farther from each other. A big question is whether there's enough matter in the universe to reverse that expansion by mutual gravitational attraction.

Neutrinos are the most abundant and least apparent subatomic particles in the universe. They traditionally have been assumed to exert no gravitational force on anything. But what if that assumption is wrong? If each neutrino exerts even a tiny gravitational force, the combined effect of all of them might reverse the expansion of the universe.

Our understanding of gravity tells us that if neutrinos exert a gravitational force, they must have at least some "rest mass"—the kind of mass that registers as weight on a scale. Do neutrinos have rest mass?

Einstein's special theory of relativity, which has turned out to describe nature accurately so far, says that any object that has rest mass—like a baseball or an airplane—must travel slower than light. So, do neutrinos travel slower than light? We got a chance to check on February 24, 1987, when the explosion of a star—a supernova—was seen in the Large Cloud of Magellan, a nearby galaxy visible from southern latitudes. At about the same time, a burst of neutrinos, presumably from the supernova, reached instruments in Japan and the United States.

Some of the neutrinos arrived at Earth a few seconds later than the others. Was the difference in arrival times due to a difference in departure times? Or were some neutrinos traveling slower—slower than light?

Do some neutrinos have rest mass and exert gravitational force? Will neutrinos reverse the expansion of the universe? The evidence is still ambiguous. We need to know the exact second that light from that supernova first reached Earth. It may or may not be possible to figure that out.

"Supernova Neutrinos," *Scientific American*, June 1987, p. 18.
"Neutrinos from Hell," *Sky and Telescope*, May 1987.

Cooking an Egg

Why does the consistency of an egg change from liquid to more or less solid as it cooks? The important change is in the arrangement of the protein molecules.

A protein molecule is a long chain of smaller molecules, called amino acids. The amino acids are linked by strong bonds between atoms. Those chains are not likely to break while you're cooking an egg. But another change happens when you turn on the heat under a raw egg.

In a raw egg each protein molecule is folded up into a compact ball. There are weak bonds between atoms that hold the protein molecule in its folded-up position. When you heat the egg, you increase the tiny random jiggling motion of the molecules. In any material warmer than absolute zero, the atoms and molecules move around at random. Higher temperature means faster random motion.

As the egg heats, the random motion gets fast enough to break the bonds that keep the proteins folded up. So the protein molecules unfold. The kind of weak bonding that once held the protein molecules in a folded position now works in another way. Here and there, a loose end of one protein molecule comes alongside a loose end of another. The loose ends overlap and bond side to side. As the egg gets hotter, the spliced proteins form a mesh, with water filling in the spaces within the mesh. As more protein molecules unfold and connect to each other, the mesh gets stronger, and the egg becomes more solid. When the mesh is strong enough for your taste, you take the egg off the heat.

So when you cook an egg, the important change is in the arrangement of the protein molecules. They unfold, connect to each other, and form a mesh that gives the egg its new, solid, cooked consistency.

Harold McGee, *On Food and Cooking: The Science and Lore of the Kitchen* (New York: Macmillan, 1985).

HOW A FIELD CAN BECOME A FOREST

The process goes by the name of ecological succession, and in the case of a field becoming a forest, it may take over a hundred years. Here's how it might happen.

Start with an abandoned farm field. The first plants to move in are weeds—the so-called pioneer colonists, including dandelions and ragweed, among others. These pioneers devote a large part of their energy to reproduction.

After two or three years, perennial grasses and shrubs begin to replace the early weeds—that's the next stage in the ecological succession.

In some areas, pine trees move in next, thanks to seeds carried into the field by wind and animals. Within a few decades, what used to be a bare field becomes a pine forest that may last for three-quarters of a century. Earlier grasses and shrubs disappear because they can't tolerate the shade under the pines.

While the pine forest develops, oak and hickory seeds enter the area. Some types of oak and hickory saplings tolerate shade well, so they grow steadily and, after many decades, become tall enough to cast shadows on the pines. Pine trees won't reproduce in shade, so they gradually disappear by attrition due to storms, disease, or old age. The oaks and hickories come to dominate the forest for a nearly indefinite number of decades, or until they are removed by some disturbance. The field has become a forest in the so-called climax stage of ecological succession.

This is ecological succession in a simple idealized example. The specifics vary from region to region, and in any case few fields remain absolutely undisturbed for a hundred years or more.

Eugene P. Odum, *Basic Ecology* (Philadelphia: Sanders College, 1983).
Robert Leo Smith, *Ecology and Field Biology*, 3rd ed. (New York: Harper and Row, 1980).

THE MOST IMPORTANT FLY IN THE HISTORY OF SCIENCE

This fly emerged in 1910—in a bottle, in Thomas Hunt Morgan's laboratory at Columbia University in New York. It was a male fruit fly with a very unusual, unexpected trait: white eyes. Fruit flies usually have bright red eyes.

Morgan was breeding fruit flies to observe patterns of heredity. Wondering which of the descendants of this unusual white-eyed fly would inherit white eyes, he bred it to its red-eyed sisters. Two fruit-fly generations later, some more white-eyed flies appeared.

The strange and surprising thing was that the new white-eyed flies were all males. Why did only male flies inherit white eyes? It can be explained in terms of chromosomes—objects in the nucleus of each cell that look like little pieces of thread under a microscope.

White eyes in a fruit fly are caused by an unusual change, an apparent defect, in the so-called X chromosome. A male fruit fly has only one X chromosome in each cell; if that chromosome is defective, the fly has white eyes. A female fruit fly, on the other hand, has two X chromosomes; if one is defective, the other serves as a backup and the female fly has normal red eyes.

Back in 1910, biologists already knew that male fruit flies have a distinctive set of chromosomes. Male fruit flies also have a distinctive capacity to inherit white eyes—that was Morgan's discovery.

Thomas Hunt Morgan's observations gave a clue that the mystery of biological inheritance might be explained in terms of chromosomes—a new idea in 1910. Now it's a basic idea in our understanding of how living things reproduce and develop.

T. H. Morgan, "Sex Limited Inheritance in *Drosophila*" (1910), reprinted in J. A. Peters, ed., *Classic Papers in Genetics* (Englewood Cliffs, N.J.: Prentice-Hall, 1959); originally in *Science* 32:120–122.

Helena Curtis, *Biology*, 4th ed. (New York: Worth, 1983).

How plants fight

For centuries people have known that few plants will grow near a black walnut tree. The tree seems to do something to the soil that inhibits the growth of other plants.

This is more than just competition. In competition, plants vie for the same resources—minerals, water, space, light. Each competing plant in effect seeks to take something from the environment, and to take more than surrounding plants. Black walnut trees use the strategy of putting something into the environment that makes life difficult or impossible for other plants. Tomatoes, for example, wilt and die near black walnut trees; alders won't survive more than about ten years.

The black walnut's weapon is a substance botanists call juglone. It's harmless within the tree, but it's chemically changed into its effective form when it mixes with ground water. Juglone added to plant beds stunts or kills the plants.

In the desert, where resources are especially precious, shrubs like sagebrush, wormwood, and salvia eliminate competition with a family of chemicals called terpenes. Desert shrubs are often surrounded by a zone practically bare of vegetation; even after a fire, new plants have trouble growing in the terpene-affected area.

Some plants even produce chemicals that inhibit their own reproduction. In the prairies of Oklahoma and Kansas, some of the so-called pioneer weeds—sunflower, ragweed, crabgrass, and others—make chemicals that inhibit the growth of other individuals of the same species, cutting out competition even from their own kind.

"Allelopathy," in *McGraw-Hill Encyclopedia of Science and Technology* (New York: McGraw-Hill, 1987) and *Yearbook* (1988).
A. Sutton and M. Sutton, *Eastern Forests* (New York: Knopf, 1985).

How Fast Are the Clouds Moving?

Go outside and glance at the clouds. Are they moving? In which direction? What's the slowest apparent motion your eyes can detect? How quickly can you detect the motion? How does your ability change under different conditions—high and low clouds, strong and light wind, day, night, moon, no moon, overcast, partly clear?

We detect motion either by comparing the position of the cloud to the position of some fixed object like a chimney, or by using our own eyes as the fixed reference. Of course, our eyes don't measure the speed of a cloud in miles per hour; we judge motion in terms of angles within our field of vision.

Our visual perceptual system is a surprisingly sensitive detector of motion. At night, an airplane or a satellite stands out among the stars purely because of its motion, even among stars that are brighter. Some people can detect motion as slow as one-thirtieth of a degree of angle per second, using a fixed object as a reference. At that speed a cloud takes about fifteen seconds to cross the disk of the sun or moon. (The sun and moon, incidentally, happen to have almost exactly the same apparent size in the sky—about one-half a degree of angle.)

Not only are we visually sensitive to slow motion, but we can judge the direction and speed of motion quickly. A brief glance may be enough to tell in which direction and how fast the clouds are moving. A good baseball outfielder can judge the direction of a fly ball within a fraction of a second after it leaves the bat.

Apparently we don't perceive motion by taking one visual snapshot now, another one later, and comparing the two. Instead, we perceive motion well because our eyes are especially sensitive to any change in the pattern of light falling on our retinas.

Marcel Minnaert, *The Nature of Light and Colour in the Open Air* (New York: Dover, 1954).

G. Johannson, "Visual Motion Perception," *Scientific American*, June 1975.

S. H. Bartley, *Introduction to Perception* (New York: Harper and Row, 1969).

K. von Fieandt and I. K. Moustgaard, *The Perceptual World* (New York: Academic Press, 1977).

Sort Nuts by Shaking the Can

If you shake a can of mixed nuts for a few seconds, the largest nuts come to the top. The spaces between nuts are not big enough for small nuts to fall through, but the small nuts end up on the bottom and the large ones on top anyway. Shaking creates momentary gaps in the mixture; small gaps occur more often than large ones.

Then the nuts are sorted by gravity. As the can shakes, the large nuts frequently move aside far enough to allow a small nut to fall into the space beneath. This happens much more often than the reverse process, in which several small nuts happen to make a gap that one large nut can fall into.

Every time a large nut moves far enough to allow a smaller nut to fall into a gap beneath it, that large nut ends up resting on top of the smaller nut. Over the course of several seconds of shaking, the large nuts slowly move up.

This is not only an amusing kitchen observation, but something with practical usefulness. In many parts of the world, construction workers separate gravel from sand by shaking the container. Coarse gravel comes up to the top. Manufacturers can exploit the tendency of large particles to move up when they need to make a mixture of particles of different sizes, in pharmaceuticals, glass making, and paint making. They can put large particles into a container first, then add smaller particles on top. Shaking the container for the right amount of time causes the large particles to move up until they're evenly distributed through the mixture.

"Nuts and Jolts," *Scientific American*, May 1987, p. 58D.

A. Rosato et al., "Why the Brazil Nuts Are on Top: Size Segregation of Particulate Matter by Shaking," *Physical Review Letters* 58:1038–1040 (March 9, 1987).
Of related interest: R. B. Prigo, "Liquid Beans," *The Physics Teacher*, February 1988, p. 101.

Everybody Talks About Genes— but What Do They Do?

The classic experiments in the history of science are often memorable not for complexity but for cleverness. Here's an example.

By the 1940s, biologists were pretty well convinced that offspring grow to resemble their parents because information of some kind is transmitted from generation to generation by the so-called genes. But what information is transmitted? Exactly what does a gene do?

The strategy of the biologists George Beadle and Edward Tatum was to "find out what genes do by making them defective." Beadle and Tatum worked in the 1940s with ordinary bread mold. They grew mold in test tubes with a simple nutrient formula: sugar, minerals, and one vitamin. Normal bread mold could make all the proteins and other substances it needed from that nutrient formula.

Then Beadle and Tatum exposed some of their mold samples to intense X-rays. A few of the X-rayed molds would no longer grow unless they had proteins added to their diet. The X-rays had destroyed the molds' ability to make those proteins.

What's more, this inability to make certain proteins, like any other inherited trait, was passed on to future generations of molds. The X-rays had caused a defect, and the defect was inherited. The real effect of the X-rays had been to damage the molds' genes.

The Beadle-Tatum experiment was important because it showed that what a "gene" conveys from generation to generation is a set of recipes—instructions—for making proteins. The next project in biology, still unfinished, is to find out how proteins make offspring resemble their parents.

G. Beadle, "The Genes of Men and Molds," *Scientific American*, September 1948; reprinted in *Genetics: Readings from Scientific American*, intro. by C. I. Davern (San Francisco: W. H. Freeman, 1981).

Looking high and low at leaves

Have you ever noticed that the same tree may have leaves of different shapes?

Next time you have a chance, look closely at the leaves on a big tree—a white oak, for example. Compare leaves at the top of the tree with leaves near the bottom. Leaves near the top often tend to be relatively small and thick, the ones at the bottom large and thin. Also, leaves near the top may have deeper lobes than those near the bottom.

It may be that these differences exist because they help the leaves to do their job better. The most obvious job of a leaf is to make food for the tree from carbon dioxide, water, and sunlight. In view of this, a small, thick leaf with deep lobes seems better suited for the sunny, hot environment near the top of a tree. A thick leaf absorbs more carbon dioxide, while losing less water, than a thin leaf of the same surface area. That's because carbon dioxide is absorbed through special cells inside the leaf; a thicker leaf has more of those special cells, for every square inch of surface area, than a thin leaf does.

Also, small size and deep lobes allow a pattern of air circulation that helps keep the leaf cool near the top of a tree. If a leaf gets too hot, it lets too much water escape into the air by evaporation. And if a tree loses too much water, it can't bring the minerals it needs up from the ground.

On the other hand, a large, thin leaf with a smooth outline seems better suited to the darker, cooler environment near the bottom of a tree. Down there, heat and water loss are not so threatening.

So the hot, sunny environment near the top of a tree seems to favor small, thick leaves; the cool, dark zone at the bottom favors large, thin leaves. On many trees, you can see that difference.

D. F. Parkhurst and O. L. Loucks, "Optimal Leaf Size in Relation to Environment," *Journal of Ecology* 60:505–537 (1972).
Susan Wintsch, "The Greedy Leaf," *Garden*, May–June 1986.

A Taste Test

An old-fashioned English lady comes to you and says: "I like milk in my tea. But I'm very particular; the milk must be added to the tea. I do not like it if the milk goes into the cup first. I can tell, just by tasting, whether the milk or the tea went into the cup first."

You, the scientist, decide to test this remarkable claim with an experiment. You prepare eight cups of tea. In four of them, you put the milk in first; in the other four, you put the tea in first. You don't tell the lady which is which. You ask her to taste all eight cups and select the four in which the milk went in first.

The English lady takes a sip from each cup of tea and sets aside four cups, saying, "These are the ones in which the milk went in first." You check your records and find she was right about three of the cups, and wrong about one.

A reporter is on the phone, asking, "Inquiring listeners want to know—can this lady tell, just by tasting, whether the milk was added first? Yes or no?" You're the scientist. What do you do?

You have to keep a cool head and consider all the possible ways the experiment could have come out. What's the probability that the lady could have achieved that degree of success just by guessing?

There are precise mathematical ways of answering that question. In this example, a little calculating shows that there's a 24 percent chance that the lady could have achieved at least that degree of success just by guessing, without having the ability she claims to have. From that you'd probably conclude that you do not have enough information to tell for sure whether the lady can really distinguish which cups of tea had milk put in first.

This is a cute example with a serious moral: a scientist has to consider not only how an experiment did come out, but also all the other ways it could have come out.

Sir Ronald A. Fisher and Ghiuean T. Prance, *The Design of Experiments*, 9th ed. (New York: Hafner, 1974), chap. II.

WHY A RUBBER BAND SNAPS BACK

Stretch a rubber band; it becomes long and thin. Let it go; it snaps back to its original short, fat shape, ready to be stretched again.

Rubber has this useful property for two reasons. First, rubber molecules have a peculiar structure and arrangement; second, those molecules are always moving around, because the rubber is warmer than a temperature of absolute zero. In any material warmer than absolute zero, the molecules are always moving around in a tiny, random, jiggling motion.

Rubber is made of molecules shaped like strands of spaghetti. If you stretch a rubber band, you pull those spaghetti-shaped molecules into a more or less straight line. But the molecules are still moving around. They shake from side to side and bump into each other. Because of that motion, the molecules tend to spread out sideways; so they must "unstraighten," curl up, kink, tangle. That makes them pull inward on the ends of the rubber band. The stretched rubber tries, so to speak, to become short, thick, and flabby so the molecules will have more room to move around sideways. The rubber band snaps back.

This picture also explains another property of rubber: unlike most materials, it shrinks when you heat it and expands when you cool it. In a warm rubber band, the molecules move faster, tend to shake sideways more, and therefore pull harder at the ends than in a cold rubber band. A rubber band will squeeze a package harder if it's been in the sun than if it's been in the freezer.

Richard P. Feynman, *The Feynman Lectures on Physics* (Reading, Mass.: Addison-Wesley, 1964), vol. I, chap. 44.

Frederick T. Wall, *Chemical Thermodynamics*, 2nd ed. (San Francisco: W. H. Freeman, 1965), chap. 15, "Statistical Thermodynamics of Rubber."

Breaking the Tension

Carefully fill a glass with water, until the surface of the water is exactly level with the brim of the glass. You may want to use a second glass to add the last of the water, rather than trying to do it at the faucet. Now gently drop a quarter into the glass. The water surface will bulge upward slightly, but water will not run over the rim of the glass.

Molecules of water attract each other. That attraction makes a film under tension at the surface of the water. Even though the water is bulging upward, surface tension keeps it from spilling.

Now the game is this: how much change can you drop into the water before water spills over the rim of the glass? Every coin displaces an amount of water equal to its own volume. In other words, the bulge at the top of the water has the same volume as all the coins added to the glass. The film at the surface of the bulging water—caused by attraction of water molecules—holds the water like a bag. How much water can that bag hold before it breaks?

Possibilities for elaboration suggest themselves. You could agree that the next-to-last person to add a coin before the water spills wins all the change in the glass.

To make the game last longer, use paper clips instead of coins. As before, carefully fill the glass with water until the water surface is exactly level with the glass brim. How many paper clips can you drop in before the surface tension breaks and water spills over the edge? Some people may guess that about ten paper clips will do it. But remember, a paper clip is just a piece of bent wire, which displaces only a tiny volume of water. You may be able to get over a hundred paper clips into the glass before the water spills.

Of related interest: Martin Gardner, *Entertaining Science Experiments with Everyday Objects* (New York: Dover, 1981).

How cockroaches get away

The all-too-familiar American cockroach almost seems to know where you're going to strike. What's the tip-off that sends the cockroach running?

Entomologists who have investigated this question have found that cockroaches detect the puff of wind generated by a nearby moving object. They run away from the wind. And it has to be a puff of wind, not a steady breeze. To make the roach run, the wind speed has to increase sharply over a small fraction of a second.

Roaches have special organs for detecting puffs of wind. Extending from the rear end of a cockroach are two tapered appendages, the so-called cerci. The underside of each cercus has about 220 delicate hairs connected to the roach's nervous system. When these hairs are struck by a puff of air, they cause nerve impulses to be sent to the insect's leg muscles.

Each hair can flex a little more easily in one direction than in others, so each hair is especially sensitive to wind from a particular direction. Nerve impulses from the hairs are sent to the roach's legs in just the right pattern to cause the roach to turn away from the direction of the wind. A puff of air from the left causes impulses to be sent to the cockroach's left legs; as a result, the roach turns right, away from the wind.

A cockroach with one cercus damaged or removed makes wrong turns. A roach with both cerci damaged or removed doesn't try to escape at all.

J. M. Camhi, "The Escape System of the Cockroach," *Scientific American*, December 1980.

THE MOON ILLUSION

For thousands of years people have been noticing that the moon looks much bigger when it's very low in the sky than when it's high overhead. This effect has come to be called the moon illusion.

It's not a physical effect; the atmosphere does not magnify the image of the moon. The atmosphere may cause the moon to appear flattened or colored, but not magnified. Photographs show that the moon's image is really the same size no matter how high or low it is in the sky. But people almost always judge the image to be larger when the moon is low.

The real cause of the moon illusion seems to be the juxtaposition of the moon and features on the distant horizon. Our perception of the distance to the horizon influences our judgment of how big the moon is. Professional psychologists have done experiments that indicate this, but you can investigate the moon illusion yourself.

Cut a hole the size of a quarter in a big piece of cardboard. Hold the cardboard at arm's length, not next to your eye. Look at the rising or setting moon through the hole. That cardboard screen blocks your view of the landscape near the moon. Does the moon look smaller with the cardboard than it does without?

Another experiment involves looking at the whole scene upside down, by bending over and looking between your legs. For most people, looking at a scene upside down weakens the impression that the horizon is far away. Does that weakened impression of distance dispel the moon illusion for you?

Looking at the rising or setting moon through a hole in a cardboard screen, and looking at it upside down are two simple tricks that may dispel the moon illusion. Try them, and get a hint of the mystery and complexity of our ability to judge distance and size.

Lloyd Kaufman and Irvin Rock, "The Moon Illusion," *Scientific American*, July 1962.

POLARIZING SUNGLASSES

How do polarizing sunglasses cut glare?

To start, an analogy. Two children hold a long jump rope stretched between them. The child at one end shakes the rope, causing waves to travel from one end of it to the other. The child can shake the rope up and down, sideways, or in any other direction. That makes waves that vibrate in different directions.

If we think of the waves traveling along that rope as a model of light waves traveling through space, then the direction in which the rope vibrates corresponds to the direction of the so-called polarization of the light. Light can be polarized horizontally, vertically, or in any other direction.

Back to our rope analogy: imagine now that the children pass the rope between the slats of a picket fence. If the child at one end shakes the rope from side to side, the vibrations will be stopped by the fence. But if the shaking is up and down, the waves will go right through.

Polarizing sunglasses are like that picket fence: they pass light that vibrates vertically but block light that vibrates horizontally. In general, light that has bounced off a horizontal non-metallic surface—like a road or a lake—vibrates horizontally. That's glare, and it's the kind of light polarizing sunglasses are designed to block.

Here's an experiment: take the polarizing glasses off, slowly rotate them to a vertical position while you look through one lens, and you'll see glare spots reappear. You are, in effect, turning the picket fence sideways, so the slats let vibrations of glare get through.

G. P. Können, *Polarized Light in Nature* (New York: Cambridge University Press, 1985).

Pros and Cons of the Mercator Projection

If you sail northeast from Caracas, Venezuela, into the Atlantic Ocean, maintaining a heading of northeast, where will you reach land? Portugal? Spain? France? England? Ireland? Scotland? Norway? It's easy to find out, if you use the right kind of map.

The right kind of map for this purpose is the Mercator projection, first published as a world map in 1569 by the German geographer and engraver Gerardus Mercator. Projection means transferring points from the round Earth onto a flat map. There are dozens of projections in use today, but Mercator's projection has a special property: the course that results from maintaining a steady compass bearing, such as northeast, comes out as a straight line. Such a course is technically called a loxodrome.

A loxodrome is not the shortest course between two points on the Earth, nor is it a straight line on the Earth. But a loxodrome is a straight line on a Mercator-projection map, and it's the simplest course on the Earth if you're navigating by compass, as people did in Mercator's time.

To get these advantages, Mercator had to introduce some famous distortions. Continents and oceans near the poles are much too large compared to features near the equator. Greenland looks much too big compared to Africa. For that reason, modern atlases avoid Mercator's projection for maps showing distribution of people or resources.

We'll leave it to you to find out where a northeast course from Caracas takes you. Just lay a ruler on the map at a forty-five-degree angle, with one end at Caracas. But for this purpose, be sure that your map is based on the Mercator projection.

"Map," in *McGraw-Hill Encyclopedia of Science and Technology* (New York: McGraw-Hill, 1987).

Encyclopaedia Britannica, 14th ed. (1968).

There is a Mercator map of the world in *Chambers's Encyclopedia* (1969), vol. XV, pp. 2–3.

A Surprise at a Shadow's Edge

On a sunny day, look closely at your shadow on a plain, smooth surface. You will see that the edge is not perfectly sharp; there's a gradual transition from the dark inside, through a range of intermediate greys, to the bright outside. Now look for something else: a bright band just outside that grey zone on the bright side. Look more carefully and you may also see a dark band just inside the grey zone on the dark side.

That bright band on the outside of the shadow and the dark band on the inside were first discussed in scientific literature over a century ago, by the Austrian physicist Ernst Mach. They're generally called Mach bands.

The Mach bands are an optical illusion: they don't represent actual variations in the amount of light hitting the surface; the bands are created by our visual system. To see them more clearly, try moving around and watching the edge of the moving shadow.

The Mach bands indicate that our visual system accentuates contrast at edges. Our visual system tells us about the difference between the dark area and the bright area by accentuating the line where they meet. That's why we can use lines to draw pictures. To make a convincing picture of, say, a coffee cup, an artist needs to draw only the edges. Our perceptual system interprets the lines to mean "coffee cup" on one side and "background" on the other.

Look for the Mach bands along a shadow's edge: an extra-bright band along the bright side, an extra-dark band along the dark side. Those bands provide a striking piece of evidence that our visual system accentuates contrast wherever we see an edge.

F. Ratliff, "Contour and Contrast," *Scientific American*, June 1972.

Marcel Minnaert, *The Nature of Light and Colour in the Open Air* (New York: Dover, 1954).

Of related interest: M. S. Livingstone, "Art, Illusion and the Visual System," *Scientific American*, January 1988.

Richard P. Feynman, *The Feynman Lectures on Physics* (Reading, Mass.: Addison-Wesley, 1964), vol. I, chap. 36.

ALGAE AS A THERMOSTAT

It has been suggested that algae in the oceans help keep Earth's climate steady. The suggested process goes like this:

Some algae living in the open sea are known to make a gas called dimethyl sulfide, or DMS. This gas escapes from the algae into the air and undergoes a chemical reaction that leaves tiny crystals, about a millionth of an inch across, suspended in the air above the oceans.

Water vapor condenses around these tiny crystals to make cloud droplets—maybe smaller-than-usual cloud droplets. Smaller-than-usual cloud droplets make whiter-than-usual clouds, which reflect more sunlight than usual back into space, cooling the climate.

Now for the more speculative part of this idea. It may be that the algae that make DMS gas prefer warm water. If so, these algae could act as a global thermostat. Here's how.

Suppose the world warmed up for some reason. These particular algae would flourish in the warm water, making more DMS, which would form more tiny crystals in the air, making more and brighter clouds. The extra clouds would reflect more sunlight into space, cooling the atmosphere and reversing the warming trend that started the whole process. In other words, if the algae get too warm, they cause clouds to form and put the ocean in the shade.

That's the theory. Is it right? Not all the evidence is in yet.

In any case, there are many other processes, including the burning of fossil fuels by humans, that could influence climate. A big job in climatology is to find out which processes are the important ones.

"Climate Control," *Scientific American,* July 1987, p. 24.
"No Longer Willful, Gaia Becomes Respectable," *Science* 240:393–395 (April 22, 1988).
R. J. Charlson et al., "Evidence for the Climatic Role of Marine Biogenic Sulfur," *Nature* 329:319 (April 24, 1987).

Balance a yardstick without looking

A yardstick is thirty-six inches long, so you know the exact center is at the eighteen-inch mark. But how could you find the center blindfolded?

You might guess something complicated, like using the distance between two knuckles to represent one inch, and measuring with that. But there's an easier way. Hold your hands in front of you, with your index fingers pointing forward. Rest the yardstick across your fingers and slowly bring your hands together under the stick. Your fingers will meet under the eighteen-inch mark.

You're actually finding the center of gravity of the stick, the point where it balances. We're assuming that your yardstick is made of wood or other material that's uniform from end to end, with no metal attachments or big holes that would cause it to balance somewhere other than the center. If that assumption is correct, the yardstick will balance at the eighteen-inch mark.

As you bring your hands together, you feel the stick sliding first over one finger, then over the other. Whenever your left hand gets closer to the center of gravity than your right hand, the yardstick presses down harder on your left index finger. More pressure causes more friction, so the left hand stops sliding. All the sliding then happens over your right index finger till your right hand gets closer to the center and reverses the situation. In other words, if one hand gets ahead, friction stops it from sliding till the other hand catches up.

All this happens with no special effort on your part. Just rest the yardstick across your index fingers and slowly, steadily, bring your hands together. Your hands will meet at the eighteen-inch mark, the center of gravity of the yardstick.

H. Steinhaus, *Mathematical Snapshots* (New York: Oxford University Press, 1950).
Martin Gardner, *Entertaining Science Experiments with Everyday Objects* (New York: Dover, 1981).

A ROCK IN A ROWBOAT

Here's a classic puzzle you'll enjoy pondering.

You're in a rowboat in a small pond. You have a huge boulder with you in the boat. You throw the boulder overboard into the water. Does the water level of the pond rise, fall, or stay the same?

Now, it's pretty clear that if you took everything completely out of the pond—yourself, the boat, and the boulder—the water level would fall. And if you stayed in the boat, in the water, and threw the boulder ashore, the water level in the pond would also fall. Since the rowboat would weigh less after you tossed the boulder ashore, the boat would float higher and displace less water. But what happens if you toss the boulder overboard, into the water?

You can simulate the situation by filling a big mayonnaise jar with water. That's the pond. Put a rock in a tin can—that's the rowboat—and float it in the water in the jar. Mark the level of water in the mayonnaise jar. Next take the rock out of the can and drop it into the jar. Now you have a rock at the bottom and the empty tin can floating at the surface. Don't let it capsize. Is the level of water in the jar higher, lower, or the same as before?

Here's the logic behind the answer. When the boulder is in the boat, it displaces an amount of water equal to its weight. That's a lot of water. Lying at the bottom of the pond, the boulder displaces only an amount of water equal to its volume. That's less water. The bolder displaces less water if it's on the bottom of the pond than if it's in the boat. Also, the boat floats higher without the rock.

So here's the answer: if you're in a rowboat with a big boulder and you throw the boulder overboard into the water, the pond water level falls.

R. J. Brown, *333 More Science Tricks and Experiments* (Blue Ridge Summit, Pa.: Tab, 1981).

WHITER AND BRIGHTER THAN NEW

The main purpose of laundry detergent is to take dirt out of fabric. But many detergents also leave something behind—an additive designed to make the fabric look whiter and brighter than new.

This additive is a so-called optical brightener. It's really a dye with a special property: it absorbs invisible ultraviolet light from the sun and gives off a faint glow of visible blue light. The blue glow counteracts the yellowish color of dirty old fabric and gives the eye the impression of white.

Optical brighteners are examples of so-called fluorescent materials. These brighteners take in energy from the ultraviolet rays of sunlight and release that energy in the form of blue light visible to the eye.

Optical brighteners can be economical to use. If you add optical brighteners to your clothes, you need less bleach to make them look clean. That can help your clothes last longer, because some bleaches weaken the fibers in the cloth.

Optical brighteners have an especially dramatic effect under black lights, which are still used in some bars and skating rinks and other places to create a festive atmosphere. Black lights produce a lot of ultraviolet light and very little visible light. Fabrics—especially light-colored fabrics—light up as the optical brighteners in the fibers change that invisible ultraviolet light into visible blue light.

"Bleaching," in *McGraw-Hill Encyclopedia of Science and Technology* (New York: McGraw-Hill, 1987).

F. L. Wiseman, *Chemistry in the Modern World* (New York: McGraw-Hill, 1985).

Hormone Insecticides

In human beings, certain hormones trigger the physical changes that make a child's body mature into an adult's body. With insects, it's different. It's the lack of a hormone that allows an insect to mature to its next life stage.

It's called the juvenile hormone, because its function is to keep the insect young—to slow down its development. Being immature for the right amount of time is important for insects. Many do most of their eating before they become adults. After they become adults, these insects mostly travel and reproduce.

Some plants make an anti-juvenile hormone—a substance that destroys the cells in an insect's body that make juvenile hormone. In particular, a bedding plant of the genus *Ageratum* makes an anti-juvenile hormone that disrupts the life cycle of milkweed bugs. Milkweed bug nymphs quickly become miniature adults after exposure to anti-juvenile hormone. That means the bugs eat less during their lifetimes, because they don't get a chance to pass through all their early life stages—the stages in which they would do a lot of their eating. This has obvious advantages for the plant. Female milkweed bugs that have been rushed into adulthood by anti-juvenile hormone are sterile. Also, they refuse to mate.

There has been no large-scale practical application yet, but if anti-juvenile hormones could be manufactured in quantity, they might be used as insecticides that affect only insects. A spraying or dusting of anti-juvenile hormone might cause a whole population of insects to become precocious adults, with a reduced appetite for food and no ability to reproduce.

W. S. Bowers et al., "Discovery of Insect Anti-juvenile Hormones in Plants," *Science* 193:542–547 (August 13, 1976).

Scott F. Gilbert, *Developmental Biology* (Sunderland, Mass.: Sinauer Associates, 1985).

AN INVERTED IMAGE

This is a simple visual experiment. To do it, you need two three-by-five index cards.

Take one of the cards and make a tiny triangle of holes in it with a straight pin. Make the three holes about a sixteenth of an inch apart. Take the other index card and poke just one pinhole in it.

Now take the card with the triangle of pinholes, and hold it very close to your eye. Hold the other card, the one with the single pinhole, about four inches in front of the first one. Face a strong light and look through the three holes at the single hole. You will see your triangle of pinholes upside down.

The holes in the two cards cast three thin beams of light into your eye, making three dots on your retina. Under normal circumstances, your retina gets a focused, upside-down image projected by the lens of your eye. Your nerves and brain in effect turn that image over to make it right side up. But in this experiment, the card with the three holes is so close to your eye that the lens can't focus the three dots into an image. The rest of your visual system, operating as usual, inverts the triangle of light on your retina anyway, and you see the pinhole pattern upside down.

It's a very striking effect; try it.

C. J. Lynde, *Science Experiences with Ten-Cent Store Equipment*, 2nd ed. (Scranton, Pa.: International Textbook Co., 1951), p. 132.

A NEW PERSON FROM A NOSE?

Can you really make a new person from a nose, the way Woody Allen did in the movie *Sleeper*?

First we have to back up. One of the most mind-boggling mysteries of our planet is this: how does a single fertilized egg cell generate the hundreds of cell types in a complete living organism?

Within that question is another question. The fertilized egg divides into two cells, then four cells, then eight, sixteen, and so on, to make all the cells in the new body. Do all those body cells preserve all the genetic information that was in the original fertilized egg? And is that genetic information always available? Would it be possible to grow a new copy of an organism from any of its cells?

It can be done with plants. It appears to have been done with frogs. But with mammals, it's another story.

In one experiment, the nucleus of a fertilized mouse egg cell was replaced with a nucleus taken from another fertilized mouse egg cell. This involves tricky microsurgery. The egg cell with the replacement nucleus, implanted in a female mouse, developed into a normal mouse.

But in another experiment, the replacement nucleus came from a fertilized mouse egg that already had divided into four cells. The egg that received this nucleus did not develop beyond a very early embryonic stage. In other words, cells in a developing mouse embryo almost immediately lose their ability to generate new, separate mice.

The real purpose of these experiments, and others like them, was to investigate that great mystery of how one cell generates a whole new organism. But the results also put a damper on fantasies about, say, cloning a political leader from cells of his nose. It appears that once a cell has become specialized enough to be part of a nose, it has long since lost its ability to become anything else.

Scott F. Gilbert, *Developmental Biology* (Sunderland, Mass.: Sinauer Associates, 1985), p. 314.

THE MYSTERIOUS NUMBER PI

If the distance across the diameter of a circle is 1 foot, the distance around that circle is approximately 3.141592 feet. That number is pi— that famous number from geometry, one of the most mysterious and remarkable numbers known. Pi relates the circumference of a circle to its diameter.

We have to say that pi is approximately 3.141592 because pi cannot be expressed exactly. The digits after the decimal point go on forever; that was proved in the 1700s.

Although mathematicians have proved that the digits of pi go on forever, no one knows what all those digits are. There are lots of formulas for calculating the digits of pi. Most of them involve some simple calculation, repeated over and over. Each repetition adds more digits. One recent calculation, done on a computer in Japan, gave the value of pi to over two hundred million digits.

Here's another strange property of the number pi: as far as anyone can tell, the digits are in completely random order. There's only one correct order, but there's no pattern to it. In the long run, every digit appears just as often as every other digit. And there's no way to guess what the two-hundred-million-and-first digit will be just by looking at the preceding two hundred million digits.

The randomness of the digits, and the fact that they go on forever, leads to another striking conclusion: any number pattern you can think of—your social security number, for instance—must be lurking somewhere among the known or unknown digits of pi.

In fact, if you assign a number to every word in the English language, then somewhere, probably trillions of trillions of digits beyond the decimal point, lies the sequence of numbers representing any book you care to name.

David Wells, *The Penguin Dictionary of Curious and Interesting Numbers* (New York: Penguin, 1986).

Petr Beckmann, *A History of Pi* (New York: St. Martin's, 1971).

"Following Pi down the Decimal Trail," *Science News* 133:215 (April 2, 1988).

Springs in the Cafeteria

You're in line at a cafeteria. You pass a stainless-steel cart that holds several stacks of plates. When you take a plate off the top of one stack, the other plates in the stack rise from below just far enough to present the next plate at the same height as the one you just took!

Underneath each stack of plates is a spring whose tension is adjusted to keep the top plate level with the top of the cart. Once the adjustment is made, the top plate will always be level with the top of the cart, no matter how many plates are in the stack.

Those cafeteria plate dispensers cleverly exploit a general property of springs: if you put twice as much force on a spring, it compresses, or stretches, twice as far. If you put twenty plates on the stack, their weight compresses the spring just twice as far as the weight of ten plates.

This property of springs was discovered about three hundred years ago by the English physicist Robert Hooke. Hooke wrote, "as the tension, so the force." Hooke noticed this principle at work in all kinds of devices that rely on springy materials: spring scales, bows, watches, and the vibrating parts of musical instruments.

In the twentieth century we've come to realize that this relationship, now called Hooke's Law, is a result of forces between atoms in solid material. If two atoms in a metal are pulled apart, they pull on each other. If you separate the atoms more, the force between them increases, in exact proportion. This is true as long as you don't pull the atoms too far.

Because of this pervasive relationship between atoms, just about all springs compress or stretch twice as far if you load them with twice the force. And because of that, cafeteria plate dispensers keep the top plate level with the top of the cart, no matter how many plates are in the stack.

Quotation from Hooke's treatise in the anthology *Moments of Discovery*, vol. 1, ed. George Schwartz and Philip W. Bishop (New York: Basic Books, 1958).

Richard P. Feynman, *The Feynman Lectures on Physics* (Reading, Mass.: Addison-Wesley, 1964), vol. I, chap. 12.

Firefly Signals

Firefly flashes are mating signals. Male fireflies cruise the evening air, flashing their lanterns in a pattern characteristic of their species, looking for females of their own kind.

The males of some species flash with a slow glow lasting several seconds; others flicker more than forty times per second. There are more than a hundred firefly species, each with a particular male flash pattern.

The female firefly emerges from her burrow after sunset and waits on the ground. When she detects the flash of a male of her species, she flashes back in a characteristic female pattern. Exchanging flashes, male and female find each other and mate. Then the female returns to her burrow, and the male returns to the air.

Sometimes, however, the male does not return to the air, because he is eaten by the female. Female fireflies of some species eat male fireflies of other species. They attract these males by detecting their flash patterns and sending a return flash pattern that imitates a female of the appropriate species. Some of these duplicitous insects have a repertoire of five or more different flash patterns.

So, every time a male firefly sees a responsive female flash in the grass, he faces a life-and-death dilemma: hesitate, and risk losing out to another male in the race to mate, or rush in and risk being eaten alive.

J. E. Lloyd, "Mimicry in the Sexual Signals of Fireflies," *Scientific American*, July 1981.

Mirages

On a hot, sunny day, the road in the distance seems to be covered with water. It reflects the blue of the sky. But when you get there, the mirage is gone.

You realize, of course, that there was never any water there in the first place. But the apparition was convincing; what you saw looked exactly like light reflected from a puddle. And as far as the reflection of light is concerned, there might as well have been water on the road.

The pavement, baking in the sun, is hot. The hot pavement heats the air near the surface to a much hotter temperature than the air higher up. A few inches above the pavement there's a boundary between hot air and cooler air—a boundary that can reflect light just like a water surface.

Light can be reflected from any boundary between one transparent medium and another. Take, for example, the boundary between air and water. If you look toward the far side of a quiet lake, you see trees and mountains beautifully reflected from the top of the water surface.

Light can be reflected from the bottom of a water surface too. If you're underwater in a swimming pool, wearing goggles so things are in focus, look up and toward the far side of the pool. If the water is quiet, you will see a mirror-like reflection from the underside of the water surface.

Light can be reflected from either side of a boundary between one transparent medium and another. The reflection is best if light hits the boundary at a glancing angle.

Back to the road: the boundary between hot air near the pavement and cooler air a few inches up reflects light exactly as a water surface would. From a distance, viewing the road at a glancing angle, it's hard to tell whether you're seeing water, or just reflection from the top of a layer of hot air—a mirage.

Marcel Minnaert, *The Nature of Light and Colour in the Open Air* (New York: Dover, 1954).

Seeing yellow

Why does a mix of red light and green light look yellow?

Imagine the colors of the rainbow. There's a continuous range of colors, from red through orange, yellow, green, and blue, to violet.

The cells in our retinas that give us color sensations come in only three types. Each type is sensitive to a fairly broad segment of that rainbow—a fairly broad range of colors—with peak sensitivity in one region. Each cell generates a signal in proportion to the total amount of light it detects. Our nerves and brain combine those signals to give us color sensations.

The perception of the color yellow calls upon two types of these cells. One type has its peak sensitivity in the green range, with less sensitivity to colors near that peak, and the other has its peak sensitivity farther toward the red range.

Suppose pure light from the yellow part of the rainbow enters our eye. There's no color-detecting cell with peak sensitivity to yellow. But yellow light does stimulate the green-sensitive cells, slightly, and the red-sensitive cells, slightly. Signals from those cells are combined by our nerves and brain to give the sensation of yellow.

Now, if a mix of red and green light falls on our retina, it's the same thing as yellow as far as our visual system is concerned. Again, red-sensitive and green-sensitive cells are both stimulated, and again their signals are combined. Again, we get a sensation of yellow.

This simple picture shows that the job of detecting what we usually call yellow light is shared by two types of color-detecting cells in our eyes. Whether those two types are stimulated by pure yellow light, or by a mix or red and green light, the signals that finally come out are the same.

Other things being equal, our eyes cannot distinguish yellow light from a mix of red light and green light.

R. Bergsten, "When Is Yellow *Yellow?*" *The Physics Teacher*, October 1986.

Why Cotton Wrinkles

A cool, dry cotton fiber springs back after being bent. A warm, damp cotton fiber doesn't. Temperature and moisture make the difference.

First, the role of temperature.

Cotton fibers, like many other materials, spring back as long as they're cooler than a certain transition temperature—the temperature at which the fiber loses its springy quality. This temperature of transition from springy to non-springy is a characteristic of the material. For dry cotton, this point is about 120 degrees Fahrenheit. Dry cotton stays springy below 120 degrees; above 120 degrees, it holds whatever shape it's bent into.

Now the role of moisture.

Water, absorbed into cotton fibers, lowers this transition temperature. In other words, damp cotton loses its springiness at a lower temperature than dry cotton.

Suppose the weather is warm and you're wearing a cotton shirt or blouse. You sit in a chair, leaning back. Perspiration lowers the transition temperature of the fabric to about 70 degrees Fahrenheit. Your skin is warmer than that, so heat from your skin is sufficient to change the cotton into its non-springy state. Your weight then presses the cotton into a new, wrinkled shape. You stand up; the cotton cools off, dries out, and resumes its springy state—this time in a wrinkled shape.

The cotton holds its wrinkled shape till you iron it flat again, probably with a steam iron. Steam lowers the transition temperature of the cotton to a point much cooler than the temperature of the iron. The iron can then press the fabric into a new, flat shape.

F. L. Wiseman, *Chemistry in the Modern World: Concepts and Applications* (New York: McGraw-Hill, 1985).

"Glass Transition," in *McGraw-Hill Encyclopedia of Science and Technology* (New York: McGraw-Hill, 1987).

DNA CAUGHT IN THE ACT

DNA, deoxyribonucleic acid, is the famous molecule that carries genetic information. A DNA molecule takes the form of a thread of two strands twisted around each other in a double helix.

Every time a cell divides, the DNA inside copies itself. The double helix unwinds. Each old strand serves as the template for a new companion strand assembled from raw materials in its vicinity. The result is two identical DNA molecules where there used to be only one. That's how genetic information is passed on.

This all-important copying process was actually photographed by the English biologist John Cairns in 1962. The experimental subjects were intestinal bacteria.

The strategy was this: feed the bacteria radioactive material that they'll incorporate into their DNA. Leave the bacteria alone for a while, then remove their DNA, spread it on a glass plate, and coat the plate with photographic emulsion. Wherever the DNA has taken up some of the radioactive material, it'll leave a mark on the emulsion. Develop the emulsion, examine it under a microscope, and you should be able to see photographic images left by the radioactive DNA molecules.

The experiment was technically difficult, but it worked. Cairns's 1962 photographs showed what looked like loops of black thread—those were the DNA molecules. And in some places, those threads divided into two strands. DNA had been caught in the all-important act of copying itself. The process that conveys hereditary information from generation to generation had been made visible.

John Cairns, "The Bacterial Chromosome," *Scientific American*, January 1966 (reprinted in the *Scientific American* anthology *Genetics*, intro. by C. I. Davern [San Francisco: W. H. Freeman, 1981]).

Newton's Rainbow

Isaac Newton, the seventeenth-century English physicist, darkened a room by covering all the windows. Then he cut a small hole in one window shade to let in a narrow beam of sunlight.

He put a triangular solid-glass prism in the sunbeam. The prism bent the sunbeam and projected it onto the opposite wall of the room, twenty-two feet away. Where the beam hit the wall, it was spread out into an oblong patch with all the colors of the rainbow—a spectrum.

Others had noticed that when sunlight goes into a glass prism, colors come out. But how? Why?

One popular explanation in Newton's time was that the prism created the colors by somehow changing the white light into other forms. Newton's interpretation was different. He guessed that those rainbow colors were all present in the original white light, but they were mixed. The prism sorted them out. Today we know Newton was right, but he had to do a lot of thinking and experimenting to convince himself.

For example, Newton figured that if the prism was really taking the white light apart, then it should be possible to put the colors back together and make white light once again. In one of his simpler experiments, Newton projected not one but three spectra on the wall and made them overlap partially, to mix the colors. The result was white light, reconstituted from rainbow colors.

So Isaac Newton, working three centuries ago, did far more than just observe the colors of the spectrum; he proposed a new explanation for the colors, and he tested his explanation with experiments. Newton not only took white light apart, he put it back together.

I. B. Cohen, "Isaac Newton," in *Dictionary of Scientific Biography* (New York: Charles Scribner's Sons, 1974).

R. S. Westfall, *Never at Rest: A Biography of Isaac Newton* (New York: Cambridge University Press, 1980).

The Elastic Ruler

Of all the home demonstrations we've described in this book, this might be the simplest. All you need is a ruler and a saucepan full of water.

Hold the ruler vertically and lower it into the water on the side of the pan farthest from you. Bring your eye down to a position just a little higher than water level and look at the ruler. The submerged part of the ruler looks shorter than the part above water. Notice that the effect becomes more pronounced as you lower your eye closer and closer to the level of the water surface.

Now try this: fix your eye just a little above water level and slowly raise the ruler out of the water. The ruler seems to stretch as it emerges from the water. And, of course, it works in reverse: dip the ruler back in and it seems to compress.

The physical principle at work here is that light is bent whenever it crosses at an angle from one transparent medium into another.

You can try to imagine following light rays as they leave the bottom of the ruler on their way to your eye. Light rays leaving the bottom of the ruler at a steep angle—say, upward at forty-five degrees—get bent toward the horizontal when they leave the water. The light rays then travel through the air at a shallow angle, closer to horizontal. Light rays reaching your eye at a shallow angle appear to come from just beneath the surface of the water.

C. J. Lynde, *Science Experiences with Ten-Cent Store Equipment* (Scranton, Pa.: International Textbook Co., 1951), p. 71.

Uncorking a Mystery

The seventeenth-century English physicist Robert Hooke was curious about the remarkable properties of cork—its ability to float, its springy quality, its usefulness in sealing bottles. He investigated the structure of cork with a new scientific instrument he was very enthusiastic about: the microscope.

Hooke cut a thin slice of cork with a penknife, put it under his microscope, focused sunlight on it with a thick lens, and looked through the eyepiece. What he saw looked like a piece of honeycomb. The cork was full of small empty compartments separated by thin walls. He called the compartments "pores, or cells." He estimated that every cubic inch of cork had about twelve hundred million of these cells.

Hooke had discovered the small-scale structure of cork. And he concluded that the small-scale structure of cork explained its large-scale properties.

Cork floats, Hooke reasoned, because air is sealed in the cells. That air springs back after being compressed, and that's why cork is springy. And that springiness, combined with the fact that the cells are sealed off from each other, explains why a piece of cork is so well suited for sealing a bottle.

Hooke's observation not only explained the properties of cork, but gave a hint that all living tissue might be made of small building blocks.

Our understanding of what those building blocks are has changed since Hooke's time. Today we'd say that what Hooke observed were dead walls that had been created by living cells when the cork was still part of the tree. But we still use the word "cell," and our usage can be traced back to the microscopic observations of cork made over three hundred years ago by Robert Hooke.

R. Hooke, *Micrographia* (New York: Dover, 1961).

R. S. Westfall, "Robert Hooke," in *Dictionary of Scientific Biography* (New York: Charles Scribner's Sons, 1972).

PSYCHOLOGICAL ACCOUNTING

Here are two hypothetical situations involving money. What would you decide to do in each situation?

First, imagine that you have decided to see a play to which admission is ten dollars per ticket. As you enter the theater, you discover that you have lost a ten-dollar bill. Assuming you have more money, would you still pay ten dollars for a ticket to the play?

When a psychologist posed this question to over 180 people, most of them—88 percent—said they would go ahead and buy the ten-dollar ticket even after discovering that they had lost a ten-dollar bill.

In the second situation, you've already bought a ten-dollar ticket to the play. But as you enter the theater, you discover that you have lost your ticket. The seat is not marked; you can't recover the lost ticket. Would you pay ten dollars for another ticket?

When this question was posed to a couple of hundred people, only 46 percent said they would pay ten dollars for a replacement ticket.

In both situations, you end up paying twenty dollars, rather than ten, to see the play. The difference in people's responses seems to be a matter of psychological accounting. In the first case, the lost money and the cost of a ticket seem to have been entered in separate accounts; losing ten dollars had no particular bearing on the decision to buy a ticket to the play. In the second situation, the lost object was the ticket itself. The cost of the new ticket and the cost of the old ticket were entered in the same psychological account; the total cost of twenty dollars then seemed excessive.

This experiment gives evidence that what we decide to do depends not only on the information we have, but also on how we organize that information. Viewing the same question two different ways, we may come up with two different answers.

Amos Tversky and Daniel Kahnemann, "The Framing of Decisions and the Psychology of Choice," *Science* 211:453–458 (January 30, 1981).

COLOR IS IN THE EYE OF THE BEHOLDER

Black and white, plus black and red, make full color, because color *is* in the eye of the beholder. That was demonstrated in the 1950s by the engineer Edwin Land, also famous as the founder of the Polaroid Corporation.

Land's procedure was this: make two photographs of the same colorful scene—say, a vase of flowers—on black-and-white film. But make the photographs slightly different by taking one picture through red glass and the other through green glass. Load these two black-and-white photographs into two slide projectors pointed at the same screen. Superimpose the projected images to make a single black-and-white image.

Now put a piece of red glass in front of the projector containing the picture originally taken through red glass. You might think this would just turn the image on the screen pink. But, astonishingly, the image on the screen takes on a nearly full range of colors, including blues and greens—even though neither blue nor green light is hitting the screen. A black-and-red image plus a black-and-white image makes a full-color image!

This experiment, and others like it, showed that how we experience light depends on context. Our visual system assigns colors to objects in a picture on the basis of differences in the light coming from different parts of the scene.

Edwin Land demonstrated in the 1950s that color is not really a property of light itself. Instead, color is in the eye of the beholder; it's a sensation created by our visual system. Our eye makes a world of color from whatever light is available.

E. H. Land, "Experiments in Color Vision," *Scientific American*, May 1959.

WINE AND LIFE

Yeast from crushed grapes turns grape juice into wine by the process of fermentation. Sugar in the juice is changed into carbon dioxide gas and ethyl alcohol.

How does yeast do that?

A hundred years ago, a lot of scientists thought yeast caused the transformation of grape juice into wine through some "vital force" present only in living things like yeast cells. According to this "vitalistic" view, fermentation is inextricably linked with life. Other scientists had a different view, namely, that all the processes of living organisms could, in principle, be explained by the same laws of chemistry and physics that describe non-living things.

A crucial experiment was carried out in 1896 by the German chemist Eduard Buchner. He mixed yeast with sand and diatomaceous earth, ground the mixture in a mortar and pestle, put the mixture in a hydraulic press, crushed it under tremendous pressure, and squeezed out a fluid that had been part of the yeast cells.

When Buchner added sugar to this fluid, the sugar changed to alcohol, and bubbles of gas came out. Fermentation happened without yeast cells. Buchner had demonstrated that fermentation was caused not by some vital force in the yeast, but by a chemical, an enzyme, that can work by itself in a test tube.

Eduard Buchner was credited with opening up a new field of research: biochemistry. Buchner specifically rejected the vitalistic viewpoint—the view that the chemistry of life was unknowable. His demonstration of fermentation without living cells also earned him the 1907 Nobel Prize for Chemistry. And since Buchner's time, biological research has been based solidly on the notion that the same laws of physics and chemistry apply to living things and non-living things.

H. Schriefers, "Eduard Buchner," in *Dictionary of Scientific Biography* (New York: Charles Scribner's Sons, 1970).

E. Buchner, Nobel Lecture, 1907, with presentation speech by K. Mörner, in *Nobel Lectures: Chemistry, 1901–1921* (New York: Elsevier, 1966).

THE SWEET SPOT ON A BASEBALL BAT

There's a right way and a wrong way to hit a ball with a bat. If you hit the ball with the wrong part of the bat, your hands get stung and the bat may break. If you hit the ball on the "sweet spot" of the bat, you get the feeling of a solid connection with the ball—no stinging, no vibration, no broken bat.

Every bat has a sweet spot. The location along the length of the bat varies, depending on the shape of the bat and on how you hold it. You can find the sweet spot by gripping the bat handle with one hand in the same place as when you're swinging. Take a hammer in the other hand and gently tap the bat at various places along its length. At some point you will feel almost no vibration when you tap. That's the sweet spot. That's the best place for the ball to meet the bat.

If you don't have a baseball bat handy, you can find the sweet spot on a pencil. Hold the pencil loosely between two fingers and tap it sharply against the edge of a hard table. Try tapping various spots along the length of the pencil, from the far end to very close to your fingers. You'll find one point where the tapping does not sting your fingers. You'll probably also notice a difference in the sound as you get closer to the sweet spot.

Any swinging object has a sweet spot, or "center of percussion," as engineers call it. A good hammer or axe is designed so that if you grip the handle at the proper place, the sweet spot is right where the tool strikes the nail or the wood. As a result, you get the optimum in power and control.

P. Kirkpatrick, "Batting the Ball," *American Journal of Physics* 31:606 (1963).

U. Ingard and W. L. Kraushaar, *Introduction to Mechanics, Matter, and Waves* (Reading, Mass.: Addison-Wesley, 1960), p. 343.

O. Eschbach, *Handbook of Engineering Fundamentals*, 2nd ed. (New York: Wiley, 1969), pp. 4–41.

Make an image without a lens

Punch a pinhole in the center of a big piece of cardboard. That pinhole can project an upside-down image onto a piece of white paper.

The effect is easiest to see if you're indoors on a sunny day, in a room with a window. Stand on the side of the room farthest from the window. Hold the card with the pinhole vertically. Hold a piece of white paper in the shadow of the card, behind the pinhole. Light coming through the pinhole will make an upside-down image of the window on the white paper.

Hold the white paper closer to the pinhole, and you get a brighter but smaller image. Make the pinhole bigger by shoving a pencil point into it, and you get a brighter but fuzzier image.

A way to see how it works is to think of rays of light traveling in straight lines from each part of the window, through the pinhole, onto the white paper. Because the pinhole is small, each point on the white paper receives light from only a tiny part of the window. So light from the window is formed into an image on the white paper.

You can also see that light from the top of the window, after going through the hole, ends up at the bottom of the projected image. That's why the image is upside down.

Making an image with a pinhole is so simple, any child can do it. But the technique is also used on the cutting edge of modern science. Some objects in space, including supernovas and black holes, emit X-rays. Ordinary lenses and mirrors cannot focus X-rays, but a pinhole can. Many X-ray telescopes aboard astronomical satellites are elaborate pinhole cameras, based on the same principle you've just demonstrated with a piece of cardboard.

G. K. Skinner, "X-ray Imaging with Coded Masks," *Scientific American*, August 1988.

C. J. Lynde, *Science Experiences with Ten-Cent Store Equipment*, 2nd ed. (Scranton, Pa.: International Textbook Co., 1951).

CHIMES, FOR YOUR EARS ONLY

This kitchen demonstration calls for a fork and a piece of string about five feet long. Tie the middle of the string tightly around the fork at the narrowest part of the handle. Hold one end of the string in each hand and let the fork hang down in the middle. Press the ends of the string to your ears and swing the hanging fork against the edge of a table so it strikes once and bounces away. If the fork you're using is made of one piece of metal, with no joints or rivets, it will ring like a bell and send a surprisingly loud and rich chiming sound through the string to your ears.

If you try the same thing without pressing the string against your ears, the sound isn't nearly as rich. The reason for the loudness is that the taut string carries the fork's vibrations much better than air does. Take the string away from your ears, and all you hear is whatever comes to your eardrums through the air.

The reason for the richness of the sound is that you've suspended the fork in a way that allows it to vibrate freely, at many frequencies, making many musical tones at the same time. If you were holding the fork in your hand, the flesh on your fingers would damp out a lot of those vibrations.

Try tying not just one but two forks, or a fork and a spoon, into the middle of the string. Allow the cutlery to hang freely, press the ends of the string to your ears, and let the cutlery strike the edge of a table. From plain, ordinary flatware you can hear a sound almost like church bells.

C. J. Lynde, *Science Experiences with Ten-Cent Store Equipment,* 2nd ed. (Scranton, Pa.: International Textbook Co., 1951).

Martin Gardner, *Entertaining Science Experiments with Everyday Objects* (New York: Dover, 1981).

IT'S NOT JUST THE HEAT; IT'S THE HUMIDITY

Our bodies generate heat. The more active we are, the more heat we generate.

To keep our inner body temperature at the level where it belongs, we must dissipate that heat. If we don't, our body temperature begins to rise. We face heat stroke at a body temperature of about 106 degrees Fahrenheit—and death at a body temperature of about 110.

Heat always flows from warmer material into cooler material, never the other way. When the surrounding air is cooler than our body temperature, our skin is cooler than the inner body. That makes heat flow out, as it should.

If the air temperature gets close to our body temperature, something more is needed to keep the skin cooler than the inner body. We sweat.

When we sweat, energy represented by heat in our skin drives water molecules apart and sends them off into the air. In other words, evaporation cools our skin; the all-important temperature difference between inside and outside is restored, and heat continues to flow outward, even if the air temperature is close to our body temperature.

We're in trouble if the air is not only very hot but also humid. If the air is nearly saturated with water vapor, evaporation effectively stops, and sweating no longer cools our skin. Heat no longer flows out of our bodies, so our body temperature rises, especially if we continue to generate a lot of internal heat through hard work.

Heavy exertion, high temperature, and high relative humidity are a dangerous combination that no one can endure for long.

R. C. Plumb, "Knowing Some Thermodynamics Can Save a Life," *J. Chem. Ed.* **49** (2):112–113 (February 1972).

Fluorescent Lamps

In an incandescent bulb, electric current flows through a tungsten filament. In a fluorescent tube, current flows through rarefied gas.

Mixed in with that gas is a small amount of mercury vapor. Mercury atoms in the vapor pick up extra energy from the electric current. When those mercury atoms give up their extra energy, they give it up as ultraviolet light. That's a kind of light not visible to the eye, so the next step is to convert that ultraviolet to visible light.

Here's where the process of fluorescence comes in. Fluorescent materials convert one form of light into another. The inside of a fluorescent tube is coated with a fluorescent phosphor—a powder that absorbs energy in the form of ultraviolet light and re-emits that energy as visible light.

So in a fluorescent lamp, electrical energy is converted to ultraviolet light by mercury atoms; then the ultraviolet light is converted to visible light by the fluorescent phosphor on the inside of the tube.

Fluorescent tubes run cool. As lighting devices go, a fluorescent tube is very efficient at converting electrical energy into lots of light and very little heat. But before the electric current gets into the tube, it must go through a so-called ballast, a device that smooths out fluctuations in the current. The ballast is by far the most inefficient part of a fluorescent lamp.

"Fluorescent Lamp," in *McGraw-Hill Encyclopedia of Science and Technology* (New York: McGraw-Hill, 1987).

H. R. Crane, "Fluorescent Lights: A Few Basic Facts," *The Physics Teacher*, November 1985, p. 502.

"News Updates (Reagan Signs Ballast-Efficiency Standards)," *Science News* 134:30 (July 9, 1988).

J. Raloff, "Energy Efficiency: Less Means More—Fueling a Sustainable Future," *Science News* 133:296–298 (May 7, 1988).

THE TRUTH ABOUT BLEACH

Bleach doesn't work by taking anything out of fabric; it works by changing what's already there.

Take a grape juice stain, for example. Grape juice looks purple because of molecules in the juice that reflect purple light and absorb non-purple light. Those molecules absorb non-purple light because their atoms are connected by electrical bonds that store just the amounts of energy carried by non-purple light. What bleach does is to rearrange those bonds, those connections between atoms, so that they no longer absorb light as they did before. The formerly purple molecules are made colorless.

One important idea here is the relation between energy and color of light. The color sensation we get from light depends largely on how much energy the light carries. Different energies appear as different colors.

Another important idea is that molecules are made of atoms connected by electrical bonds. To say that a molecule absorbs light means that the molecule stores the energy brought to it by the light. The electrical bonds are the storage batteries. Different bonds hold different amounts of energy, so different bonds absorb light of different colors. Change the bonds between atoms and you change the molecule's color.

What bleach does is to rearrange the bonds between atoms so the formerly colored molecule doesn't absorb energy from light as it did before. The stuff that caused the stain is still in the fabric—bleach just makes it invisible.

F. L. Wiseman, *Chemistry in the Modern World* (New York: McGraw-Hill, 1985).

"Bleaching," in *McGraw-Hill Encyclopedia of Science and Technology* (New York: McGraw-Hill, 1987).

CARBON DATING

If an object contains plant or animal material of any kind—cotton, wool, or leather, for example—the technique of carbon dating may reveal the object's age.

Occasionally, subatomic particles from space hit nitrogen atoms in the Earth's atmosphere. The impact changes the nitrogen atoms into so-called carbon-14 atoms. A definite, small percentage of all the carbon atoms on our planet are carbon-14. They're pretty much like ordinary carbon atoms, but they're unstable: sooner or later, each carbon-14 atom changes back into nitrogen. It takes about six thousand years for half the carbon-14 atoms in any object to change back to nitrogen.

Plants and animals take in carbon, including carbon-14, from their environment while they live. Plants get carbon from carbon dioxide in the air; animals eat the plants. But when a plant or an animal dies, it stops taking in new carbon. In the dead body, the amount of ordinary carbon stays the same, while the carbon-14 gradually disappears—it keeps changing into nitrogen.

So, to determine the age of something by the carbon-14 method, you measure the total amount of carbon in the object, then measure how much of that is still in the form of carbon-14. The less carbon-14, the longer it has been since the death of whatever plant or animal the object was made from.

Carbon-14 dating works best for objects less than about fifty thousand years old. There are other dating methods that work for inanimate objects millions or billions of years old, using other unstable atoms.

"Radiocarbon Dating," in *McGraw-Hill Encyclopedia of Science and Technology* (New York: McGraw-Hill, 1987).

M. W. Rowe, "Radioactive Dating: A Method for Geochronology," *Journal of Chemical Education* 62:580–584 (July 1985).

R. F. Flint and B. J. Skinner, *Physical Geology* (New York: Wiley, 1974).

SOAP BUBBLES AND BUTTERFLY WINGS

We can think of light as waves traveling through space, like ripples across a pond. Light can have different wavelengths—different distances between the crest of one wave and the crest of the next. Different wavelengths of light give us the sensation of different colors.

Those are some abstract but basic ideas about light. Here's how to see those ideas in action.

Make a solution of soapy water in a shallow bowl. Take a coffee cup and lower it, mouth down, into the soapy water, then lift it out gently. You want a thin soap-bubble film across the mouth of the cup.

Now turn the cup sideways so the soap-bubble film is vertical. Hold the cup so you can see the reflection of a bright light—the sky, for instance—in the surface of the bubble. After a few seconds you'll see bands of color appear near the top of the bubble, slowly moving downward.

The soapy water has no color of its own. The thickness of the bubble makes the colors. Wherever the bubble is thick enough to accommodate a whole number of waves of, say, red light, red light will be reflected to your eye, because red-light waves bouncing off the back side of the bubble will be exactly in step with red-light waves bouncing off the front of the bubble. The same goes for other colors. As the bubble's thickness changes, so do the colors.

This is the same process that makes colors in oil floating on water. And most of the blue colors in bird feathers and butterfly wings also come about in the same way—not through colored dyes, but through reflection of light from both sides of a thin film.

C. J. Lynde, *Science Experiences with Ten-Cent Store Equipment*, 2nd ed. (Scranton, Pa.: International Textbook Co., 1951).

Richard P. Feynman, *QED: The Strange Theory of Light and Matter* (Princeton: Princeton University Press, 1985).

TRACING THE ROOTS OF ENERGY

In 1841, the German physician Julius Mayer went to the East Indies as the doctor on a Dutch merchant ship. While treating European sailors in Java, he was struck by the color of their blood. Mayer was treating the sailors by bleeding, as physicians of the nineteenth century often did. He noticed that blood from the veins of these sailors had a much brighter red color than usual—almost as bright as blood from arteries.

When Mayer saw this, he boldly guessed that the sailors were using less blood oxygen than usual because they were in a hot, tropical climate new to them. In those days, physicians were beginning to realize that body heat resulted from something like slow burning of food and oxygen. Mayer guessed that since the sailors were getting so much heat from outside their bodies, they didn't need to make as much heat inside, so they used less of the oxygen in their blood.

Mayer's observations of the sailors' blood led him to guess that energy—he called it "force"—is never created or destroyed; it just changes from one form into another. The way Julius Mayer said this was vague and hard to evaluate in the 1840s, but his hunch contributed to an idea—the conservation of energy—that is now basic to all science.

Today, for example, we say that nuclear energy from the sun is sent to Earth in the form of light. Plants store it as chemical energy; animals, including us, eat the plants and change the stored chemical energy into energy of motion and into heat.

At each stage of the process, energy income and energy outgo must balance exactly, as in a bank account. Energy is a kind of common currency. Today we interpret every event in nature as the transformation of energy from one form to another.

R. S. Turner, "Julius Robert Mayer," in *Dictionary of Scientific Biography* (New York: Charles Scribner's Sons, 1974).

Why Fan Blades Stay Dirty

Turn off your window fan for a moment, and you see fine dust on the fan blades. It seems strange—when the fan is running, there's air blowing over the blades hour after hour. Yet that wind doesn't carry the dust away.

When you look at dirt on fan blades, you're looking at a manifestation of one of the most complex processes in nature: air flowing over a solid surface. Figuring out the details requires the fastest supercomputers in existence. But the overall picture is something like this:

If you could get small enough to sit on a spinning fan blade, you'd feel a strong breeze—it would be like riding in a convertible with the top down. But here's the strange and mysterious part: as you got still smaller and closer to the surface, you'd feel less and less breeze. Within a fraction of a millimeter from the fan blade surface, you'd feel no breeze at all!

Because of friction between air and fan blade, there's a very thin layer of air next to the surface that doesn't move over the blade. Any dust particles small enough to stay within that quiet surface layer never feel the breeze, so they stay put.

This fact has other practical implications. Blowing on a phonograph record won't get rid of the very smallest dust particles, especially the ones at the bottom of the grooves. And blowing on a camera lens will never get it really clean. In both cases you have to use a brush that touches the surface to get the fine dust off.

In his autobiography *Slide Rule* (Portsmouth, N.H.: Heinemann, 1954), Nevil Shute Norway describes calm air near the surface of a 750–foot-long airship built in 1930: "When the ship was cruising at about sixty miles an hour, as soon as you got to the top, or horizontal, part of the hull you were in calm air crawling on your hands and knees; if you knelt up you felt a breeze on your head and shoulders. If you stood up the wind was strong. It was pleasant up there sitting by the fins on a fine sunny day" (p. 101).

Richard P. Feynman, *The Feynman Lectures on Physics* (Reading, Mass.: Addison-Wesley, 1964), vol. II, chap. 41.

A. Khurana, "Numerical Simulations Reveal Fluid Flows near Solid Boundaries, *Physics Today*, May 1988.

C. Donald Ahrens, *Meteorology Today*, 2nd ed. (St. Paul: West, 1985) (discussion of saltation, p. 260).

I. Peterson, "Reaching for the Supercomputing Moon," *Science News* 133:172 (March 12, 1988).

S. Weisburd, "Record Speedups for Parallel Processing," *Science News* 133:180 (March 19, 1988).

I. Peterson, "Friction Features," *Science News* 133:283 (April 30, 1988).

Brown Apples and Brown Tea

When you bite or cut into an apple, you crush some of the cells the apple is made of. Substances that normally occupy separate compartments within cells now have the chance to combine. Chemical reactions happen that would not happen in an uninjured apple, and one of those reactions leads to browning.

In particular, a family of substances called phenols from one compartment of each apple cell come into contact with oxygen from the air. When certain enzymes, the so-called phenolases, reach that mixture, a whole chain of chemical reactions takes place, and one of the end products is a brown-colored pigment. That pigment doesn't change the apple's taste or nutritional value, but it does hurt its visual appeal.

To prevent cut apples from browning, you must either inactivate the browning enzymes with heat or with acid such as lemon juice, or you must cut off the oxygen supply by immersing the fruit in water or by coating it with salad dressing. Vitamin C also prevents browning by starting a chemical reaction that uses up oxygen.

Browning also happens with bananas, pears, avocados, peaches, and raw potatoes, among other fruits and vegetables. The process apparently benefits the fruit, because it produces not only the brown pigment but also a substance that attacks fungi that might otherwise become established in the injured fruit tissue.

This "enzymic browning" has a practical application. In the processing of tea, the green leaves are crushed and exposed to the air for a few hours. Crushing of cells, mixing of substances, reaction with oxygen, and production of brown pigment all happen basically as they do with an apple. We don't like brown fruit, but we do like brown tea.

Harold McGee, *On Food and Cooking: The Science and Lore of the Kitchen* (New York: Macmillan, 1984).

T. P. Coultate, *Food—The Chemistry of Its Components* (London: Royal Society of Chemistry, 1984).

Owen R. Fennema, ed., *Food Chemistry*, 2nd ed. (New York: M. Dekker, 1985).

Optics and Glue

Fill a clean, dry glass with lukewarm water—lukewarm so that you don't get condensation of water from the air on the outside of the glass. Make sure your hand is completely dry, then pick up the glass and look down into the water, at the inside walls of the glass. You'll see a mirror-like reflection of the bottom. What you won't see is your hand holding the glass. You might see fingerprints here and there, but not much more. Wherever there's air between the glass and your skin, light is reflected back into the glass without ever reaching your skin.

Now dip your hand in water and pick the glass up with wet fingers. Look at the inside of the glass again and you'll see your fingers. When your hand is wet, water fills the tiny gaps between skin and glass, so light from i..side the glass can travel all the way out to your skin and back, allowing you to see your skin.

This not only demonstrates something about optics, it also shows why solid objects don't usually stick together: dry surfaces actually touch in only a few places.

Here's where glue comes in. It fills the gaps between objects and keeps them filled. Then the objects are held together by attraction between molecules, which is very strong if a lot of molecules are involved.

Water fills gaps in some materials, but it's not good glue because it runs out too easily. To glue your hand to the glass, you'd need either a stiff substance like the adhesive on duct tape, or something that hardens, like epoxy glue.

So, solid objects that seem to be in contact are actually separated by a lot of air. The job of glue is to fill in the gaps and keep them filled.

N. A. de Bruyne, "The Action of Adhesives," *Scientific American*, April 1962, and "How Glue Sticks," *Nature* 180:262–266 (August 10, 1957).

"Adhesive," in *McGraw-Hill Encyclopedia of Science and Technology* (New York: McGraw-Hill, 1987).

LIGHT TAKES TIME

In September 1676, the Danish astronomer Olaus Roemer went before the French Academy of Sciences in Paris and predicted that the eclipse of Jupiter's moon Io, which was expected the following November 9th at 5:25 A.M., would occur ten minutes late. His explanation for the delay was that earlier calculations of Io's motion had failed to consider the time needed for light to cross Earth's orbit. Roemer's prediction, and his explanation, turned out to be right.

Io is one of Jupiter's four largest moons. It's easy to see in a small telescope as it goes around Jupiter once every forty-two and a half hours. Eclipses of Io happen when it disappears into the shadow of Jupiter during part of each orbit.

The astronomers studying Io were working on ways to improve navigation methods. To steer by the stars, you have to know the time. They hoped to produce an almanac with the correct times of future eclipses of Io, so that navigators could check the time at sea by watching Jupiter and Io through a spyglass.

Roemer collected timings of Io's eclipses and saw an irregularity in the numbers: the interval between eclipses varied, depending on whether Earth was moving closer to Jupiter or farther away. Roemer concluded that light from Jupiter did not travel instantaneously as was generally believed, but took some time to reach Earth.

From those eclipse timings, Roemer calculated that light takes about twenty-two minutes to go all the way across Earth's orbit. He wasn't too far off: it actually takes about seventeen minutes, traveling at 186,000 miles per second.

Olaus Roemer is now remembered for having made, in 1676, the first careful measurement of a fundamental quantity of the universe: the speed of light.

Heinz Tobin, "Ferdinand Roemer," in *Dictionary of Scientific Biography* (New York: Charles Scribner's Sons, 1975).

I. B. Cohen, "Roemer and the First Determination of the Velocity of Light (1676)," *Isis* 31:327–379 (1940).

Read Fine Print Through a Pinhole

Hold a page with fine print on it about an inch from your eye. Probably you won't be able to get the print in focus well enough to read it. The lens in your eyeball can't make a sharp image of an object that close.

Now try this: punch a small hole in an index card with a straight pin. Put down the pin and hold that pinhole very close to one eye—close enough so that the card touches your eyelashes. If you wear glasses, take them off.

Look through the pinhole at fine print an inch away. The letters will appear amazingly sharp. Take the pinhole away, and the view becomes blurry again.

The pinhole, being as small as it is, allows each point on your retina to get light only from one small part of the object you're looking at. As a result, all the light rays coming through the pinhole make an image of the fine print on your retina. That's how the pinhole makes such a big difference in what you see.

The image even looks magnified, because things look bigger when they're closer, and you're not accustomed to looking at things at such close range. This pseudo-magnification effect is more striking if you bring the print very close to the pinhole—a quarter of an inch or so. Keep the pinhole very close to your eye. Move the letters past the pinhole, and you'll see the middle of each letter bulge as it goes by.

So a pinhole functions something like a lens, but it works over a wider range of distances. Look through a pinhole and you can read fine print only an inch away.

C. J. Lynde, *Science Experiences with Ten-Cent Store Equipment,* 2nd ed. (Scranton, Pa.: International Textbook Co., 1951).

Get Your Bearings with Two Thumbtacks

Here's a way to learn a lot about your surroundings from one of those U.S. Geological Survey quadrant maps. They cover just a few square miles each, in tremendous detail. You can get one for your area from the

U.S. Government Printing Office or, possibly, from a local sporting-goods store.

Lay the map out flat on a table near a window. Find your location. Shove a thumbtack through that point on the map into the table below. Now the map is free to rotate around the thumbtack, but the point corresponding to your location stays fixed.

Next, look out the window and find some prominent landmark, preferably a few miles away—a hilltop, for example, or a fire tower. Find the symbol for that landmark on your map. Rotate the map around the thumbtack until a straight line drawn from the thumbtack through the map symbol points to the landmark. Stick one more thumbtack through that map symbol into the table. You've now oriented the map using two known points: your location, and a landmark you can see from your location.

Now that the direction to one landmark is correct, the directions to every other landmark will also be correct. A line of sight from the central thumbtack to, say, a hill whose name you don't know will pass through the symbol for that hill on your map. Look at the map, and you may find a name for the hill. Of course, if there's more than one hill along that line of sight, you may have to estimate the distance to the one you're looking at.

But you can get your bearings with two thumbtacks. Tack down your location first, then orient the map by referring to a landmark you can see. This works best with maps showing an area so small that the curvature of the Earth is not noticeable.

P. J. Davis and W. G. Chinn, *3.1416 and All That* (Boston: Birkhauser, 1985), p. 160.

A GLOBE AS A SUNDIAL

It's very easy to set up your globe as a miniature model of the real Earth, with the same orientation in space. Simply place your globe in a sunny spot, then tilt and turn it until your hometown is on top—so that a penny, laid flat on your hometown, doesn't slide off. Now turn the globe till the north side faces north. That's all there is to it. Leave the globe alone and let Earth's motion do the rest.

What you've done is to orient the globe so that its axis is parallel to the axis of Earth, and so that an imaginary line from your hometown on the globe, through the center of the globe, passes through your hometown on Earth and the center of Earth.

Now ponder how sunlight strikes the globe. The dividing line between sunlight and shadow on the globe corresponds exactly to the dividing line between the day side and the night side of Earth, right now. You can see where in the world the sun is rising, and where it's setting, at the present moment.

Since your globe is attached to the turning Earth, it will now turn every twenty-four hours. At different times of day, different times of year, different places in the world, the lighting on the little globe matches the lighting on the big Earth.

Anyone else in the world with a similarly oriented globe will see it lit exactly the same way as yours at exactly the same time. That person's globe, like yours, models the Earth we all share.

R. M. Sutton, "A Universal Sundial," in C. L. Strong, ed., *The Scientific American Book of Projects for the Amateur Scientist* (New York: Simon and Schuster, 1960), pp. 62–72.

An ink ring in a glass of water

For this experiment you need a tall glass of water (the taller the better), a bottle of ink, and an eyedropper.

After you fill the glass with water, put it on a steady table and leave it alone for a few minutes, to allow all the turbulence in the water to settle down. Now take some ink in the eyedropper and release one drop from a height of one inch above the center of the water. The ink will form an expanding ring, descending through the water like a smoke ring traveling through the air.

The ring keeps its shape because of the way water moves in it. You can get the idea by thinking of a rubber O-ring—maybe something like the rubber rings that are used as drive belts in upright vacuum cleaners. You can twist one of those rings inside out without changing its overall circular shape. What's happening with the water is something like that. The ink ring that you see is actually turning itself inside out as it travels to the bottom of the glass. The turning motion was started by the ink drop falling into the water.

The ring stays sharp and clear as it descends. That shows that water and ink in the ring don't mix very much with the rest of the water in the glass—at least not at first. There is some friction between the water in the ring and the surrounding water, and after traveling a long way, the ring will start to get fuzzy around the edges. But within the dimensions of a drinking glass, the ink ring will stay amazingly sharp and clear all the way to the bottom.

Richard M. Sutton, *Demonstration Experiments in Physics* (New York: McGraw-Hill, 1938), p. 103.

Richard P. Feynman, *The Feynman Lectures on Physics* (Reading, Mass.: Addison-Wesley, 1964), vol. II, chap. 40.

WHY AFTER-DINNER MINTS TASTE COOL

There are at least two reasons why chocolate-covered after-dinner mints make your mouth feel cool: the sudden melting of chocolate, and the strange cooling effect of menthol.

Most chocolate candy is about half cocoa butter. Cocoa butter is a natural component of cocoa beans and, like butter from milk, falls into the chemical category of fats and oils. But unlike butter from milk, butter from the cocoa bean has a remarkably uniform chemical composition; in other words, it contains only a few different kinds of fat molecules. That uniformity gives cocoa butter what chemists call a sharp melting point. As cocoa butter is heated, it changes suddenly from a brittle solid to a liquid as its temperature passes through about 93 degrees Fahrenheit.

When any substance melts, it absorbs heat from its surroundings. Anything that absorbs heat from your body when you touch it usually feels cool. When cocoa butter melts suddenly in your mouth, it absorbs a relatively large amount of heat in a short time, yet it does not get warmer right away. So you may notice that absorption of heat as a sensation of coolness.

The sudden cool sensation is especially noticeable because cocoa butter melts at about 93 degrees—very close to body temperature. That means that, just before it melts in your mouth, chocolate candy is likely to feel neither warm nor cold.

Now to the mint at the center of the candy. Mint flavor usually comes from oil of peppermint. The active ingredient in oil of peppermint is menthol, a fairly simple chemical with a remarkable effect: menthol tastes cool.

Apparently, menthol produces its cooling effect in the mouth not through the taste buds or even through the receptors for smell, but by fooling the cells that respond to temperature. In particular, menthol works on the receptors that detect cold, in your mouth or elsewhere. In small concentrations, menthol causes the sensors that detect cold to become active at a higher-than-usual temperature. So menthol makes things feel cooler than they really are. When you eat a mint containing menthol, the normal temperature of the inside of your mouth—body temperature—feels cool.

Menthol is also used in liqueurs, cigarettes, toothpaste, and shaving cream, among other products, to give a cool sensation to whatever part of the body the product touches.

P. W. Atkins, *Molecules* (New York: Scientific American, 1987).

Harold McGee, *On Food and Cooking: The Science and Lore of the Kitchen* (New York: Macmillan, 1984).

Owen R. Fennema, ed., *Food Chemistry*, 2nd ed. (New York: M. Dekker, 1985).

A LEAF FALLS

Where the stalk of a leaf meets the stem, there is a special layer of cells, the so-called separation layer. The separation cells are more closely spaced than cells in the surrounding tissue. In some plants, the separation layer is present even before the leaf matures; in other plants, those special cells develop later. Before the leaf falls, it dies, and whatever salvageable nutrients it contains are brought back into the tree.

When it's time for the leaf to fall, the cells of the separation layer produce enzymes that digest the walls between cells. Meanwhile, the separation cells closest to the plant get bigger, while those closest to the leaf don't. With the cell walls weakened and cells growing only on one side of the separation layer, the connection between leaf and stem soon breaks, and the leaf falls off.

Some of the separation layer is left behind on the stem. It forms a protective layer of cork that joins with the cork of the stem.

The whole process goes by the name of abscission, a word that comes from the same root as "scissors." Apparently abscission is controlled by a complex interaction among several plant hormones. With deciduous trees, it happens every year. Abscission can be triggered by cold, drought, decreasing day length, or polluted air, among other factors.

Left behind on the stem after abscission is a leaf scar with small raised dots inside it. Those dots are the so-called bundle scars, the sealed-off ends of the vessels that once carried fluids into and out of the leaf. Often, somewhere near the leaf scar, you can see the bud of next year's leaf.

"Abscission," in *McGraw-Hill Encyclopedia of Science and Technology* (New York: Mc-Graw-Hill, 1987).

Frank B. Salisbury and Cleon W. Ross, *Plant Physiology,* 3rd ed. (Belmont, Calif.: Wadsworth, 1985).

A DOT, A LINE, A CREASE, A BEAUTIFUL CURVE

Take a piece of paper and a pencil. Draw a straight line somewhere on the paper—it doesn't matter where. Then draw one dot somewhere else on the paper—again, it doesn't matter where.

Now fold the paper over so that dot comes down somewhere on the line. Hold the dot on the line and crease the paper at the fold.

Open the paper up and re-fold it at a different angle. Put that dot somewhere else on the line, hold it there, and crease the paper at the fold.

Do this a few more times, always folding the paper at a different angle, but always putting that original dot somewhere on the line before you crease the paper.

Flatten the paper out, and you see that the creases form a curved boundary around the dot. The more creases, the smoother the curve. You can trace through the curve with a pencil.

Technically speaking, that curve is a parabola, one of the most famous curves of mathematics and physics. The path of a stream of water squirting out of a garden hose is close to a parabola; so is the path of a ball thrown through the air. Air resistance and the curvature of the Earth cause slight deviations from the parabolic ideal.

In space, where there's no air resistance, high-speed comets follow parabolic paths around the sun. The dot on your paper marks the position of the sun in the parabolic orbit. Make the dot and the line farther apart and you'll get a close-up of the portion of the comet's orbit nearest the sun.

Martin Gardner, "The Abstract Parabola Fits the Concrete World," *Scientific American*, August 1981.

DIRECTING A LIVING CELL

The cells of plants, animals, protozoans, and fungi contain a nucleus. To a large extent, the nucleus directs the cell. That was beautifully demonstrated in the 1930s by the German biologist Joachim Hämmerling, using single-celled plants known as *Acetabularia*, which grow in seawater.

Each plant is about one or two inches tall—small for a plant, huge for a single cell. One *Acetabularia* species looks something like a tiny palm tree. Another looks like a little parasol with an open canopy. Both types have a thin stalk, anchored to whatever the plant is growing on by a sort of foot. Within that "foot" is the cell nucleus.

Hämmerling cut the "foot" off one type of *Acetabularia* and grafted it onto a cut stalk of the other type. He was really transplanting the nucleus. After a few weeks, the stalk would grow a new cap.

What kind of cap? If Hämmerling put a palm-tree-type nucleus into a parasol-type stalk, that stalk would eventually grow a palm-tree cap. And a parasol nucleus in a palm-tree stalk would make a parasol cap.

Fifty years later, Hämmerling's experiments with *Acetabularia* plants are remembered for demonstrating the normal flow of information in cells—all kinds of cells. For the most part, the nucleus directs the cell. Information is transcribed from the famous DNA molecules in the nucleus into so-called RNA molecules, then translated into proteins which do the mechanical work of building.

J. Hämmerling, "Nucleo-cytoplasmic Relationships in the Development of Acetabularia," *International Review of Cytology* 2:475–498 (1953).

Scott F. Gilbert, *Developmental Biology* (Sunderland, Mass.: Sinauer Associates, 1985).

Dancing Pollen Grains

In the summer of 1827, the Scottish botanist Robert Brown looked through his microscope at pollen grains immersed in water. The grains were moving—they tumbled and jiggled back and forth as they drifted across the field of view. Brown wondered if the pollen grains were moving because they were alive.

Brown looked at pollen grains from dried plants that had been dead twenty years, at particles knocked loose from old wood and from coal, and at particles of soot from the air. They all moved when suspended in water. He then looked at particles that had never been part of anything living—dust knocked loose from rocks, including a rock supposedly taken from the Sphinx. The Brownian motion, as it's now called, was always there.

Clearly, this microscopic motion of tiny particles had nothing to do with life. But Brown couldn't explain it in 1827. After 1827, evidence accumulated indicating that all material bodies are made of atoms and molecules, and that temperature is a measure of the constant random motion of those atoms and molecules. The hotter the temperature, the faster the motion. The Brownian motion turned out to be caused by randomly moving water molecules knocking pollen grains back and forth on the microscope slide.

By 1905 the full significance of the Brownian motion was explained by a young physicist who showed that by watching how far a particle gets kicked by the Brownian motion in a certain amount of time, you can calculate how many molecules there are in a cubic centimeter of water. That young physicist was Albert Einstein.

Robert Brown, "A Brief Account of Microscopical Observations . . . on the Particles Contained in the Pollen of Plants . . . "; and A. Einstein, "The Elementary Theory of the Brownian Motion," both reprinted in Henry A. Boorse and Lloyd Motz, eds., *The World of the Atom* (New York: Basic Books, 1966).

Wet Weather Means Brighter Colors

There are several things you associate with dry summers, but one which you might not have noticed is that they are not as colorful. When wet weather returns, so do some of the colors we have been missing. Not only leaves, but rocks, soil, and road surfaces all have more intense color when they're wet than when they're dry.

Take a wet reddish-colored rock, for example. A wet rock is coated with a film of water. The water is smooth on the surface, and it fills all the tiny valleys and pits in the surface of the rock.

When light from the sky strikes this wet reddish-colored rock, the water bends the light downward, into those tiny valleys and pits. The light gets reflected back and forth from one side of each little valley to the other. At each bounce, more non-reddish-colored light is absorbed by the rock surface. The light that bounces becomes fainter and redder. A small amount of light bounces back up to the surface of the water film, and some of that light passes through the water surface into the air on its way to your eye. So when you look at a wet rock, you're seeing light that has bounced off the rock surface many times. A wet rock looks dark and strongly colored.

In the case of a dry rock, there's no water to bend light downward into the little valleys and pits. When you look at a dry rock, you're seeing light that has bounced off the rock surface only once, or just a few times. Relatively little light is absorbed by the rock surface, so the light that reaches your eye from a dry rock is whiter and more intense than light from a wet rock.

Because water fills the nooks and crannies in the surface, not only rocks but pavement, sand, soil, dead leaves, and bare wood look darker and more strongly colored when they're wet.

Marcel Minnaert, *The Nature of Light and Colour in the Open Air* (New York: Dover, 1954), p. 345.

THE SPINNING EARTH AND THE WEATHER

You and a friend sit on opposite sides of a big, flat turntable—a merry-go-round. With the turntable not moving, you toss a ball to your friend on the other side. If you toss accurately, the ball goes to the other person, who catches it.

Now the turntable begins to spin counterclockwise. Because of the turning, you begin moving to your right. You toss the ball to your friend on the other side once again. If you aim as you did before, you'll miss; the ball will turn right from your point of view. Your friend on the other side will have to lunge to his or her left to catch the ball. Because you're moving, the velocity of the turntable combines with the velocity of your throwing arm to send the ball off to the right. (If the turntable were spinning clockwise, the ball would turn left after you threw it.)

This effect was first analyzed in detail in 1835 by the French physicist Gaspard Gustave de Coriolis, who was making a theoretical study of the forces on moving parts of machines. Now we understand the tremendous importance of the Coriolis effect, as it has come to be called, in explaining how things move long distances over the Earth—air masses, for instance.

The Earth is, in effect, a giant turntable. As seen from the North Pole, the Earth spins counterclockwise every twenty-four hours. Because of that spinning, air flowing out from a northern-hemisphere high-pressure area turns right, just like the ball leaving your hand, and that causes clockwise wind circulation.

The Coriolis effect of the Earth's rotation is noticeable only with things traveling very long distances—things like winds and ocean currents. Contrary to what we sometimes hear, it's too weak to have a noticeable effect on water going down the drain in a sink.

Pierre Costabel, "Gaspard Gustave de Coriolis," in *Dictionary of Scientific Biography* (New York: Charles Scribner's Sons, 1971).

C. Donald Ahrens, *Meteorology Today*, 2nd ed. (St. Paul: West, 1985).

J. B. Marion, *Classical Dynamics of Particles and Systems*, 2nd ed. (Orlando: Academic Press, 1970).

INFECTION: A STRUGGLE BETWEEN TWO ORGANISMS

By 1882, the Russian biologist Elie Metchnikoff had collected many observations of how cells deal with foreign particles. Roundworms, for example, digested food with special cells that engulfed food particles. And white blood cells had been seen eating particles of the coloring matter in ink. Metchnikoff's observations led him to the hunch that animals, including humans, defend themselves against infection with special moving cells that devour invading objects.

One day in 1882, while his family was at the circus, Metchnikoff had an idea. As he described it, he guessed that "a splinter introduced into the body of the starfish larva . . . should soon be surrounded by mobile cells, as is to be observed in a man who runs a splinter into his finger."

Outside, in the garden, was a tree decorated for Christmas. Metchnikoff "fetched from it a few rose thorns and introduced them at once under the skin of the beautiful starfish larva, transparent as water." By the next morning, special cells—called "eating cells" in those days—had gathered around the splinter. The starfish larva was defending itself against the splinter.

After this 1882 experiment, Metchnikoff was convinced that infection was really "a struggle between two organisms."

Metchnikoff was a pioneer in the study of what is now called cell-mediated immunity, in which special cells gather around and attack intruders. There's another kind of immunity—antibody-mediated immunity—in which special molecules, the antibodies, circulate in the bloodstream in search of foreign molecules.

E. Metchnikoff, *Lectures on the Comparative Pathology of Inflammation* (1891; New York: Dover, 1968).

Quote taken from Olga Metchnikoff, *Life of Elie Metchnikoff* (1921; reprint, New York: Arno, 1972).

G. H. Brieger, "Elie Metchnikoff," in *Dictionary of Scientific Biography* (New York: Charles Scribner's Sons, 1974).

Why doesn't a pregnant woman reject her fetus?

The human body has ways of dealing with cells that don't belong to it. Sometimes the body rejects organ transplants and tissue grafts because they are made of foreign cells.

This leads to an interesting question. An unborn fetus is made of tissue foreign to the mother. The fetus is "foreign" because about half its genes come from the father, and its proteins are assembled according to its unique genetic program. So why doesn't a mother's immune system reject her fetus?

The answer seems to be that part of the mother's immune response is suppressed while she's pregnant. Understanding of this has come about fairly recently, but evidence had been accumulating for a long time.

For example, decades ago in the rural southern United States, pregnant women were given quinine every day to try to protect them from malaria; and women who had had tuberculosis as young girls were considered completely cured if the tuberculosis did not return when they became pregnant. Behind these traditions was a recognition that resistance to these diseases is weak during pregnancy. Meanwhile, farmers and veterinarians had noticed that sheep had more worms when they were pregnant than when they were not.

More recently, experiments with mice have shown that pregnant mice are more susceptible to malaria than non-pregnant mice. And non-pregnant mice injected with hormones to imitate pregnancy are more susceptible to herpes than mice in a control group.

Why doesn't a pregnant woman—or any pregnant mammal—reject her fetus? Because her immune response is, so to speak, turned down as long as she's pregnant. The immune system must compromise between protecting the mother and protecting the fetus.

Eugene D. Weinberg, "Pregnancy-Associated Immune Suppression: Risks and Mechanisms," *Microbial Pathogenesis* 3:393–397 (1987).

THE FLOATING CORK TRICK

Cut a slice about a quarter of an inch thick from the end of a cork and drop it into a glass of water. Watch the cork for a few seconds and you'll see it drift over to the side of the glass. Challenge everyone at the table to make the cork float exactly in the center of the water. Let people push the cork around, turn it over, drop it in in some special way. No matter what they try, it will always drift to one side, for the uninitiated.

The trick is to leave the cork in the glass and add more water. Pour it in slowly from another glass. Keep pouring slowly and carefully until the water surface bulges above the rim of the original glass. You may be surprised at how much water will fit into that bulge without spilling.

The water bulges because molecules of water attract each other. The molecules at a water surface make a film under tension. That film of surface tension holds the water like a bag and keeps it from spilling. The same thing happens in a water drop.

Bring your eye down level with the rim of the glass and look at the profile of the water. You'll notice that it curves gently across the mouth of the glass, with the highest point of the bulge at the center. By this time you'll also notice that the buoyancy of the cork causes it to be pulled up the sloping water surface to that central high point.

Why didn't the cork float in the center before the glass was full? Pour some water from the glass and look carefully at the surface. Now you won't see the bulge in the center, but you can see that the water climbs up the sides a little all around the edge. This is because the water molecules are attracted to the glass. When the glass is not full, the water is higher at the edges than in the center, so the buoyancy of the cork still causes it to float to the highest point, but that is now at the edge rather than the center.

Martin Gardner, *Entertaining Science Experiments with Everyday Objects* (New York: Dover, 1981).

A THOUSANDTH OF A SECOND

A thousandth of a second is the shortest exposure time, the fastest shutter speed, on many cameras. That's especially helpful to sports photographers, who use fast shutter speeds to take pictures of high-speed motion. A runner who covers a hundred meters in about ten seconds goes only about a third of an inch in a thousandth of a second, so the runner's image will hardly be blurred in that short time.

In a thousandth of a second, a car going 55 miles per hour moves about an inch. A jet plane flying at 600 miles per hour goes about a foot. The strings in a piano that make the note middle C go through one-quarter of a complete back-and-forth vibration.

In the human body, a single molecule of the enzyme carbonic anhydrase makes about 100 molecules of carbonic acid from carbon dioxide and water in a thousandth of a second. That process helps regulate the amount of carbon dioxide in the bloodstream.

In a thousandth of a second, a mosquito flaps its wings once.

In a thousandth of a second, the electronic clock inside many personal computers makes about 15,000 ticks, each of which triggers another logical operation—that's why computers can do arithmetic so fast.

Here are some other things that happen in a thousandth of a second:

A beam of light or a radio wave travels about 186 miles—roughly the distance from Chicago to Indianapolis.

A spacecraft in low Earth orbit travels about 25 feet.

The Earth travels about 100 feet in its orbit around the sun; the planet Pluto travels about 17 feet in its orbit.

And our solar system gets about 46 feet closer to the star Vega and travels about 740 feet in its great orbit around the center of the Milky Way galaxy—in the brief interval of one one-thousandth of a second.

Based on a discussion in A. Bakst, *Mathematics: Its Magic and Mystery*, 3rd ed. (Princeton, N.J.: Van Nostrand, 1967).

The enzyme statistic comes from Helena Curtis, *Biology*, 4th ed. (New York: Worth, 1983), p. 168.

TOUCHING AND BEING TOUCHED

Our so-called sense of touch has at least two parts: passive touch, which tells us, for example, that something has landed on our arm; and active touch, in which we use the sensations of pressure on our skin to explore the world.

One of the first scientific studies of the difference between active and passive touch was done almost thirty years ago by the psychologist James Gibson. The study measured people's ability to distinguish shapes of six different cookie cutters—a triangle, a star, a crescent, and so on—without looking.

People's judgment of the shape was least accurate when the cookie cutter was steadily pressed into their outstretched palms by a mechanical lever—passive touching. People identified the shape correctly only about 29 percent of the time.

The subjects did better if the cookie cutter was attached to a mechanical gadget that slowly rotated it around a vertical axis while pressing it into their palms. About 72 percent of the judgments were correct.

The highest percentage of correct judgments, 95 percent, came when the cookie cutter was held still and the subjects were allowed to move their fingers to explore the shape—active touching.

These early experiments by James Gibson revealed something almost paradoxical. When we hold our hand still and allow something to touch it, the pressure on our hand is an exact image of the shape of the object; yet we usually can't tell what that shape is. But if we move our fingers over the object, we can form a very accurate idea of the shape, even though the pattern of pressure on our fingers has no resemblance to the shape. As Gibson wrote, "a clear unchanging perception arises when the flow of sense impressions changes most."

J. Gibson, "Observations on Active Touch," *Psychological Review* 69:477–491 (1962).

Philip G. Zimbardo, *Psychology and Life*, 12th ed. (Glenview, Ill.: Scott, Foresman, 1988).

ON A CLEAR DAY, HOW FAR CAN YOU SEE?

How far you can see depends on the condition of the atmosphere and on whether anything is blocking your view. But if we assume that the air is perfectly clear and the horizon is unobstructed, how far can you see?

Because the Earth is round, the higher you are, the farther you see. In case you're the calculating type, here's the formula: multiply the square root of your height, in feet, by a factor of one and a quarter; that gives the approximate number of miles to your horizon.

In case you're not the calculating type, here are some results:

If your eyes are five feet above ground level, your horizon is about two and three-quarters miles away.

If you're on the tenth floor of a tall building—about a hundred feet up—your horizon is about twelve miles away.

From fourteen hundred feet up—that's roughly the height of the Empire State Building—you can see forty-six miles if the air is perfectly clear.

From a jet at thirty thousand feet you can see about 210 miles; from a spacecraft a hundred miles up, about 890 miles.

That formula once again: multiply the square root of your height in feet by a factor of one and a quarter. That gives you the approximate number of miles to your horizon—on the Earth.

Elsewhere, the formula changes. On the moon, for instance, if your eyes are five feet off the ground you can see only about a mile and four-tenths. Since the moon is smaller than Earth, the surface curves more sharply and the horizon is closer.

If you could stand on the sun, you'd be standing on a surface more nearly flat. From five feet above the sun, with nothing blocking your view, you'd see thirty-one miles.

The flatter the surface, the farther you see. If the Earth were absolutely flat, then on a clear day you really could see forever.

A. Bakst, *Mathematics: Its Magic and Mystery*, 3rd ed. (Princeton, N.J.: Van Nostrand, 1967), chap. 29.

Edison and the Bulge-Heads

In 1880, while working on his early carbon-filament electric light bulbs, Thomas Edison noticed something strange: after a bulb had burned for a while, a black deposit appeared on the inside. Edison figured that particles of carbon were being carried from the hot filament to the glass. He attacked the problem by sealing another wire into the bulb—a platinum wire connected to one terminal of the power supply, to attract the carbon particles.

When the improved light bulb was turned on, an electric current flowed through that extra platinum wire, even though the extra wire was not part of a complete circuit. Evidently electricity was flowing through empty space inside the bulb, from the regular filament to this extra wire! At that time no one would have imagined this was possible. A visiting English engineer named the phenomenon the Edison effect.

Not until the turn of the century did it become known that there were elementary particles of electricity (such as electrons) that could travel through empty space.

Thomas Edison apparently had little interest in either pure science or scientists. He patented the special bulbs and went on to other things. In a letter about the Edison effect, he wrote, "I have never had time to go into the aesthetic [i.e., theoretical] part of my work. But it has, I am told, a very important bearing on some laws now being formulated by the Bulge-headed fraternity."

In fact, electricity flowing through empty space can be controlled with much greater speed and precision than electricity flowing through a wire. When Edison made his contemptuous remark about "the bulge-headed fraternity," he was unaware of the implication of his discovery. His light bulbs with the extra wire inside were the first electronic devices; they would lead to the vacuum tubes that would make radio possible.

Matthew Josephson, *Edison* (New York: McGraw-Hill, 1959), pp. 274ff.

THE SHAPE OF SOUND

For this kitchen demonstration you need a candle, a piece of paper, and a big knife. Roll the paper around the candle, then put the candle on a cutting board and cut it in two with the knife. But cut it diagonally, like a green bean—in other words, cut straight down, but with the knife at an angle to the candle, not perpendicular to it.

Now unroll the paper and look at its cut edge. It's shaped in an undulating curve like the profile of ripples on a pond. That's one of the most important curves of mathematics and physics, the so-called sine curve.

Sine curves describe the nature of sound. The wavy edge of your paper could represent air pressure in a series of sound waves. Where the curve goes up, the air pressure is slightly higher than average; where the curve goes down, pressure is lower. When regular alternations of high and low pressure strike your eardrum, you hear a musical tone.

Look at the wavy edge of your paper and notice how far apart the waves are—the wavelength, as a physicist or engineer would call it. The distance between waves corresponds to the musical pitch of the sound. If the waves are closer together—in other words, if the wavelength is shorter—you hear a higher pitch. You can get a shorter wavelength by wrapping paper around a thinner candle and cutting it as you did before.

Look at the wavy edge and notice how far up and down the waves go.

That corresponds to the loudness of the sound wave. You can vary that by changing the angle of the knife when you cut through the candle. If the knife is more nearly parallel to the candle, you'll get a sine curve with higher highs and lower lows.

Hugo Steinhaus, *Mathematical Snapshots* (New York: Oxford University Press, 1950).

THE WRONG FORMULA FOR WATER

Most of us have heard that the chemical formula for water is H_2O. In other words, a molecule of water is made of two hydrogen atoms and one oxygen atom. But for a long time in the nineteenth century, chemists thought the formula was HO: one atom of hydrogen and one atom of oxygen in each water molecule.

That incorrect formula arose from the work of the nineteenth-century English chemist John Dalton, who published *A New System of Chemical Philosophy* in 1842. Dalton's reasoning went like this:

He was convinced that matter was made of atoms of different kinds: hydrogen was made of hydrogen atoms, oxygen was made of oxygen atoms, and so on. Dalton was also convinced that atoms could hook up in different combinations to make molecules, and that's why there are so many different chemical substances in the world.

In Dalton's time, chemists knew of only one substance that could be made from hydrogen and oxygen: water. Dalton figured, therefore, that a molecule of water was made of one atom of hydrogen and one atom of oxygen, because that was the simplest possible combination. The formula must be HO.

Dalton's reasoning was sound, but he was missing some important facts. He didn't know—no one knew in 1842--that water is not the only chemical that can form from hydrogen and oxygen. Dalton's mistake was in assuming that hydrogen and oxygen would combine in only one simple way.

John Dalton is one of the great figures in the history of science. His work in the early 1800s provided important evidence about the nature of atoms and how they combine. But because certain laboratory discoveries about hydrogen and oxygen had not yet been made in his time, Dalton came up with the wrong formula for water.

Aaron J. Ihde, *The Development of Modern Chemistry* (New York: Harper and Row, 1964).
J. Dalton, excerpt from *New System of Chemical Philosophy*, reprinted in Henry A. Boorse and Lloyd Motz, eds., *The World of the Atom* (New York: Basic Books, 1966).

Discovering Viruses

Virus is Latin for "poisonous fluid." That's the guise under which viruses first became apparent a century ago.

In 1890 the Russian Department of Agriculture asked the botanist Dmitri Iosifovich Ivanovsky to investigate a so-called mosaic disease wiping out tobacco plants on the Crimean peninsula. Ivanovsky found that just the sap from an infected plant could cause mosaic disease in a previously healthy plant. Remarkably, even if all bacteria were filtered out, the sap could still make a healthy plant sick. Ivanovsky guessed that some living particle smaller than any known bacterium was causing the disease.

Meanwhile, in Holland, Willem Martinus Beijerinck was also studying tobacco mosaic disease in the 1890s. Beijerinck also found that filtered sap could infect a previously healthy tobacco plant. Sap from that second plant could then infect a third, and so on indefinitely. Beijerinck guessed that the virus, as he called the mysterious infectious agent, reproduced by using the reproductive machinery in plant cells.

Today, both Dmitri Ivanovsky and Martinus Beijerinck are credited with discovering viruses in the 1890s. But it took decades more to figure out how viruses really operate. Biologists now understand a virus to be a particle, much smaller and simpler than a cell, that attacks a preferred type of target cell and causes the chemical machinery inside that cell to make new viruses. Viruses reproduce only inside living cells. As Ivanovsky and Beijerinck guessed, viruses are unlike any other living organism.

V. Gutina, "Dmitri Iosifovich Ivanovsky," and S. S. Hughes, "Martinus Willem Beijerinck," in *Dictionary of Scientific Biography* (New York: Charles Scribner's Sons, 1973, 1978).
G. R. Taylor, *The Science of Life: A Picture History of Biology* (New York: McGraw-Hill, 1963).

CELLS GET OLD AND DIE

All living cells come from other cells. A cell makes new cells by dividing. But experiments first done in the 1960s showed that some cells won't keep dividing forever.

Some cells that make soft tissues of the human body, for instance, won't divide more than about fifty times. This was observed in experiments in which human tissue cells were cultivated in laboratory glassware. The cells somehow count divisions and stop dividing around the fiftieth division, even if they have nourishment and room to grow. After that, the cells die. Temperature and other factors influence the time interval between divisions, but not the final number of divisions.

Do we get old and die because our individual cells get old and die after fifty divisions? That's an intriguing thought, but the fifty-division limit can't be the whole explanation. For one thing, when old people die, many of their cells haven't yet reached the fifty-division limit. Also, that fifty-division limit was observed in a type of cell that divides especially frequently. Many of the changes associated with aging happen in types of cells that divide much less often. So the real significance of the limit on cell divisions is still unknown.

There are some cells that have a kind of immortality—they'll keep dividing indefinitely, no matter how crowded they are, as long as they get nourishment. They are cancer cells.

L. Hayflick, "Cell Senescence and Death," in *McGraw-Hill Encyclopedia of Science and Technology* (New York: McGraw-Hill, 1987).

"The Cell Biology of Human Aging," *Scientific American*, January 1980.

R. A. Weinberg, "Finding the Anti-oncogene," *Scientific American*, September 1988.

SORTING OUT MUSICAL PITCHES

Sing into the strings of a piano with the damper pedal held down, and you hear reverberation of the notes you just sang. Pressing the pedal lifts the dampers from the strings, leaving the strings free to vibrate. The sound of your voice then causes the strings to vibrate—but not all equally. The strings that vibrate most energetically, and that keep vibrating after you stop singing, are the ones tuned to the pitches you sang.

Something a little like that happens in the human ear. Curled up in a fluid-filled capsule in the inner ear is a piece of tissue about an inch and a half long, the so-called basilar membrane, which is free to move in response to vibrations that come to it from outside. Just as different strings in the piano vibrate at different frequencies and make different musical pitches, different parts of the basilar membrane vibrate most energetically at different frequencies.

But there's a difference between the basilar membrane and a piano. The basilar membrane is one solid piece of elastic tissue, precisely shaped—thick at one end and thin at the other, like a tiny chisel. The basilar membrane does not have tuned strings; it has this special shape enabling it to sort out pitches.

The most energetic vibration is at the thick end for high frequencies, and at the thin end for low frequencies. Nerves connected to the membrane send signals to the brain indicating which part is vibrating most energetically.

If two or more musical notes sound together, the basilar membrane will vibrate strongly in two or more different places. That's why we can pick out individual notes in a musical chord. The basilar membrane of the inner ear, because of its special shape, sorts out vibrations by frequency.

The highest pitches humans can hear correspond to about twenty thousand vibrations per second. How do we do that? Not by counting vibrations.

A nerve, such as the nerve connecting the ear to the brain, cannot transmit twenty thousand impulses per second—in fact, a nerve may have trouble transmitting more than about five hundred or one thousand impulses per second.

Here is how our ear and brain deal with this inability of nerves to transmit such high frequencies. One area of the basilar membrane resonates at twenty thousand vibrations per second. Nerves connected to that area send the brain not twenty thousand nerve impulses per second, but a message that stands for twenty thousand vibrations per second. The brain then translates that message into a pitch sensation.

Incidentally, low notes—like a bass note at one hundred vibrations per second—are handled differently. For a low note, our ear does send one impulse to our brain for each and every vibration of the eardrum—one hundred impulses per second for that bass note.

J. G. Roederer, *Introduction to the Physics and Psychophysics of Music*, 2nd ed. (New York: Springer-Verlag, 1975).

THE ECHO OF A TRAIN

If you stand near a railroad track while a train goes by with its horn blowing, you hear the pitch of the horn drop as the train passes.

Imagine sound as waves of slightly compressed air, emitted from the horn, traveling through the air. The pitch you hear depends on how many sound waves reach your eardrum every second. More sound waves per second means higher pitch.

As the train approaches, the horn emits each new sound wave when it's a little closer to you than it was for the one before. So the sound waves are crowded together when they get to your ear; you hear a higher pitch than if the train were standing still.

As the train goes away, the horn emits each new sound wave a little farther from you than the one before; the sound waves are relatively spread out when they get to your ear, and you hear a lower pitch.

So, between the time of approaching and the time of going away, as the train passes, the horn's pitch drops: a familiar case of the so-called Doppler effect.

Try listening for this after the train passes: listen to the horn's echo from surfaces farther down the track. The echo has a higher pitch than the sound directly from the horn. The surface reflecting the sound to make the echo is getting crowded-together sound waves, because the train is approaching that distant surface. That reflecting surface isn't moving, so it doesn't change the pitch before returning the sound to you.

So when a train is going away from you, listen for the horn honking at one pitch, followed by an echo of that honk at a higher pitch.

MICROBURSTS AND AIRPLANE CRASHES

Turn on the kitchen faucet; watch the water hit the sink below and spread out in every direction. You're looking at a model of one of the principal causes of airplane crashes. Descending water from the faucet represents an intense, localized downdraft in the air—a so-called microburst—that comes out of some storm clouds.

Take an imaginary trip across the bottom of your sink while the water is running. As you approach the descending water column, you're going upstream, into the current. Then you get right under the faucet and feel a tremendous force pushing you downward. Finally, you emerge from the other side of the descending water column. The current is coming from behind you now; you're going downstream.

This analogy shows why it's dangerous to fly through a microburst in the atmosphere. First, the airplane approaching a microburst encounters a strong headwind that increases the speed of air over the wings, increasing the lift. Recall that airplane wings generate lift only if air flows over them at high speed. Then, suddenly, the plane hits a hundred-mile-an-hour downdraft that shoves it toward the ground. A few seconds later, the plane gets a strong tailwind that reduces the speed of air over the wings, undermining the lift and robbing the pilot of control of the aircraft. An airplane thousands of feet up may have time to recover from this; an airplane about to land may not.

Instruments are being installed on airplanes and at some airports to detect microbursts so that pilots and traffic controllers can better avoid them. But even with these instruments, airplanes will have to continue to avoid situations where microbursts are even likely.

Donald Ahrens, *Meteorology Today,* 3rd ed. (St. Paul: West, 1988).
"Airlines Told to Arm Planes against Wind Threat," *New York Times,* Friday, September 22, 1988, p. 13.

WHAT'S INSIDE AN ATOM?

If you were to wrap a steel marble in fluffy cotton, then shoot BBs at it, most of the BBs would go right through the cotton. But a few would hit that steel ball at the center and bounce back. Those ricocheting BBs would tell you that something small, heavy, and hard was inside that cotton. That's basically how the nucleus of the atom was discovered back in 1911.

Hans Geiger, Ernest Marsden, and Ernest Rutherford at the University of Manchester in England shot tiny particles at atoms and watched where the particles went. The tiny particles came from radium, which is radioactive—it emits so-called alpha particles in all directions. Geiger and Marsden let these alpha particles hit pieces of thin metal foil. To see where the particles went afterward, they made a special screen—a piece of glass coated with a chemical that would make a flash of light when it was hit by a particle.

By putting the screen in different places around the foil and counting the flashes, Geiger and Marsden could measure how many particles were coming from the foil in each of several directions. The results: most of the alpha particles passed right through the metal foil. But a small percentage bounced back.

Ernest Rutherford came up with an interpretation: the atoms in the foil were mostly empty space. But within each atom must be something hard and small and heavy—a nucleus. If a particle from the radium happened to hit a nucleus, it would bounce back.

So in 1911 Geiger, Marsden, and Rutherford shot tiny particles at some atoms, noticed that some of the particles bounced back, and from that concluded that an atom has a nucleus.

The following papers are reprinted in Henry A. Boorse and Lloyd Motz, eds., *The World of the Atom* (New York: Basic Books, 1966):

Hans Geiger and Ernest Marsden, "On a Diffuse Reflection of the Alpha Particles" (1909).

Ernest Rutherford, "The Scattering of Alpha and Beta Particles by Matter and the Structure of the Atom" (1911).

Hans Geiger and Ernest Marsden, "The Laws of Deflexion of Alpha Particles through Large Angles" (1913).

Dew-bows

You've probably looked for a rainbow in the sky after a thunderstorm on a warm afternoon. Try looking for a dew-bow in the grass on a cool, clear morning.

A dew-bow looks pretty much like a rainbow, but it's on the ground, and it's upside down compared to a rainbow. To see one you must have the sun at your back. Look toward the shadow of your head. The dew-bow—if it's there—forms part of a big circle around the shadow of your head.

The principle behind dew-bows and rainbows is the same. When sunlight hits a water droplet, it gets bent as it enters the water, then gets reflected from the back of the droplet, then gets bent again as it re-emerges into the air. The upshot is that most of the light comes back from a water droplet at an angle of about forty-two degrees from the direction it went in.

That forty-two-degree angle is characteristic of spherical water droplets. If rain and dew were made of some liquid other than water, the angle would be different.

The forty-two-degree figure is not exact. Different colors of light get bent at slightly different angles—that's why a rainbow or dew-bow separates white sunlight into colors.

On a bright, cool, dewy morning, the grass before you is covered with millions of water droplets, all illuminated by the sun. When you see a dew-bow—or a rainbow—you see light from only those droplets that happen to be in the right place to send sunlight back to your eye.

Marcel Minnaert, *The Nature of Light and Colour in the Open Air* (New York: Dover, 1954).

Halogen Lamps

Ordinary light bulbs grow dimmer with age. As the light bulb burns, atoms evaporate from the hot tungsten filament and land on the inside of the glass. As more tungsten builds up on the inside of the bulb, less light gets out. Eventually the filament loses so much tungsten that it breaks—the bulb "burns out."

Halogen lamps are designed to fight this tungsten loss. The bulbs contain gas from the so-called halogen family of chemical elements. Iodine gas is frequently used. Inside a halogen lamp, iodine atoms combine with tungsten atoms evaporating from the filament to make a new molecule that won't stick to the inside of the bulb, as long as the inside of the bulb is very hot. Instead, this new iodine-tungsten molecule drifts to the filament and puts the tungsten atom back on it! The iodine atoms are then free to pick up more evaporated tungsten.

For this to work, the inside of the bulb has to be very hot—up to about

2,000 degrees Fahrenheit. The bulb of a halogen lamp is made small so it will be close to the filament and get hot. It's made of quartz instead of ordinary glass so it won't melt. And that tiny, delicate quartz bulb is often enclosed in a big glass bulb to protect it and to keep people's fingers off the hot quartz.

Because of their special construction, halogen lamps cost more but stay brighter and last longer than ordinary light bulbs.

H. R. Crane, "How Things Work: Halogen Lamps," *The Physics Teacher*, January 1985, pp. 41–42.

WHEN POP BOTTLES DON'T BLOW UP . . . AND WHEN THEY DO

Carbonated beverages in airtight bottles contain dissolved carbon dioxide gas ready to escape when the cap seal is broken. Let a factory-sealed bottle of carbonated beverage sit upright, quietly, all day, then carefully remove the cap. You hear a puff of escaping carbon dioxide, but the liquid stays put. On the other hand, everybody knows that if you shake the bottle for five seconds, then open it, you get a near-explosion with significant and lasting effects on nearby furniture and carpeting.

You might conclude that shaking the bottle increases the pressure inside. But it doesn't. Shaking does create bubbles. The beverage swirls and splashes and falls back on top of itself inside the shaking, sealed bottle. Here and there, carbon dioxide gas gets trapped below the liquid surface, making bubbles in the liquid that were not there before. The pressure is the same, but there are now more bubbles. When you open the bottle, those bubbles suddenly expand because the gas pressure inside them is higher than atmospheric pressure. The rapidly expanding bubbles push liquid out through the bottle neck.

If you don't shake the bottle, the liquid has few bubbles or none at all. Most of the carbon dioxide gas that's not dissolved invisibly in the liquid is above the liquid, and from there it can escape harmlessly when you loosen the cap.

However, a large and sudden temperature change can indeed alter the pressure inside a pop bottle and cause it to explode. Heating not only causes expansion of the carbon dioxide already present, but also makes more carbon dioxide come out of solution in the pop and rise to the surface as gas, raising the pressure even more.

So, as long as the temperature doesn't change, merely shaking a factory-sealed pop bottle will not increase the pressure inside—it just makes more bubbles. When you remove the cap, those expanding bubbles push liquid out of the bottle with a force whose ultimate application depends on your wisdom and judgment.

D. W. Deamer and B. K. Selinger, "Will That Pop Bottle Really Go Pop? An Equilibrium Question," *Journal of Chemical Education*, June 1988.

IT'S NOT WHAT YOU HEAR—IT'S WHEN YOU HEAR IT

You're sitting near the back of a big auditorium, and someone on the stage is talking. If you can hear the talker clearly, there's probably a sound-reinforcement system at work—a system involving microphones, amplifiers, and loudspeakers.

In some auditoriums, the talker's voice is fed not into one loudspeaker at the stage but into many loudspeakers mounted in the ceiling or along the side walls of the room. This approach puts a loudspeaker near everyone in the audience. But this approach creates a problem. Electronic signals can travel almost instantly to the back of a big room, while the live sound takes a noticeable fraction of a second to travel to the back through the air. So the best sound-reinforcement systems delay the electronic signal by a fraction of a second before sending it to loudspeakers at the back.

How long should that delay be? It might seem best for the amplified sound to reach you through the loudspeakers at exactly the moment live sound reaches you through the air. But audio engineers and psychologists have found that, for the most natural sound, the delay has to be just a little longer than that—maybe a fiftieth of a second longer.

This is because of a so-called precedence effect in human hearing. If the live sound reaches your ear about a fiftieth of a second before the amplified sound, then all the sound will appear to come from the stage, not from speakers in the ceiling. This is true even if the loudspeaker sound is somewhat louder than the live sound!

Sound appears to come from whichever source produces it first. If the delays in a sound-reinforcement system are set just right, you may never be aware that amplification is being used at all.

"Sound-Reinforcement System," in *McGraw-Hill Encyclopedia of Science and Technology* (New York: McGraw-Hill, 1987).

H. F. Olson, *Music, Physics and Engineering* (New York: Dover, 1967).

WEIGHTLESS WATER

Punch a hole somewhere near the bottom of an empty tin can. Fill the can with water. Of course, a stream of water squirts out of the hole. Now refill the container and drop it from a height of five or six feet. Notice that while the container is falling, water does not squirt out of the hole. The water is weightless with respect to the can as long as it is falling.

You can see how this happens by remembering that the force of gravity makes all falling objects—water, cans, and everything else—accelerate toward the ground at the same rate. (We're neglecting air resistance here, because it doesn't affect the main point.) When the punctured can sits on a table, it cannot accelerate toward the ground because it's not free to move. But the water presses against the sides of the container, escapes through the hole, and accelerates toward the ground.

When you drop the punctured can, gravity makes the can as well as the water accelerate toward the ground—at the same rate. Gravity pulls on the water, but it also pulls on the can. So the weight of the water does not press on the sides and bottom of the can. The water is weightless, and no longer squirts through the hole.

The water-filled can does not have to fall straight down for this demonstration to work. You might throw it sideways, for instance. However you throw it, once the can leaves your hand, no water squirts through the hole.

You might want to ponder this: if you could throw the can sideways at seventeen thousand miles an hour, it would be going as fast as an orbiting space shuttle. Again, the water inside would be weightless—and for the same reason that the shuttle astronauts are weightless in orbit.

D. R. Kutliroff, *101 Classroom Demonstrations and Experiments for Teaching Physics* (West Nyack, N.Y.: Parker, 1976).

WARMTH FROM A COLD LAMP

Find a lamp that has been turned off for several hours, so that the light bulb is stone cold. Touch the bulb with your fingers. It feels just about as warm or cool as any other glass object in the room.

Now, with your hand near the bulb but not touching it, switch the lamp on for five seconds, then switch it off. During the five seconds the lamp is on, you feel what seems to be heat coming from the bulb. Touch the bulb again immediately after you switch the lamp off; the bulb will feel almost as cool as it did before. It seems paradoxical—a light bulb that's not hot can make your hand feel warm.

What this experiment really demonstrates is that light and heat are not the same thing. When you turn on the bulb, what hits your hand is light—lots of visible light, and even more invisible infrared light. Light of any kind is really energy traveling though space. When light, visible or not, strikes matter—your hand, for instance—that energy can be converted to other forms. Here, the energy of light is converted to tiny random motions of the atoms in your skin: in other words, heat.

Heat can also be communicated directly by matter. If your hand is above the light bulb, you will soon receive additional heat from air, warmed by the bulb, rising to your hand. But you will feel warmth as a result of the light even if your hand is in the cool air below the bulb.

The sun warms the Earth by the same process: sunlight—visible and invisible—travels through 93 million miles of airless space, changing to heat only when it strikes the Earth or some other object, such as a spacecraft. It's true that the sun's surface is hot—like the filament inside the light bulb—but that heat is not directly communicated to faraway objects. The *light* from the sun is what warms the Earth.

Julius Sumner Miller, "Further Enchanting Things to Think About," *The Physics Teacher*, September 1979.

Mirror, Mirror on the Wall

Suppose you want a mirror to hang on the wall—a mirror big enough that you can see yourself full-length, from haircut to shoeshine, in one view. How big does that mirror have to be?

You might at first think that the mirror has to be as tall as you are. But that's not correct. If you hang it so the top edge is approximately even with the top of your head, the mirror has to be only about one-half your height to give you a full-length view of yourself, from head to foot.

To see why that's true, remember that looking into a mirror is something like looking through a hole in the wall. You can see big things through small openings. You can see a six-foot person through a keyhole if you get your eye close to the keyhole and if the six-foot person stands back from the other side.

Looking into a mirror is something like looking through a keyhole, with an important difference: the opening, represented by the mirror, is always exactly halfway between you and your reflection. If you stand three feet in front of a mirror, your reflected self appears three feet behind it. No matter where you stand, the mirror is always exactly halfway between you and your reflection. So looking at a mirror is like looking through a window located exactly halfway between you and your reflection. Because this window is halfway between you and your reflected self, it has to be only half as big as your reflected self to show all of your reflected self.

T. B. Greenslade, "Nineteenth Century Textbook Illustrations XXIV: The Half-Length Mirror," *The Physics Teacher*, September 1978.

Artificial Flavoring Means Fewer "Chemicals"

Chemists have found over one hundred different chemical compounds in ripe apples that contribute to their flavor. There are, of course, large amounts of sugars that give an apple its sweetness, and acids that add sourness. But the characteristic apple flavor comes from a balance of very small amounts of the rest of those hundred-plus different compounds. The flavors of other things we eat and drink arise from similar mixtures of many substances. In coffee, almost sixty compounds have been identified as contributing to the flavor; in Scotch whisky, over three hundred.

Just about all these compounds can be made in quantity in the laboratory, then mixed in the right proportions to reconstruct a particular flavor. The question facing a cost-conscious food processor is, how many of those dozens or hundreds of compounds are really necessary to make a convincing artificial flavoring? Just a few of the most important ones may be sufficient to simulate a natural flavor pretty well. Why make, say, a raspberry flavoring with one hundred compounds if a flavoring made with only ten comes close enough to the flavor of real raspberries?

Actually, one patented artificial raspberry flavor formula uses only seven different compounds. A patented strawberry formula calls for eight compounds; a patented chocolate formula uses just four. So, although we may tend to think of artificial flavoring as involving more "chemicals" than natural flavoring, the opposite is likely to be true. If an artificial flavoring tastes artificial, the reason may be that it contains not too many chemicals, but too few.

T. P. Coultate, *Food—The Chemistry of Its Components* (London: Royal Society of Chemistry, 1984). The raspberry formula (U.S. patent 3,886,289) is on p. 145.

Catch a Falling Dollar

I have here a crisp, straightened-out one-dollar bill. I hold it by a short edge between the thumb and forefinger of my left hand, allowing the bill to dangle flat and vertical. Now I place the thumb and forefinger of my other hand around the bottom edge of the hanging bill, not quite touching it.

I shall demonstrate my quick reaction time by releasing the bill with my left hand and catching it with my right hand before it has time to fall through my fingers. I've done some figuring, and I estimate that a dollar bill takes about a fifth of a second to fall a distance equal to its own length after I release it. I, however, am so quick that I can catch the bill before it has fallen even half its own length. There—I have caught the bill so that my thumb is over George Washington's portrait.

Now you try it. I'll dangle the bill so the bottom edge is between your fingers. Without warning, I drop the bill. You aren't quick enough to catch it. Again and again, you fail.

Actually I'm cheating. When I drop the bill and catch it myself, I do not demonstrate my own reaction time. My brain issues both the "drop" and "catch" instructions, so I am not really reacting to the motion of the bill. I can make the drop and the catch happen as close together in time as I want. I can even catch the bill before I drop it.

You, however, must see the bill begin to fall before doing anything. Messages must travel from your eyes to your brain to your hand—only then do your fingers close. All that takes time—more time than the dollar bill takes to fall a distance equal to its own length.

Do you think you'll react faster if I use a five-dollar bill instead of a one?

Martin Gardner, *Entertaining Science Experiments with Everyday Objects* (New York: Dover, 1981).

OSMIC RAYS

In 1912, the Austrian physicist Viktor Hess spent several nights hovering over Vienna in a balloon. During these flights, Hess measured how quickly a small piece of metal foil, charged with static electricity and sealed in an airtight can, would lose its electric charge at different altitudes.

Most of us have shuffled across a carpet on a cold, dry day to build up a personal static charge, and have felt that static electricity suddenly discharge in a miniature lightning bolt when we touch a faucet or something else connected to the ground.

Actually, any object charged with static electricity eventually loses its charge even if it's never grounded; the air always contains a few electrically charged atoms, or ions, that neutralize the static charge. Many of those ions are created by the Earth's natural mild radioactivity. Subatomic particles emitted by elements like uranium in the ground make ions by stripping electrons off atoms in the air. So measuring how quickly something loses static electricity, as Hess was doing, is really a way of measuring the general intensity of particles.

In 1912 it was generally thought that if you got higher above the ground, you'd detect fewer of these particles, because air between you and the radioactive ground would absorb some of the radiation. In his balloon flights, Hess found that radiation does taper off with altitude— but only up to a height of about one mile. Above one mile, Hess found increasing radiation—radiation coming from the sky.

Viktor Hess, in 1912, had discovered what are now called cosmic rays—fast subatomic particles from outer space. Physicists and astronomers now think that cosmic rays originate in exploding stars or bright centers of galaxies. But no one knows for sure.

V. F. Hess, "Penetrating Radiation in Seven Free Balloon Flights" (1912), trans. and reprinted in Henry A. Boorse and Lloyd Motz, eds., *The World of the Atom* (New York: Basic Books, 1966).

D. J. Helfand, "Fleet Messengers from the Cosmos," *Sky and Telescope*, March 1988.

CHOCOLATE BLOOM

Chocolate bloom is the gray film that sometimes appears on chocolate candy.

Most chocolate candy is about half cocoa butter, and there are six different forms of cocoa butter. They are all made of the same fat molecules, but their melting temperatures range from about 63 to about 97 degrees Fahrenheit. The difference is not in chemical composition, but in how the fat molecules are stacked up to make solid cocoa butter. Melting is basically the dismantling of the stacking pattern by heat. Some stacking patterns are more easily dismantled than others, so different forms of cocoa butter have different melting points.

Of these six different forms, only the fifth—the one that melts at about 93 degrees—has the nice glossy surface that everybody likes on chocolate candy. Much of the art of chocolate making involves getting the melted cocoa butter to solidify into that form and not into any of the other five forms.

If the chocolate isn't made correctly, or if it is subjected to a lot of temperature variations—making many trips into and out of the refrigerator—some of the fat molecules in the cocoa butter will be jostled out of their proper stacking pattern. Those molecules will emerge on the surface of the candy and settle into another stacking pattern—usually the one that melts at 97 degrees Fahrenheit rather than 93. That 97–degree form doesn't have a glossy surface.

So the gray film that sometimes develops on chocolate candy is made by fat molecules from cocoa butter separating from the chocolate and settling into a new stacking pattern with a dull surface.

Owen R. Fennema, ed., *Food Chemistry*, 2nd ed. (New York: M. Dekker, 1985).

T. P. Coultate, *Food—The Chemistry of Its Components* (London: Royal Society of Chemistry, 1984).

P. W. Atkins, *Molecules* (New York: Scientific American, 1987).

GETTING ROBBED IN THE CAMERA OBSCURA

"Camera obscura" literally means a dark room. For at least twenty-five hundred years, people have known that a single small hole in one wall of a closed, dark room will cause an image of the scene outside to be projected onto the opposite wall. A lens in the hole can brighten the image, but isn't absolutely necessary.

Since light travels in straight lines, each point in the projected image is formed by a ray of light coming through the hole from one point in the landscape outside.

The image projected by a hole in the wall is upside down. Light from the top of the landscape passes through the hole and ends up at the bottom of the projected image; light from the bottom of the landscape ends up at the top of the image. The ninth-century Chinese philosopher Shen Kua explained this with an elegant analogy: light rays going through a hole are constrained like an oar in a rowlock. When the handle of the oar is down, the blade is up, and vice versa. Some arrangement of lenses or mirrors can be added to make the image right side up.

A French writer of the seventeenth century tells about a camera obscura near a park reputed to be a hangout for young couples of low morals. Fashionable patrons would pay to step into the camera obscura and watch projected images of various scandalous activities among the trees and bushes. The patrons were astonished not only by what they were seeing but by how they were seeing it—most of them didn't realize that because light travels in straight lines, a hole in a wall can project an image.

According to this seventeenth-century account, there were some other things these patrons didn't know: first, that most of the amorous action they were watching had been staged by the operators of the camera obscura, and second, that while they stood in the dark room, captivated by the projected image, their purses were being stolen!

J. H. Hammond, *The Camera Obscura: A Chronicle* (Bristol: Adam Hilger Ltd., 1981), p. 29.

Cfcs and CO₂

The news frequently mentions two gases in the atmosphere whose names sound similar but which are connected with different problems.

CFCs are chlorofluorocarbons, a family of man-made chemicals once used as propellants in spray cans and still used in air conditioners, refrigerators, and foam cushions. From the point of view of safety, CFCs at first glance seem ideal: they're non-toxic, non-flammable, and non-corrosive; they react chemically with very few substances.

But those desirable qualities are also the reason for the CFC problem. Chlorofluorocarbons can survive for decades in the lower atmosphere. That gives time for CFC molecules to rise to the upper atmosphere, where ultraviolet light from the sun strips chlorine atoms off the molecules. Those chlorine atoms break up molecules of the naturally occurring ozone in the upper atmosphere, in complicated reactions involving high-altitude clouds.

A molecule of ozone is made of three oxygen atoms bound together; a molecule of the oxygen we breathe has two oxygen atoms. The three-oxygen molecule blocks the sun's ultraviolet light, which would disrupt life on Earth if it reached the ground in large amounts.

In 1987 representatives of thirty-one countries, including the United

States, signed the so-called Montreal Protocol on Substances That Deplete the Ozone Layer, which includes guidelines for cutting back on CFCs during the 1990s. But some calculations indicate that even if chlorofluorocarbons are banned completely, the atmosphere may need a century to recover from damage already done.

CO_2, on the other hand, is carbon dioxide. CO_2 is exhaled by animals and people, and it's also generated by burning fossil fuels like petroleum, coal, and wood. Concern about carbon dioxide arises from observations that the percentage of carbon dioxide in the atmosphere has been increasing in the twentieth century, presumably because of human activity. Carbon dioxide traps infrared light generated by the Earth's warm surface—that's the so-called greenhouse effect.

Too much carbon dioxide in the atmosphere would trap too much infrared light and perhaps cause the world's climate to gradually warm up. Some studies indicate that the warming has already begun.

So CFCs and CO_2 have similar-sounding names, but are connected with two different atmospheric problems. CFCs, chlorofluorocarbons, are associated with depletion of the ozone layer; CO_2, carbon dioxide, is connected with the greenhouse effect.

R. Monastersky, many articles in *Science News,* including "The Decline of the CFC Empire," April 9, 1988; "Clouds without a Silver Lining," October 15, 1988; "New Chemical Model, New Ozone Fear," September 3, 1988; "Has the Greenhouse Taken Effect?" April 30, 1988.

R. A. Stolarski, "The Antarctic Ozone Hole," *Scientific American,* January 1988.

T. Beardsley, "Winds of Change: International Talks Address Human Effects on Climate," *Scientific American,* September 1988, pp. 18–19.

THE SHAPES OF SNOW

Snowflakes are ice crystals, and ice crystals can form as hexagonal plates, needles, or hexagonal columns, as well as the familiar starlike shapes.

All ice-crystal shapes are based in one way or another on the hexagon, the six-sided geometrical shape we also see in the cells of a honeycomb. The hexagon is basic to ice crystals because water molecules, when they link up to form ice, take positions corresponding to the corners of a hexagon.

Apparently, just about every snow crystal begins when a tiny amount of water freezes on a piece of dust high in the atmosphere. As this micro-scopic particle drifts through a cloud, it picks up more and more water molecules from the surrounding humid air. Each new molecule hooks into the existing hexagonal pattern of the crystal. Eventually this process makes an ice crystal, big enough to see, with some kind of six-sided symmetry.

Meteorologists have found that the final shape of an ice crystal is very sensitive to the temperature at which it forms. Below about minus 10 degrees Fahrenheit, ice crystals form as hollow hexagonal columns—something like the shape of a pencil. Up to about 3 degrees Fahrenheit above zero, ice crystals form hexagonal plates; between 3 and 10 above, the branching star-shaped types, the so-called dendrites, appear. In warmer air, ice crystals come out as plates, needles, or solid hexagonal columns, depending on the exact temperature.

If an ice crystal drifts through several different temperature regions within a cloud as it forms, it may come out as a hybrid. One of the most beautiful hybrid types is a hexagonal column with a flat plate at each end. These have been named tzuzumi crystals, after the Japanese drums they resemble.

Charles and Nancy Knight, "Snow Crystals," *Scientific American*, January 1973.
B. J. Mason, "The Growth of Snow Crystals," *Scientific American*, January 1961.
(The previous two articles are reprinted in the *Scientific American* anthology *Atmospheric Phenomena*, intro. by David K. Lynch [New York: W. H. Freeman and Co., 1980].)
Donald Ahrens, *Meteorology Today*, 3rd ed. (St. Paul: West, 1987).

Skidding downhill

Let a toy car roll down a long, steep wooden ramp. If all four wheels turn freely, the car will be going pretty fast when it gets to the bottom.

Now lock all four wheels, maybe with tape stuck to the wheels across the fenders. The car now skids, out of control, down the ramp.

What happens if you lock only the rear wheels? You might guess that the car will now go down the ramp front end first, since the rear wheels skid while the front wheels roll, and friction from the skidding wheels pulls the rear end back—right?

Well, try it—lock only the rear wheels, leave the front wheels free to turn, point the toy car down the ramp, and let it go. You'll probably see an amazing result: the car spins around and goes down the ramp backwards—that is, with the locked wheels ahead and the freely rolling wheels trailing behind!

Rolling wheels have better contact with the road than skidding wheels because the bottom point of a rolling wheel is always at rest on the road. Also, it's always harder to start something sliding, or skidding, over a surface than it is to keep something sliding once it's started: static friction is greater than sliding friction.

So, as the car goes down the ramp, static friction under the front wheels maintains good contact with the ramp. The front end becomes a pivot. Meanwhile, the much smaller sliding friction under the locked rear wheels allows the rear end to come around to the front.

This demonstrates one safety advantage of anti-lock brakes on a real car. As long as the wheels roll rather than skid, you're using static friction rather than sliding friction to bring your car to a stop. Also, you can steer better when you're rolling than when you're skidding.

INFRARED

Around 1800 the German-born English astronomer William Herschel decided to study the sun. He figured that since the sun is the star nearest to the Earth, if he could learn something about the sun he might understand something about the other stars.

Some of Herschel's conclusions turned out to be wrong—such as his idea that sunspots are mountains. But Herschel was right when he concluded from his experiments that there is more to sunlight than meets the eye. He allowed sunlight to pass through "various combinations of differently-coloured darkening glasses." Herschel wrote: "What appeared remarkable was, that when I used some of [these darkening glasses], I felt a sensation of heat, though I had but little light; while others gave me much light, with scarce any sensation of heat." Sunlight apparently contained invisible rays of heat as well as visible rays of light.

Herschel let sunlight pass through a prism to separate it into a spectrum of rainbow colors and placed a thermometer in different parts of the spectrum to see how much heat it picked up. Rays carrying the most heat were beyond the red end of the spectrum, where almost no light could be seen. Soon Herschel demonstrated that these rays beyond the red end of the spectrum could be bent and focused by prisms, mirrors, and lenses, just like ordinary visible light.

William Herschel, in the year 1800, had discovered a form of light not visible to the eye—what is now called infrared light. Hot objects like the surface of the sun and incandescent light bulbs give off a lot of infrared light.

"William Herschel," in *Dictionary of Scientific Biography* (New York: Charles Scribner's Sons, 1972).

DARK MEAT AND LIGHT MEAT

Chickens and turkeys have dark, and sometimes greasy, leg muscles and light, dry breast muscles. On the other hand, flying game birds like ducks and geese have dark breast muscles. These differences are connected with how different muscles get energy.

The dark color of dark meat comes not so much from blood as from a special protein that stores oxygen in muscles that move the skeleton. This protein goes by the name of myoglobin. When a myoglobin molecule is loaded with oxygen, it's deep red in color. When it loses oxygen, it becomes pale purple. When it's cooked, myoglobin turns brown.

Muscle fibers rich in myoglobin fall into the broad category of slow-twitch muscle fibers. They tend to be especially well suited to slow or sustained activity, like walking around a barnyard. Muscles that store oxygen in myoglobin and fuel in the form of fat can operate steadily even when the oxygen supply from the blood is low. So dark meat tends to come from muscles that are used constantly—for instance, from the leg muscles of chickens and turkeys and the breast muscles that operate the wings of ducks and geese.

The other broad category of muscle fibers is the fast-twitch category, suited for brief spurts of high power. Fast-twitch muscle fibers store less oxygen than slow-twitch fibers because they contain less myoglobin. So fast-twitch fibers tend to be light-colored. They burn not fat but carbohydrates—mainly glucose brought in by the bloodstream. Oxygen to burn the glucose must also come from the bloodstream. High-powered spurts of activity have to be brief because fast-twitch muscle fibers can operate for only a short time after they use up the available oxygen supply.

P. W. Atkins, *Molecules* (New York: Scientific American, 1987).

Helena Curtis, *Biology*, 4th ed. (New York: Worth, 1983).

Harold McGee, *On Food and Cooking: The Science and Lore of the Kitchen* (New York: Macmillan, 1987).

Sperm Meets Egg: What Really Happens

In the 1870s biologists knew that, as a rule, animal egg cells would start to develop only when they had been "fertilized"—whatever that meant. But good microscopes and new techniques of that era made it possible to see what really happens.

In 1874 the German zoologist Oscar Hertwig studied fertilization of sea urchin eggs. Sea urchins are relatives of starfish and sand dollars, abundant near seashores, and still favorites among biologists. Fertilization of sea urchin eggs is easy to observe because it happens in open water.

Hertwig saw that before fertilization the sea urchin egg had a single nucleus, a distinct body inside the cell that divides when the cell divides; but immediately after fertilization there were not one but two nuclei, which soon fused into one. Hertwig concluded in 1875 that the extra nucleus had been added to the egg by a sperm cell. At about the same time a French biologist, Hermann Fol, actually saw a sea urchin sperm cell penetrate an egg cell.

By about 1900 the observations of Hertwig, Fol, and others were brought together to make the now-familiar picture: a single sperm cell penetrates the egg cell; the nucleus of the sperm merges with the nucleus of the egg; then development begins.

These observations suggested but did not yet prove that the sperm contributes something essential to the new individual. Not till the twentieth century was it demonstrated that one function of a sperm cell is to add genetic information to the nucleus of the egg. The other function of the sperm is to trigger development of the egg into an embryo.

Garland E. Allen, "Hermann Fol," and Robert Olby, "Wilhelm August Oscar Hertwig," in *Dictionary of Scientific Biography* (New York: Charles Scribner's Sons, 1971, 1972).

Oscar Hertwig, *Allgemeine Biologie*, 3rd ed. (Jena: G. Fischer, 1909), pp. 292ff.

Do you *really* have a one-track mind?

This is a psychology demonstration in which I ask you, my volunteer subject, to perform three tasks.

First, I show you a list of names of colors—"red," "blue," "green," "orange," and so on—written in clear black letters on white paper. I ask you to read the list aloud as fast as possible. You have no trouble with this.

For your second task, I show you another list of color names, which I have written not in black ink but in ink of various colors, using a different felt-tip marker for each color name. Again I ask you to read the list aloud as fast as possible, and again you have no trouble.

For your third and final task, we use the colored list again. I ask you not to read the color names on the list, but to tell me as fast as you can what color of ink I used to write each color name. Now you have trouble! You see that I've used each marker to write the name of a color different from the color of ink in the marker. I've written the word "red" in blue ink, the word "yellow" in green ink, and so on.

When you look at the word "yellow" written in green ink, it's hard not to blurt out "yellow" instead of naming the color of the ink as I asked you to do. You have to resist the tendency to read.

What this shows is that our perceptual system has one part that reads and another part that judges color. This test, in which the name of one color is written in ink of another color, forces both those parts of the perceptual system to generate color names at the same time. That rarely happens in everyday life.

J. R. Stroop, "Studies of Interference in Serial Verbal Reactions," *Journal of Experimental Psychology* 18:643–662 (1935).
H. R. Schiffman, *Sensation and Perception: An Integrated Approach* (New York: Wiley, 1982).

The season of static electricity

As everybody knows, you can acquire a personal charge of static electricity by shuffling across a carpet on a dry winter day. When you do this, atoms in your shoes give up a few electrons to atoms in the carpet. You may be surprised to hear that the exact details of how that happens are not completely known. But the result is that you are left with a slight electron deficit relative to other objects, while the carpet ends up with a slight electron surplus. In other words, you and the carpet acquire equal and opposite static charges.

Now bring your finger near a faucet or another person, and electrons will jump across the gap to your finger, wiping out your electron deficit in a miniature lightning bolt.

This kind of thing happens most often on cold, dry winter days, because on those days indoor relative humidity is likely to be low. In dry air, objects with surplus electrons keep them more easily, and objects short on electrons can't pick up electrons easily through the air. In other words, dry air is a good insulator. Humid air, on the other hand, has a slight ability to conduct electricity; that allows static charges to drain away.

Next question: why is indoor air in winter so often dry? Remember that the amount of water vapor cold outdoor air can hold is smaller than the amount that same air can hold when it's warmer. Bring cold air in from outside, heat it up, and you lower its relative humidity—not by removing water vapor, but by increasing the air's capacity for water vapor.

So you're most likely to see effects of static electricity indoors on cold days, because indoor air on those days is likely to have low relative humidity, and because dry air is a good insulator.

A. D. Moore, "Electrostatics," *Scientific American*, March 1972.

A. D. Moore, ed., *Electrostatics and Its Applications* (New York: Wiley, 1973).

D. S. Ainslie, "What Are the Essential Conditions for Electrification by Rubbing?" *American Journal of Physics* 35:535–537 (1967).

Richard P. Feynman, *The Feynman Lectures on Physics* (Reading, Mass.: Addison-Wesley, 1964), vol. II, chap. 1.

WHAT SOAP DOES TO WATER

Water molecules attract each other. The molecules at the surface of a body of water make a film under tension. That film is strong enough to support a needle or a small insect like a water strider. Surface tension also pulls water into round droplets. Soap breaks surface tension, and here's how to see it happen.

You need a clean dinner plate, some talcum powder, and a bar of soap. Rinse the plate thoroughly to get rid of any grease or soap. Fill the plate with water and sprinkle a trace of talcum powder on the surface.

Now take the bar of soap and touch one corner of it to the water surface near the edge of the plate. The talcum powder will be pulled suddenly to the opposite side of the plate.

The talcum powder doesn't dissolve in the water and it doesn't sink; it lies on the water surface, supported by surface tension. The effect of the soap is to break that film of surface tension. At the place where soap touches water, molecules of water attract molecules of soap rather than each other. Meanwhile, on the other side of the plate, water molecules still attract each other. Touching the soap to the water is like cutting a stretched rubber band. The surface tension on the far edge of the plate yanks the talcum powder away from the soap.

C. J. Lynde, *Science Experiences with Home Equipment,* 2nd ed. (Princeton, N.J.: Van Nostrand, 1949).

Roll over, George Washington

Put a quarter on the table, with George Washington's head right side up. Hold the quarter down with your finger. Now put another quarter flat on the table, again with Washington right side up, so the edge of the second coin touches the twelve o'clock position on the edge of the first coin. If you roll the second coin halfway around the edge of the first coin, from the twelve o'clock position to the six o'clock position, will George Washington come out right side up or upside down?

As you roll from twelve o'clock to six o'clock, exactly half the circumference of the rolling coin touches the edge of the coin you're holding down. So it seems that the rolling coin goes through half a turn, and Washington should come out upside down. But when you try it, George Washington comes out right side up!

How can that be? If you roll a twenty-five-cent piece along a straight edge, like a ruler, for a distance equal to half its circumference, Washington comes out upside down, because the coin rolls half a turn in that situation. But when you roll one twenty-five-cent piece halfway around another, the curvature of the edge of the coin you're holding down with your finger adds another half-turn. The two half-turns add up. The rolling coin in our demonstration actually goes through one full turn.

And that's how George Washington comes out right side up.

R. J. Brown, *333 Science Tricks and Experiments* (Blue Ridge Summit, Pa.: Tab, 1981).
Martin Gardner, *Entertaining Science Experiments with Everyday Objects* (New York: Dover, 1981).

DON'T BELIEVE YOUR FINGERS

Most of the illusions we hear about and enjoy playing with are optical illusions. This is a tactile illusion.

To experience this illusion, all you need is a marble or a pea. Cross your fingers, extending the middle finger over the index finger so the two fingertips are next to each other, but reversed from their normal arrangement. Now roll the marble around on a table with your crossed fingertips. Almost immediately you'll probably get the distinct impression that there are two marbles, not just one.

Crossing your fingers makes information travel to your brain through unusual channels. Normally the outside of your middle finger and the inside of your index finger face away from each other. Crossing your fingers brings those two sides together. When the marble gets between your crossed fingertips, it touches areas that normally would be touched only if there were two marbles. Cross your fingers, and one marble feels like two.

This effect has been known long enough to be called Aristotle's illusion. Here are some modern variations.

Try touching your nose instead of a marble. Your fingertips may give you the impression that you have two noses.

Try different fingers: cross your middle finger over your ring finger. Then lay a pencil over the two crossed fingertips so the barrel of the pencil touches one fingertip and the point touches the other. See if you can tell, just by touch, which way the pencil is pointing. Rocking the pencil gently back and forth may enhance the strangeness and vividness of the sensation.

W. James, *Principles of Psychology*, vol. 2 (New York: H. Holt, 1890), p. 86, "Illusions of the First Type."

THE CURVE OF A MEANDERING RIVER

It's a peculiar kind of curve. You can spot it easily on a map anywhere it appears—for example, along the Mississippi River between Arkansas and Tennessee. The curve is not a series of pieces of a circle connected together. And it's not one of the familiar curves used in science and engineering to describe waves. It's something different.

It comes about because a river, in a manner of speaking, doesn't like to make sharp turns. A sharp turn offers resistance to the flow of the water. A river seeks the path that distributes that resistance to flow as evenly as possible along the length of the river. So the path is not jagged like the letter W, but curved in a particular way something like the letter S.

You can see that curve elsewhere—for instance, in the hem of a pleated curtain. The pleats at the top of the curtain try to bend the hem at the bottom into some kind of zigzag, but the fabric resists bending and makes a smooth, even curve like the curve of a meandering river. The ruffles on a ruffled blouse and the loops of a ribbon bow make versions of that meandering-river curve.

What all these examples have in common is that whatever it is that's being bent offers a uniform resistance to bending—and that determines the final shape.

Luna Leopold and W. B. Langbein, "River Meanders," *Scientific American,* June 1966 (reprinted in the *Scientific American* book *The Physics of Everyday Phenomena,* ed. Jearl Walker [San Francisco: W. H. Freeman, 1979]).
John S. Shelton, *Geology Illustrated* (San Francisco: W. H. Freeman, 1966).

CURVED SPACE IN A CHRISTMAS ORNAMENT

The Christmas ornaments we're talking about here are those glass spheres with a mirror-like reflecting surface. Actually, for this observation you don't need a Christmas ornament; any ball-shaped object with a surface that reflects like a mirror will do.

As you look at your reflecting ball, you see the reflection of your own face at the center. Around your head you see the whole room—walls, floor, and ceiling. The farther you look from the center of the ball, the more the image is distorted. That's why your nose looks extra large: the rest of your face is smaller because of the distortion.

As you look more closely, you see that the ball reflects almost the whole world as seen from where the ball is. The only part left out is the tiny piece of the scene right behind the ball, as you view it.

Now suppose someone behind you spreads a square red tablecloth on the floor and measures the edge of it with a ruler. The reflected tablecloth certainly isn't square; the reflection is distorted. But the reflected ruler still shows all four sides to have the same length, because the ruler is distorted too.

The distorted reflection in a shiny ball is a model of curved space, one of the more esoteric concepts of mathematics. People living in a curved space may not know that they live in a curved space, because their rulers and measuring instruments are curved just like everything else.

Marcel Minnaert, *The Nature of Light and Colour in the Open Air* (New York: Dover, 1954), p. 13.

GUESTS IN EVERY CELL

Mitochondria are the indispensable power plants of living cells, including the cells we're made of. They convert the stored energy of carbohydrates from food into other forms the cell can use. Mitochondria use oxygen to do this. We need to inhale oxygen because our mitochondria need it.

In photographs taken with electron microscopes, mitochondria often appear as potato-shaped things inside a cell. A cell may contain anywhere from a few to a few thousand mitochondria.

In some ways mitochondria resemble bacteria. Inside their host cell, mitochondria reproduce by dividing, just as bacteria do. Each mitochondrion has its own DNA molecule to store genetic information, and that molecule is in the form of a loop, just like the DNA in bacteria. Other striking chemical similarities between mitochondria and bacteria have been found. Those resemblances point to the conclusion that today's mitochondria are really descendants of free-living bacteria of long ago.

The presumed ancestors of mitochondria might have distinguished themselves a billion or so years ago by (so to speak) mastering the trick of using oxygen to manage energy. Back then, oxygen in the air was a new thing; other types of bacteria were starting to make oxygen as a byproduct of photosynthesis. Somewhere, a bacterium of the oxygen-using type took up residence inside a larger cell and, in so doing, conferred upon its host the ability to thrive in an oxygen-rich atmosphere. That host cell then became the ancestor of today's plants and animals, including us.

So today we have guests in every cell: mitochondria, distant descendants of free-living bacteria of a billion years ago.

L. Margulis, "Symbiosis and Evolution," *Scientific American*, August 1971 (reprinted in the *Scientific American* anthology *Life: Origin and Evolution* [San Francisco: W. H. Freeman, 1979]).

The Glory

Next time you fly, try to get a window seat on the shady side of the plane, not above the wing. You want a clear view of the airplane's shadow on clouds below. Look for a bull's-eye pattern of bright rings, tinged with rainbow color, surrounding the shadow on the clouds: the so-called glory.

The glory is not the same thing as a rainbow. A rainbow is made of sunlight coming back from water droplets at an angle of about forty-two degrees from the direction it went in. The glory, on the other hand, is light coming out of the droplet in a direction almost exactly opposite to the incoming sunlight. Physicists have found the explanation extremely complicated, but part of the story goes like this:

Light encountering a spherical water droplet in a cloud has, so to speak, several options. One is to enter one side of the water droplet at a glancing angle, bounce once off the inner surface of the back of the droplet, then exit the droplet on the other side—basically making a U-turn. Another option for a light ray is to bounce not once but fourteen times off the inside of the droplet, making three and a half trips around the droplet in the process (like a car searching a lot for a parking space), then to exit the droplet.

It turns out that light that has bounced once and light that has bounced fourteen times will emerge from the droplet going in almost exactly the same direction. A doubly strong light ray goes almost straight back toward the sun, and hence, toward your airplane. But this complicated process also breaks white light into its colors, and different colors emerge in slightly different directions. That's why the glory is tinged with color.

So, if you have a window seat on the shady side of a plane flying not too high over clouds, look for the glory: a mysterious bull's-eye pattern of colored rings surrounding the shadow of the airplane.

H. C. Bryant and N. Jarmie, "The Glory," *Scientific American*, July 1974 (reprinted in the *Scientific American* book *Atmospheric Phenomena*, intro. by D. K. Lynch [New York: W. H. Freeman and Co., 1980]).

THE WATERFALL EFFECT

Sit next to a stream and stare at a waterfall. After a few minutes of watching the falling water, look away. For a few seconds you get the impression that everything else is rising!

Psychologists who have studied this so-called waterfall effect have found evidence of separate detectors in our visual system for upward motion and downward motion. Even when we look at something that's not moving, the "up" and "down" detectors are both active. But they are equally active, so their signals balance out to give us an impression of no motion.

Staring at a waterfall apparently tires the downward-motion detectors, so they become less active. Meanwhile, our upward-motion detectors continue to send the same signal as for a stationary object. When we look away from the waterfall, we get the "up" signal, but without much of a "down" signal to balance it. So the "up" signal dominates and gives us the impression that a stationary landscape is rising.

Watch for a similar effect when you're riding as a passenger in a car or a bus. Look at the landscape going by the window. Stare at some object on the ground in the middle distance. Your motion makes the landscape appear to rotate around the point you're staring at. Things closer to you appear to move backward; things farther away appear to move forward. As you shift your gaze from point to point, the landscape appears to rotate in the same direction around each new point. All this stimulates, and soon tires, your detectors for that direction of rotation.

Now, what happens when your vehicle stops? For a few seconds those fatigued rotation detectors can't balance the signal coming from detectors sensitive to rotation in the other direction. When you stop, the landscape appears for a moment to rotate the wrong way!

O. E. Favreau and M. C. Corballis, "Negative Aftereffects in Visual Perception," *Scientific American*, December 1976.

Marcel Minnaert, *The Nature of Light and Colour in the Open Air* (New York: Dover, 1954).

Philip G. Zimbardo, *Psychology and Life*, 11th ed. (Glenview, Ill.: Scott, Foresman, 1985).

White sky, gray snow

If you go outside on a completely overcast day when the ground is covered with snow, you get the impression that the sky is gray and the snowy ground is white—brighter than the sky. But that impression is wrong. If you don't believe it, prop a hand mirror in the snow so it reflects the cloudy sky, then step back and look at the mirror in comparison to the snow. The overcast sky, relected in the mirror, will look brighter than the snow.

The snow cannot possibly reflect more light than it receives from the sky. The snow may be almost as bright as the sky, but it cannot be brighter. The apparent whiteness of the snow is a psychological effect, perhaps generated by contrast between the snow and dark objects like trees. (We're assuming here that the sky is uniformly overcast, absolutely featureless, with no difference in sky brightness from one place to another.)

You may have noticed the effect we're talking about if you've ever taken a picture of a white house on an overcast day. You know the house is white, but it looks disappointingly gray in the photograph. The camera records the sky as bright and the house as less bright, the way they really are.

A photograph taken on a cloudy day does not match the impression given by the eye because a camera does not have the complex system for interpreting images that our visual system has.

Marcel Minnaert, *The Nature of Light and Colour in the Open Air* (New York: Dover, 1954).

Why Chickens Don't Have Webbed Feet

In a certain embryonic stage, chickens have at least the beginnings of webbed feet. Embryologists have observed that as toes develop in a chick embryo's foot, cells grow between the toes. The same thing happens in the embryonic foot of a duck.

But one of the differences between a chicken and a duck is that in a duck most of those cells between the toes survive to become webbing. In the chicken embryo those cells die in a later stage of development, leaving the chicken with separated toes. In other words, a chicken's foot is sculpted not only by genetically programmed formation of new cells, but also by genetically programmed death of existing cells.

This doesn't seem to be the most efficient way to make a chicken's foot. How did it come about that a chick embryo makes cells between its toes, only to kill them off a short time later? This extra step seems to indicate that chickens and ducks have both inherited a plan of development, a schedule for getting the right cells into the right places at the right times, from some common ancestor. The chicken's foot represents a modification of that original plan. The result of all this is that ducks have feet suited for swimming, and chickens have feet suited for walking.

Genetically programmed death of certain cells has been seen in other situations too. In newborn mammals, many muscle fibers have more than one connection to the nervous system. But in the first few weeks of life, most of the original nerve-to-muscle connections die off, leaving only one nerve fiber connected to each muscle fiber.

Death of specific cells may also be the process that separates the two parallel bones in our forearms, the ulna and the radius, when our skeletons are developing.

Scott F. Gilbert, *Developmental Biology*, 2nd ed. (Sunderland, Mass.: Sinauer Associates, 1988).

CAN YOU DRAW A PENNY FROM MEMORY?

There are eight important features on a U.S. penny: a head; "In God We Trust"; "Liberty"; a date; since 1959, a building; "United States of America"; "E Pluribus Unum"; and "One Cent." Now, can you draw both sides of a penny from memory, putting each feature in the right place, with the right orientation?

Can you remember whose head is on the penny? Which way is the head facing? What is the building? Does the building have columns, or a dome, or chimneys?

Two psychologists, Raymond Nickerson and Marilyn Adams, asked a group of adult U.S. citizens to draw a penny from memory. Even when given that list of eight features to include in their drawings, no one in a group of twenty people located all eight features correctly.

Of course, in real life we need to recognize pennies, not draw them from memory. So Nickerson and Adams did another experiment. They showed people fifteen drawings of a penny, all but one of which had some feature missing or misplaced. Only fifteen out of thirty-six people could pick out the correct drawing, and those people didn't indicate a very high degree of confidence.

Why do we have such a poor memory for a common object? Psychologists are working on this question, partly because it bears on the important practical issue of the reliability of eyewitness testimony. Maybe we remember just enough to distinguish a penny from other coins.

Another factor impairing our memory of a penny may be interference from memories of other coins. Have you ever noticed that the head on a penny faces the opposite direction from heads on other U.S. coins? If your drawing of a penny had the head facing the wrong way, maybe you were in some way remembering a nickel or a dime.

R. S. Nickerson and M. J. Adams, "Long-Term Memory for a Common Object," *Cognitive Psychology* 11:287–307 (1979).

E. Loftus, *Memory: Surprising New Insights into How We Remember and Why We Forget* (Reading, Mass.: Addison-Wesley, 1980).

Warren E. Leary, "Novel Methods Unlock Witnesses' Memories," *New York Times,* Tuesday, November 15, 1988.

Clouds in a Jar

In 1894 the English physicist Charles Thomson Rees Wilson stood on a hilltop in Scotland, watching the play of sunlight on the clouds below. Wilson saw and remembered the glory, a bull's-eye pattern of colored rings of light that surrounds shadows on clouds.

Back at his lab, Wilson tried to make artificial clouds in a jar in order to study the glory more closely. The basic idea was to seal humid air in a jar, then cool the air suddenly by making it expand, using a hydraulic gadget. Wilson's cloud chamber worked: when the air was expanded suddenly by the right amount, dense fog appeared in the jar.

Wilson was imitating what happens in the atmosphere: humid air rises, expands, and cools, just like air escaping from a high-pressure nozzle. Cool air cannot hold as much water vapor as warm air, so conditions are right for water vapor to condense into cloud droplets.

Wilson knew that a cloud droplet is most likely to form if there's something for the water vapor to condense on—a tiny piece of dust, or even an electrically charged air molecule. This gave him an idea.

In 1911 Wilson put radioactive material near his cloud chamber and saw not a fog but "little wisps and threads of cloud" in the jar. He realized that those wisps and threads of cloud were tracks left by subatomic particles from the radioactive stuff, flying through the jar, knocking electrons off air molecules in their path, leaving those molecules electrically charged. Cloud droplets formed first around the charged air molecules.

Wilson's cloud chamber, invented for meteorology, turned out to reveal tracks of particles smaller than the atom, and soon became one of the most important tools in nuclear physics.

"Charles Thomson Rees Wilson," in *Dictionary of Scientific Biography* (New York: Charles Scribner's Sons, 1976).

C. T. R. Wilson, "On an Expansion Apparatus for Making Visible the Tracks of Ionising Particles in Gases and Some Results Obtained by Its Use" (1912), reprinted in Henry A. Boorse and Lloyd Motz, eds., *The World of the Atom* (New York: Basic Books, 1966).

Ultraviolet

Let sunlight pass through a prism, let the emerging rays strike a screen, and you get a spectrum of rainbow colors. The order of colors is always the same: red, orange, yellow, green, blue, violet. At each end of the spectrum, light fades into invisibility.

In 1800 the astronomer William Herschel discovered that sunlight contains invisible rays beyond the red end of the spectrum—rays now called infrared light. News of the discovery quickly reached a German philosopher, Johann Wilhelm Ritter, who believed in the Romantic idea that the world was built on a principle of polarity: positive and negative electricity, north and south magnetic poles, and so on. Ritter guessed that if there were invisible rays beyond the red end of the solar spectrum, there might also be invisible rays beyond the other end—the violet end.

Ritter looked for these rays by using paper soaked in a chemical that would turn black when exposed to light—a primitive photographic emulsion. He found the greatest blackening just beyond the violet end of the spectrum, where no light was visible to the eye. Ritter, in 1801, had discovered what is now called ultraviolet light.

Johann Wilhelm Ritter seems to have been inspired by an individual philosophical belief. But his discovery was scientific in that anyone, of any philosophical bent, could repeat his experiment and see that there are invisible rays, ultraviolet rays, beyond the violet end of the spectrum.

R. J. McRae, "Johann Wilhelm Ritter," in *Dictionary of Scientific Biography* (New York: Charles Scribner's Sons, 1975).

Reproduction and Sex: What's the Difference?

Some living things reproduce without sex. An amoeba, for instance, is a single-celled organism that simply divides to make two individuals out of one. As the biologists Rollin Hotchkiss and Esther Weiss once wrote, if humans reproduced that way, then each of us, at about age twenty-five, would abruptly divide into two identical people; twenty-five years later, each of those people would divide again, and so on.

Sex, in the technical sense, is the process in which genes from two individuals are combined in new arrangements—like dealing a new hand of cards. In some living things there is sex without reproduction. The single-celled paramecium, for example, joins with another of its kind, exchanges genes with its partner, then separates with a new genetic identity. The process makes no new individuals, but it does create variations among existing paramecia that help the species to adapt and survive. That seems to be the real advantage of sex.

If people were like paramecia, sex would not result in pregnancy, but would alter the eye color and the height of both partners! Of course, this is absurd and impossible because people are made of so many cells. There's no way to make identical genetic alterations in all our cells at once.

In humans and other organisms made of many cells, the combining of genes—the dealing of the new hand of cards—happens only when sperm and egg meet. Development of the egg into an embryo then begins immediately. For us, sex and reproduction are inextricably linked.

R. D. Hotchkiss and E. Weiss, "Transformed Bacteria," *Scientific American*, November 1956 (reprinted in the *Scientific American* anthology *Genetics*, intro. by C. I. Davern [San Francisco: W. H. Freeman, 1981]).

Scott F. Gilbert, *Developmental Biology* (Sunderland, Mass.: Sinauer Associates, 1985).

A COMB, A SOCK, AND A FAUCET

A comb and a wool sock can demonstrate the structure of a water molecule.

On a day of cold, dry weather, turn on the bathroom faucet just enough to get a stream of water the diameter of a pencil lead. Now rub a comb on a wool sock. Slowly bring the teeth of the comb near the water stream. If conditions are right, the comb attracts the water. You may be able to bend the water stream through an angle of ninety degrees or even more.

This happens because you've given the comb a charge of static electricity by rubbing it on the sock. But why should a charged comb attract water? It happens because water molecules are asymmetrical; one side of each water molecule has a positive electrical charge, the other side a negative charge.

Remember that in the world of electricity, like charges repel and opposites attract. If the comb has a negative charge, it'll attract the positive side of each water molecule and repel the negative side. So water molecules in the stream will turn around so their positive sides are nearest the comb.

But there's more. The electric force field gets stronger as you get closer to the tip of each comb tooth. Each water molecule's positive side is a little closer to the comb than its negative side. So the attraction between the comb and the positive side of the water molecule is a little stronger than the repulsion between the comb and the negative side of the same molecule. The attractive force therefore wins out, and the water molecule is drawn toward the comb.

So a comb, charged with static electricity by being rubbed on a wool sock, will attract a stream of water. Notice that the sock will attract the stream, too, because the rubbing gives the comb and the sock charges that are opposite but equal.

Many similar experiments are described in C. J. Lynde, *Science Experiences with Ten-Cent Store Equipment* (Scranton, Pa.: International Textbook Co., 1951).

A. V. Baez, "Some Observations on the Electrostatic Attraction of a Stream of Water" (letter to the editor), *American Journal of Physics* 20:520 (1952).

R. Gardner, *Ideas for Science Projects* (New York: F. Watts, 1986).

OUR MOST DISTANT RELATIVES

Are we humans more closely related to earthworms or to jellyfish? The answer is not obvious—we don't look like either one.

Biologists have developed a molecular method to find out about distant relationships among living things. The idea is to look not at body structure but at the molecular structure of ribosomal ribonucleic acid— "ribosomal RNA" for short. Every living cell has ribosomal RNA; it's indispensable for executing the cell's genetic instructions.

A ribosomal RNA molecule is a long chain of thousands of smaller molecules, hooked up like cars in a train. Those smaller molecules come in only four types and are connected in a very specific order in each species. In other words, each ribosomal RNA molecule is like a long coded message spelled in a four-letter alphabet.

Now there are laboratory techniques to determine the spelling of the message, the order of smaller units in the ribosomal RNA molecule. It turns out that the spelling of this message is slightly different from one species to another. Species that spell the message almost exactly the same way are almost certainly more closely related than species whose spellings differ more.

This molecular method indicates, among other things, that we humans are in fact more closely related to earthworms than to jellyfish. The sequence of smaller units in our ribosomal RNA is closer to the sequence in earthworms than to the sequence in jellyfish.

This implies, in turn, that humans and earthworms had a common ancestor, long ago—and that humans, earthworms, and jellyfish had a common ancestor even farther back. Today's molecular similarities record yesterday's family trees.

K. G. Field et al., "Molecular Phylogeny of the Animal Kingdom," *Science* 239:748–753 (February 12, 1988).

CHEAP IMITATION IVORY

In 1863 the American firm of Phelan and Collander, manufacturer of traditional ivory billiard balls, offered ten thousand dollars to anyone who could develop a substitute for natural ivory.

The American printer John Wesley Hyatt responded in 1868 with a material he called celluloid. It was one of the first synthetic plastics. The name came from one of the ingredients, cellulose, which makes up the cell walls in green plants and which could be obtained from sawdust or cotton. Making celluloid also required nitric acid, sulfuric acid, ether, ethyl alcohol, and camphor, combined in the right order in a tricky, dangerous procedure. A few variations in the recipe would give you not a plastic but an explosive, guncotton.

Hyatt's recipe produced a material completely different from any of its ingredients. Celluloid was hard, waterproof, and capable of being colored, molded, sawed, drilled, sanded, and polished. But it did have its drawbacks: its colors faded in sunlight; above 140 degrees Fahrenheit, it would decompose into a reddish vapor; worst of all, it was extremely flammable, especially in thin sheets. Nevertheless, Hyatt used celluloid to make billiard balls, false teeth, collars, cuffs, knobs, and handles. Celluloid had its heyday in the brief period when it was used for motion-picture film. Numerous movie-theater fires led to adoption of the safety film we use today.

Celluloid's flammability may lie behind an anecdote told by Hyatt himself in 1914. It seems that a Colorado saloonkeeper bought some celluloid-coated billiard balls. Occasionally, collisions between the cheap imitation billiard balls would make a crack loud enough to cause every man in the establishment to draw his gun.

Robert Friedel, *Pioneer Plastic: The Making and Selling of Celluloid* (Madison: University of Wisconsin Press, 1983), p. 35.

"Celluloid," *Nature,* August 19, 1880, pp. 370–371.

"Plastics," in *Encyclopaedia Britannica,* 14th ed. (1968).

FREEZING HOT WATER PIPES

If you have uninsulated water pipes running through a crawlspace under the house, the hot water pipe is likely to freeze before the cold water pipe during cold winter nights.

It doesn't seem to make sense. The cold water pipe is originally closer to the temperature of the outside air, so it seems logical that it would be the first to get cold enough to freeze. The monkey wrench in this argument is that hot water and cold water do not have the same freezing point—that is, the temperature required to make ice is generally lower if you start with cold water than if you start with hot water. The reason for the difference in freezing point is that cold water can hold more dissolved air than hot water. When you dissolve anything in water, you lower its freezing point.

Freezing temperature depends not only on what a substance is, but on what's dissolved in it. That's why antifreeze, dissolved in the water in a car radiator, enables that water to stay liquid below 32 degrees Fahrenheit, the freezing point of pure water. Salt does the same thing to water on the street.

Anyway, hot water holds less dissolved air than cold water, so it doesn't have to be made quite as cold before it freezes. So the hot water pipe is likely to freeze before the cold water pipe because hot water generally has less dissolved air and therefore has a higher freezing point than cold water.

This relationship between temperature and dissolved gas is also part of the reason that warm champagne and warm soda pop go flat so fast: the warm beverage loses its dissolved carbon dioxide faster than a cold beverage. This principle also explains why life is usually more abundant in cold streams than in warm streams: cold water holds more dissolved oxygen.

Ronald A. Delorenzo, *Problem Solving in General Chemistry* (Lexington, Mass.: D. C. Heath, 1981).

THE RISING WATER MYSTERY

You may well have seen this experiment in school. But did you get the right explanation? An article in the journal *The Physics Teacher* entitled "Questionable Physics Tricks for Children" points out that some of us may have gotten the wrong story.

The experiment is simple: put a burning candle in the middle of a saucer. Fill the saucer with water. Now put a drinking glass upside down over the candle, so the rim of the glass is in the water.

After a few seconds, of course, the flame uses up the oxygen in the glass and goes out. This we all expect. Now we're asked to look at the water level inside the glass. We notice that the water has risen a fraction of an inch in the glass, indicating that the volume of gas inside is less than before. And, traditionally, we're told that this shows how the oxygen in the glass has been consumed.

There are a couple of things wrong here. First, oxygen is about 20 percent of fresh air, and the volume of gas in the glass doesn't decrease by nearly that much. We have to remember that even though the flame uses up oxygen, it also makes a roughly equal volume of carbon monoxide and carbon dioxide. The same thing happens when wood burns, or any fossil fuel such as coal or oil. Second, notice how the water rises in the glass quickly, not gradually, and that it rises only after the candle goes out.

Now you can see what really happens when you invert a drinking glass over a candle in a saucer full of water: heat from the burning candle makes the air under the glass expand; after the candle goes out, the gas quickly cools and contracts. Pressure inside the glass therefore falls, and atmospheric pressure pushes more water up into the glass.

G. Grimvall, "Questionable Physics Tricks for Children," *The Physics Teacher*, September 1987, pp. 378–379.

Would you drink this?

Would you drink a mixture of the following ingredients: acetaldehyde, a close chemical relative of the embalming fluid formaldehyde; ethyl acetate, best known as a varnish solvent; acetone, famous as nail-polish remover; acetic acid, also known as vinegar; and a few of the compounds known as hexenals, which give freshly cut grass its characteristic odor?

It sounds horrible. But, in fact, just about all of us have drunk this mixture. These are some of the ingredients of natural grape juice. That list leaves out the three ingredients present in the greatest amounts, namely, water, sugars, and citric acid. But it's the acetaldehyde, ethyl acetate, acetone, acetic acid, and hexenals, among other substances—in small quantities and in the right proportions—that give natural grape juice its characteristic flavor.

Small quantities and correct proportions are important. Take another chemical, hydrogen cyanide, for example. Hydrogen cyanide is naturally present in small amounts in cherries, and contributes to their characteristic aroma. But in large quantities, it is a poison.

Another thing you can see from these examples is that the scientific name of a chemical is not likely to tell you whether that chemical is, so to speak, friend or foe.

Which would you rather smell: hydroxyphenol-2-butanone, or trimethylamine? You'd never know from the names alone that the first chemical contributes to the aroma of ripe raspberries, and the second causes the stench of rotten fish!

P. W. Atkins, *Molecules* (New York: Scientific American, 1987).

IS IT EVER TOO COLD TO SNOW?

Meteorologists who have looked at the records tell us that it's never too cold to snow. Snowfall has been observed at temperatures as low as 53 degrees below zero Fahrenheit.

There are several reasons we might not associate snowfall with very cold weather. First, cold air holds less water vapor than warm air. Snowflakes ultimately need water vapor to form; therefore, the less vapor, the fewer flakes. Nevertheless, there is always at least some water vapor available, no matter how cold the air gets. And under the right conditions, that vapor might produce clouds and snow.

Another reason we tend not to associate snowfall with very cold weather is that, here in the United States at least, the coldest weather tends to occur in strong high-pressure areas without clouds. In particular, we may tend to associate the deepest cold with crystal-clear nights. Clear nights feel especially cold partly because our body heat is lost directly to interplanetary space. Every warm object, including the surface of the Earth and every human being, releases heat energy in the form of invisible infrared light. On a clear night, that infrared light goes off into space, never to return. Clouds, if they're present, reflect some of that infrared light back to the ground and to us. When the infrared light hits our skin, some of its energy is converted back to heat, which makes us feel a little warmer than we would under a clear sky.

So it's never too cold to snow. But snow and extreme cold don't usually go together because the coldest nights are usually clear nights.

Donald Ahrens, *Meteorology Today,* 3rd ed. (St. Paul: West, 1987).

IS IT EVER TOO WARM TO SNOW?

Snowflakes are ice crystals; water turns to ice at a temperature no higher than 32 degrees Fahrenheit, or 0 degrees Celsius. So at first it might seem that if the temperature outside is above 32 degrees Fahrenheit, it won't snow.

Remember, though, that the atmosphere generally gets colder as you go higher. Even on a warm summer day, the air temperature above about fifteen thousand feet is below 32 degrees, making it possible for snow-flakes to form at high altitudes. In fact, meteorologists have concluded that most of the raindrops that fall in our part of the world originate as ice crystals which then melt as they pass through warm air on their way to the ground.

So snowflakes can form high above the ground even if the temperature near the ground is above freezing. Whether we on the ground see rain or snow depends on whether the snowflakes melt completely before they get to us.

A snowflake that has partially melted may be saved by evaporation. A snowflake in warm air picks up heat from that air. But water evaporating from the surface of a melting snowflake carries heat away from the snow-flake. Energy in the form of heat is consumed in driving water molecules from the wet snowflake into the air.

Evaporation of sweat from our skin cools our bodies in exactly the same way.

Snowfall is possible at ground temperatures above 32 degrees. If evaporation can carry heat away from a falling snowflake fast enough to balance the heat coming in from warm surrounding air, that snowflake may survive long enough for us on the ground to see it.

Donald Ahrens, *Meteorology Today,* 3rd ed. (St. Paul: West, 1987).

ALCOHOL CONTENT

According to the old story, a gunfighter walks into a saloon and orders a drink at the bar. He takes a shell from his gunbelt, breaks it open, and dumps a little pile of gunpowder on the counter. Then he pours some of the booze onto the gunpowder and touches a lighted match to the damp powder. If the powder burns slowly and evenly, the customer has *proof* that there's a proper amount of alcohol in the drink.

Nowadays, we look for a proof number, which is roughly twice the alcohol content: 100 proof means about 50 percent alcohol. Tradition-ally, of course, the alcohol in wine, beer, and liquor comes from fermen-tation: yeast consumes sugars or starches and makes ethyl alcohol, or ethanol, as a waste product. Sugars may come from grapes or other sweet fruits; starches from barley, wheat, corn, or potatoes, among other things.

Ethyl alcohol is poison even to the yeasts that make it. Once the alcohol content of a fermenting liquid reaches about 15 percent, the yeast dies in its own waste. That's why you don't see natural wines with alcohol content above about 15 percent.

Liquors with higher alcohol content are usually made by distillation, a process based on the fact that alcohol boils at a lower temperature than water. As a result, the vapor above a boiling liquor has a higher alcohol content than the liquor. That vapor can be passed over a cold surface, where it condenses into a new liquor, just as water vapor condenses on a cold glass. That's what happens in the coiled pipe on a moonshine still.

The distilled liquor has a higher alcohol content than the original. It also has a higher concentration of ingredients that give flavor and aroma. And, if it's not made just right, the distilled liquor will also have a dangerous concentration of potent poisons collectively named fusel oil, from the German word for "rotgut."

P. W. Atkins, *Molecules* (New York: Scientific American, 1987).

Harold McGee, *On Food and Cooking: The Science and Lore of the Kitchen* (New York: Macmillan, 1985).

SUMMER ANTIFREEZE AND CANDY

Why use antifreeze in the summer?

Add antifreeze to the water in your car's cooling system, and you protect the cooling system from freezing in winter. The solution of antifreeze in water freezes at a much lower temperature than either water or antifreeze alone.

A general chemical principle is that when you dissolve anything in water, you lower the freezing temperature—and raise the boiling temperature of the solution. In summer heat, the coolant has to remain liquid to carry heat out of your engine. A solution of antifreeze in water protects your cooling system in summer because the solution can get hotter without boiling than can water alone.

Another application of this principle is in candy making, when you dissolve sugar in water and heat the solution. Candy recipes often specify a particular temperature to which the sugar solution is to be heated, so the sugar will crystallize in the right way and make candy of the right consistency. As you heat the water solution, water begins to boil away. The sugar stays behind, so the sugar solution becomes more concentrated.

Now you exploit the connection between concentration of sugar and boiling temperature: a more concentrated solution has a higher boiling temperature. As more water boils away, the sugar solution becomes more concentrated and the temperature of the solution rises.

Just as antifreeze raises the boiling temperature of water in your radiator, sugar raises the boiling temperature of water in a saucepan on your stove. The gradual boiling away of the water gives you precise control over the temperature of the candy mixture.

The concentration of sugar determines the temperature at which the mixture boils; the temperature at which the mixture has been boiled, in turn, determines the consistency the candy will have when it cools. The main difference between syrup, soft candy, and hard candy is in their boiling temperatures.

Ronald Delorenzo, *Problem Solving in General Chemistry* (Lexington, Mass.: D. C. Heath, 1981).

Harold McGee, *On Food and Cooking: The Science and Lore of the Kitchen* (New York: Macmillan, 1985).

Contents

Acknowledgments

This is the "would-not-have-been-possible-without" section, and even though the phrase might have been overused over the years, it is certainly true. Whether through financial, technical, or moral support, it took the combined efforts of many to make the radio series happen, and by extension this book (as well as its predecessor, *Why You Can Never Get to the End of the Rainbow, and Other Moments of Science*).

The material in this book came directly from the scripts for the radio series *A Moment of Science*®. The programs have been produced and aired nationally since 1988 by WFIU-FM at Indiana University in Bloomington.

During the period from which the scripts in this book were taken, much-appreciated corporate underwriting came from the Indiana Corporation for Science and Technology and Exmin Corporation. Gratitude is extended to Indiana University for the support provided by the Office of Research and the University Graduate School, the Office of the Chancellor in Bloomington, the Office of the Vice President, the Office of the President, and the Radio and Television Services.

Producing a science radio series or compiling a book on science necessitates that both live up to the implication that the information contained in them is correct, at least to the best of the knowledge at the time. Scientists who volunteered their time and expertise to help ensure accuracy for these pieces were Jeffrey Alberts, Moya Andrews, Susan Berg, Geoffrey Bingham, Jessica Bolker, William Boone, Jesse L. Byock, John Carini, Andrew Carleton, John Castellan, Ken Caulton, James Craig, Marti Crouch, Vladimir Derenchuk, Russell Dukes, David Easterling, Heather Eisthen, Andrew Ellington, John Ewing, Gerald Gastony, Steven Girvin, Michael Hamburger, George Hegeman, Margaret Intons-Peterson, Susan Jones, John Kissel, William Krejci, Ken Kuikstra, Alice Lindeman, Michael List, Charles Livingston, Alan Longroy, Bruce Martin, Anthony Mescher,

Lawrence Montgomery, Harold Ogren, Robert Peterson, Henry Prange, Rudolf Raff, Stephen Rennard, Edward Robertson, Unni Rowell, Bill Rowland, Steven Russo, Dolores Schroeder, Marc Schuckit, Sarita Soni, Catherine Souch, Joel Stager, Joseph Steinmetz, Milton Taylor, Esther Thelen, Larry Thibos, Christopher Tyler, Eugene Weinberg, Jeffrey White, David Williams, and David Wise.

Two people who had nothing to do with this book deserve recognition here because they get so little otherwise: Pat Hawkins Smith and John Shelton of WFIU's engineering and production staff. John has provided superb technical expertise, and engineered a number of programs. For years Pat has been the ever-present person on the other side of the glass (no pun intended), engineering the recordings, listening for technical glitches, as well as offering much-appreciated "esthetic" advice.

Special gratitude is extended to John Woodcock in the Indiana University English Department for his years of volunteer association with *A Moment of Science,* and the countless hours he has spent reviewing hundreds of scripts to help us stay on target at making science fun and understandable to everyone. Even when one of us thought we had gotten the text just right, John had an incredible knack for making suggestions that made it better.

Read on now and enjoy the fruits of our labors.

The Shape of the Earth

Ancient civilizations described the earth as a flat plate, a dome, or even a huge drum. Today, with the help of photographs from space, we know the earth is a sphere. Yet even by the fourth century B.C., Greek astronomers with no more evidence than you could collect in your own backyard believed that the earth was spherical.

Aristotle, for example, based his argument for a spherical world on the shape of the earth's shadow during a lunar eclipse. A lunar eclipse occurs when the sun and the moon line up on opposite sides of the earth. When that happens, the shadow of the earth moves across and eventually covers the moon. Although the moon is too small to show us the entire shadow of the earth, the edge of the shadow that we can see is always curved, regardless of where the moon and sun are in relation to the surface of the earth. The only shape that could cast a round shadow from every angle is a sphere. A round, flat plate would cast a round shadow only if the light were coming from above or below; from any other angle, the shadow would be an oval or a straight line.

1

In fact, anyone driving west across the country will notice that the peaks of the Rocky Mountains appear before the foothills. If we say that this is because the foothills are still below the horizon, we are implying—quite correctly—that the curvature of the earth gets in the way. At closer range, there is no horizon between us and what we are looking at, and so the earth appears flat. But if the earth were really flat, the only limit to how far we see would be the power of our vision, and on a clear day the full height of the Rockies would be visible from Kansas.

Cohen, Morris R., and I. E. Drabkin. *A Source Book in Greek Science.* Cambridge: Harvard University Press, 1958.

Kuhn, Thomas S. *The Copernican Revolution.* Cambridge: Harvard University Press, 1957.

A Rising Fastball

Suppose a baseball pitcher releases the ball with a sharp downward snap of the wrist. That snap of the wrist imparts backspin to the ball. Backspin is opposite in direction to the spin of a ball just rolling on the ground. If the ball has backspin, then the ball's top surface moves in the same direction as the flow of air over the ball, and the bottom surface moves in the opposite direction to the flow of air. So, because of friction between the surface and the air, the top surface of a ball with backspin helps the air along, so to speak. And the bottom surface slows the air down.

Now, a famous principle: A fast-moving air stream has lower pressure than slow-moving or still air around it—a principle named after the eighteenth-century physicist Daniel Bernoulli, who discovered it.

From the point of view of a ball with backspin, the air on top moves faster and therefore has lower pressure than air on the bottom. The result is a force pushing the ball up. A baseball thrown hard enough, with enough backspin, will rise—or at least seem to be suspended—as it approaches the plate. That's your basic fastball.

This effect was first described in 1852 by the German physicist Heinrich Magnus. He was thinking about spinning cannonballs rather than spinning baseballs, but the principle is the same: Spin makes air flow faster along one side of the ball than the other. That makes a difference in air pressure, which in turn influences the flight path.

Gray, H. J., and Alan Isaacs, eds. *A New Dictionary of Physics*. London: Longman, 1975.
"Magnus Effect." In *Oxford English Dictionary*, 2nd ed. New York: Oxford University Press, 1989.
Prandtl, Ludwig. *Essentials of Fluid Dynamics*. London: Blackie, 1952.

Pine Tar Home Runs

It's against the rules of baseball to put pine tar on the fat part of the bat. Why? What's the unfair advantage of a tarred bat?

A couple of Tulane University physicists, Robert Watts and Steven Baroni, published an article about this in a journal for teachers. They pointed out that tar increases friction between bat and ball, so a tarred bat can give the ball faster spin. Specifically, an uppercut ball has backspin. Other things being equal, a fly ball with fast backspin will travel farther—dozens of feet farther, according to the physicists' calculations—than a fly ball with no spin.

The reason takes us back to Bernoulli's principle: A fast-moving air stream has lower pressure than still air around it. The top surface of a backspinning, traveling ball sweeps air back over the ball. From the ball's point of view, the air on the top moves faster and therefore has lower pressure than the air on the bottom. The result is a force pushing the ball up. A ball with fast backspin seems to float through the air.

Watts and Baroni concluded that the best strategy for hitting home runs is to hit the ball slightly below center, so as to give the ball a fast backspin rate and a low launch angle. A tarred bat is illegal but gives faster spin.

Watts, Robert G., and Steven Baroni. "Baseball-Bat Collisions and the Resulting Trajectories of Spinning Balls." *American Journal of Physics*, January 1989.

The Force of a Tornado

Tornadoes are known for their powerful winds, but the winds alone cause only part of the damage. In addition, the high winds create an area of extremely low pressure that can actually cause buildings to explode.

To understand how the winds cause the pressure to drop, we can review Bernoulli's principle, the same principle that explains the curve ball. Bernoulli's principle states that a fast-moving air stream has lower pressure than slow-moving or still air around it.

So when the very high winds of a tornado blow over a house, they cause the pressure to drop to a level far below that of the still air inside the house. The higher pressure in the house can then force the roof off the top of the house. As the roof comes up, the tornado winds pick it up and carry it away.

To see how this works on a much smaller scale, hold a dollar bill on the back of one hand. With the other hand, hold the edge that is away from you so the bill doesn't fall off. Now, blow hard across the top surface of the bill, and it should lift up off your hand. If you blow down onto the paper it won't work, but if you blow parallel to the surface of the bill, you should be able to decrease the air pressure above the paper enough to cause it to rise. Once it rises slightly, your breath will catch the underside of the bill and blow it back across your other hand.

When a window is broken in a tornado, the glass usually lands outside the house. This is because the force is exerted from the area of higher pressure inside the house toward the area of lower pressure outside the house.

Ahrens, C. Donald. *Meteorology Today: An Introduction to Weather, Climate, and the Environment.* St. Paul: West Publishing Company, 1991.

Anemia

Most cells in the body are capable of repairing themselves and of reproducing new cells just like themselves. One type of cell, however, for which this is not the case is the red blood cell. The red blood cell has no nucleus or chromosomes, and so is incapable of either reproducing or repairing itself. Instead, the body keeps up a constant supply of these very important cells in the bone marrow to replace red blood cells as they wear out.

Red blood cells are responsible for carrying oxygen from the lungs to the other cells, and for carrying carbon dioxide back to the lungs. Normally the body keeps an appropriate number of red blood cells, but in some people the bone marrow either produces too few or produces defective cells. This condition leads to a loss of energy as the body's cells cannot get enough oxygen. The name for this condition is anemia.

The most common cause of anemia is poor diet. Pernicious anemia is caused by a deficiency of vitamin B_{12}. Vitamin B_{12}, which is an essential component of red blood cells, is available only from animal products.

Iron is also an essential part of red blood cells. Iron deficiency is most common among children, whose pool of red blood cells is increasing. Because all the iron in red blood cells is recycled by the body when a cell is destroyed, adults need iron only if they have lost blood.

If the body does not have enough iron, red blood cells are still produced, but they are small and less effective.

Still other forms of anemia are hereditary and strike certain segments of the population more often than other segments. These forms include sickle-cell anemia, primarily among people of African descent, and thalassemia, found mainly among people of Mediterranean descent.

Newton, Tennis, and the Nature of Light

The seventeenth-century English physicist Isaac Newton allowed a beam of sunlight to pass through a triangular glass prism. A rainbow of colors emerged from the prism and fell on the wall opposite the window. Newton wondered why different colors fell on the wall in different places. He wrote: "I began to suspect, whether the rays, after their trajection through the prism, did not move in curve lines, and according to their more or less curvity tend to divers parts of the wall. I remembered that I had often seen a tennis ball, struck with an oblique racket, describe such a curve line." 5

A tennis ball struck obliquely, or a baseball thrown with a snap of the wrist, curves because it is spinning. As the ball moves through the air, spin makes air flow faster along one side of the ball than the other. Pressure is lower on the side where the air moves faster. The ball is deflected toward the low-pressure side.

Newton toyed with the idea that light might be made of little balls that were somehow made to spin while passing through the prism. Then these balls might follow curved paths from the prism to the wall. Newton soon rejected the curve-ball idea when he saw that colored light emerged from the prism in straight lines, not curves. Centuries later, physicists learned that particles of light, the so-called photons, bear almost no resemblance to little balls.

But Isaac Newton's attempt to relate light to tennis balls, even though it turned out to be wrong, shows how a first-class thinker searched through all his experience for a picture to help him understand a puzzling phenomenon.

Feynman, Richard P. *QED: The Strange Theory of Light and Matter.* Princeton, N.J.: Princeton University Press, 1985.

Newton, Isaac. "Dispersion of Light." In *Philosophical Transactions, Abridged*, vol. I (1672). Reprinted in *Moments of Discovery*, vol. I, ed. George Schwartz and Philip W. Bishop. New York: Basic Books, 1958.

Stereo in 1881

If you had attended the 1881 Electrical Exhibition at the Palace of Industry in Paris, you might have stood in line for one of the most popular demonstrations at the Exhibition—a telephone, conveying music from the stage of the Paris Opera. When your turn came, you would have placed a receiver over each ear and listened to a few minutes of whatever was being performed at the opera at that moment.

This might have been your first chance to hear a telephone in person, since in 1881 the telephone was a recent invention. But even people familiar with telephones noticed something peculiar about that demonstration at the Paris Electrical Exhibition. The sound was reported to have "a special character of relief and localization" that a single telephone receiver could not produce.

The sound had this special character because of the way this particular telephone system was hooked up. The receiver over the listener's left ear was connected to a microphone on the left side of the opera stage, and the receiver for the right ear was connected to a microphone on the right side of the stage.

A contemporary article in the magazine *Scientific American* attempted to describe the resulting effect with such terms as "binauricular auduition" [*sic*] and "auditive perspective." Today we'd use the word "stereo," from a Greek word meaning solid, to describe the sound.

It was not until 1957 that the first stereo music recordings were sold to the public. But back in 1881, if you were lucky, you might have been one of the very first people to hear music transmitted in stereo.

Clark, H. A. M.; G. F. Dutton; and P. B. Vanderlyn. "The 'Stereosonic' Recording and Reproducing System: A Two-Channel System for Domestic Tape Records." *Journal of the Audio Engineering Society*, April 1958. Reprinted from *Proceedings of the Institution of Electrical Engineers*, September 1957.
"The Telephone at the Paris Opera." *Scientific American*, December 31, 1881.

A Water Magnifier

Punch a hole about an eighth of an inch in diameter in the bottom of a paper or foam-plastic cup. Now push the cup down into a deep bowl of water. Look down into the cup while you push it into the water. Of course you'll see water come in through the hole you punched. But as the cup fills, you'll notice something else. You'll notice that the hole in the bottom of the cup appears magnified. You can make the hole appear bigger by pushing down harder on the cup. Push down more gently, and the magnification is reduced.

This happens because rays of light are bent when they cross from one medium to another. In this case, rays of light that make up the image of the hole in the bottom of the cup are bent as they cross from water into air. The rays are bent in just the right way to create a magnified image of the hole from your point of view.

The reason those light rays are bent in that particular way has to do with the shape of the water surface. When you push down on the cup, water spurts upward through the hole in the bottom. That upward-spurting stream of water makes a bulge in the water surface more or less like the bulge in the surface of a glass magnifying lens. By varying the downward pressure on the cup, you can vary the size of the bulge in the water surface. That, in turn, varies the amount of magnification.

McMath, T. A. "Refraction—A Surface Effect." *The Physics Teacher,* March 1989.

Bowled Over by a Sound Wave

In the 1870s the Irish physicist John Tyndall was famous all over Great Britain as a lecturer on science. One of Tyndall's lecture demonstrations showed how sound travels through air. Tyndall described it like this:

"I have here five young assistants, A, B, C, D, and E, placed in a row, one behind the other, each boy's hands resting against the back of the boy in front of him. I suddenly push A; A pushes B, and retains his upright position; B pushes C; C pushes D; D pushes E. Each boy, after the transmission of the push, becoming himself erect. E, having nobody in front, is thrown forward. Had he been standing on the edge of a precipice, he would have fallen over; had he stood in contact with a window, he would have broken the glass; had he been close to a drum-head, he would have shaken the drum. We could thus transmit a push through a row of a hundred boys, each particular boy, however, only swaying to and fro.

"Thus, also, we send sound through the air, and shake the drum of a distant ear, while each particular particle of the air concerned in the transmission of the pulse makes only a small oscillation."

If you try John Tyndall's demonstration yourself, you'll see that each person in line can't help pushing the next person. It's a reflex to keep from being knocked over.

John Tyndall had a knack for memorable physics demonstrations. He believed they were important. He wrote: "Scientific education ought to teach us the invisible as well as the visible in nature; to picture with the eye of the mind those operations which entirely elude the eye of the body."

"Tyndall." In *Dictionary of Scientific Biography*, Charles Coulston Gillispie, Editor-in-Chief. New York: Scribner, 1971.

Tyndall, John. *Sound.* 1867. Reprinted in *The Science of Sound.* New York: Philosophical Library, 1964.

How Fast Are the Winds of a Tornado?

The speed of tornado winds is difficult to estimate for two reasons. For one, weather instruments are often destroyed in a tornado. The other is that the winds are traveling at different speeds in different parts of the tornado.

Tornado winds travel in a circle around the center but, like any weather system, the tornado itself is also moving. Because the winds of a tornado travel in a circle, the winds on opposite sides of the tornado are always traveling in opposite directions. So, if the wind at one point is traveling due south, the wind on the opposite side is traveling due north.

Imagine now that a tornado with 150-mile-per-hour winds is traveling due north at 50 miles per hour. The winds on one side will also be traveling north. To figure out how fast the wind will be on the ground in that part of the tornado, we have to add the speed of the tornado as a whole—50 miles per hour—to the circular speed of its winds—150 miles per hour. At that point on the ground, you would feel winds of 200 miles per hour.

The winds on the opposite side, however, are traveling in the opposite direction, and so the two forces partly cancel each other out. The wind speed on the ground in that side of the tornado will be much lower, only 100 miles per hour.

Most tornadoes turn counterclockwise, and so as the tornado advances, the highest winds will be on the left-hand side as you face it. Or, to look at it another way, since most tornadoes in North America travel northeast, the highest winds are most often on the southeast side of the tornado.

Ahrens, C. Donald. *Meteorology Today: An Introduction to Weather, Climate, and the Environment*. St. Paul: West Publishing Company, 1991.

Sickle-cell Anemia

Anemia develops when the body either can't produce enough red blood cells, or produces defective cells instead. Because red blood cells are responsible for carrying oxygen from the lungs to the rest of the body, people with anemia feel weak and have difficulty exerting themselves.

Sickle-cell anemia is a dangerous disease with an interesting side benefit. Dietary deficiencies are responsible for most forms of anemia, but sickle-cell anemia is hereditary and occurs most commonly among people of West African descent. Sickle cells are red blood cells with a slightly different chemical composition from normal red blood cells. When the oxygen level in the blood drops too low, the defective cells crystallize into sickle-cell shapes. In this condition the blood cells can no longer transport oxygen. The result for the person affected is shortness of breath, stomach pains, internal bleeding, and sometimes even blood clotting.

An individual may inherit either one or two genes for sickle-cell. True sickle-cell anemia requires two genes—one from each parent. With only one gene, the condition is called "sickle-cell trait." Sickle-cell trait is still dangerous at high elevations, or in other situations involving low levels of oxygen, but it is rarely fatal and is usually not even noticeable.

In Africa, sickle-cell trait carries a distinct advantage. The chemical composition of the sickle cell prevents it from being invaded by malarial parasites, making people with sickle cells immune to malaria. In West Africa, where malaria is a problem, as much as 20 percent of the population has sickle-cell. In the United States, where malaria is not a problem, sickle-cell offers no advantage. Here, fewer than 10 percent of African Americans carry genes for sickle-cell. And the incidence of sickle-cell anemia is even lower, at only 1 in 400.

Rust

Water and oxygen are both necessary for metal to rust, but equally important is the flow of electrons from the metal into the surrounding water. In order for iron to be dissolved in water, it has to have some kind of electrical charge. All atoms begin with a balanced number of negatively charged electrons and positively charged protons. So when the iron gives up electrons, it then has a net positive charge.

Once the iron is positively charged, it can react with oxygen dissolved in the water to form iron oxide, or rust. As the rust forms, the iron loses its positive charge. Now it can give up more electrons to the water, and so the cycle continues.

Usually rust forms at two different sites in two different ways. For example, a spike stuck partway into the ground rusts fastest underground, where the metal can give up electrons into the moist soil. As the spike gives up electrons, the whole spike becomes positively charged. When that happens, the metal at the top of the spike, which is exposed to the oxygen in the air, also forms a coating of rust.

We've seen how metal exposed to salt, whether it be seawater or salt put on the roads in winter to melt snow and ice, rusts faster. Salt speeds up corrosion because salt water conducts electricity better than fresh water, making it easier for iron to give up electrons.

In the 1930s, scientist Michael Faraday was the first to explain metal corrosion as an electrochemical process. Since then we have learned a lot more, but there is still a great deal that is not known about how rust works. A more recent wrinkle is that scientists have found that bacteria, too, are involved in metal corrosion, making it a biological process as well. So if you drive an old car, it may have even more bugs in it than you think. Rust involving bacteria is called "biocorrosion."

Bacteria can work to either slow down or speed up rust by creating what is called a "biofilm" over the metal. This biofilm, made up of living bacteria, can act like a coat of paint or rustproofing, protecting the metal from the corrosive effects of moisture.

But the biofilm can also have the opposite effect if other types of bacteria get to the metal first. For example, sulfate-reducing bacteria draw dissolved sulfur out of the water and release sulfuric acid. The sulfuric acid is extremely attractive to electrons, and causes the metal to corrode much faster than normal. But sulfate-reducing bacteria work better when there is no oxygen present. If the sulfate-reducing bacteria get to the metal before the biofilm forms, the film can actually cover and protect the damaging bacteria from exposure to oxygen and water currents. Sealed under the biofilm, the sulfate-reducing bacteria can work away at the metal relatively undisturbed.

"Metals, Corrosion of." In *Collier's Encyclopedia*. New York: Macmillan Educational Company, 1987.
Sienko, Michell J., and Robert A. Plane. *Chemistry*. 5th ed. New York: McGraw-Hill, 1976.

How Can You Tell If a Spider Is Dead?

If a spider is not moving and all its legs are flexed—that is, pulled in toward its body—it's likely to be dead. Although spiders' legs have flexor muscles—muscles that bend the legs in toward the body—they do not have extensor muscles—muscles that would cause the legs to straighten and point away from the spider's body.

So a spider flexes its legs by using its flexor muscles. But how does a spider extend its legs? In the 1940s the zoologist C. H. Ellis noted that, as a rule, dead spiders have flexed legs. Evidently, whatever straightens a spider's legs in life is inoperative in death.

Ellis and other zoologists demonstrated that spiders extend their legs with a hydraulic system. The legs of a living spider contain fluid under pressure that tends to straighten the legs, just like water pressure stiffening a garden hose, or hydraulic fluid pressure lifting a car at a garage. The spider increases fluid pressure when it wants to extend its legs more forcefully. If a spider's leg is cut, the spider can't straighten that leg until it seals off the fluid leak.

If the spider dies, it can't maintain its internal fluid pressure. The leg flexor muscles may contract one more time, but without fluid pressure there will be no opposing force to straighten the legs again. That's why a motionless spider with flexed legs is likely to be dead.

Vogel, Steven. *Life's Devices: The Physical World of Animals and Plants.* Princeton, N.J.: Princeton University Press, 1988.

Degradable Plastics

Past ages have been called the Stone Age, Iron Age, and Bronze Age. Future archaeologists may call this the Plastic Age.

Plastics are widely used in part because they can't be broken down by natural agents, as can some of the material they have replaced. But the fact that plastics don't break down is troublesome. Plastic litter outlasts litter made of natural materials. So as we run out of space in landfills, plastics become more and more of a problem.

There is no perfect solution, but we may find some help from a new and seemingly contradictory technology: degradable plastics.

Biodegradable trash bags combine starch and plastic. When bacteria eat the starch, much of the bag then turns to dust. The bag still doesn't break down completely, but microorganisms can at least get to the garbage inside, which otherwise is isolated for as long as the trash bag holds together.

Photodegradable plastic breaks down after a few months' exposure to the sun. Photodegradable plastic won't help with trash buried under a landfill, but it could help with litter.

In the long run, recycling may solve more of our problems with plastic waste. But plastic is harder to recycle than glass or metal, partly because there are many different kinds of plastic with different chemical properties.

Ultimately, degradable plastic presents a dilemma. If we make plastics that can be broken down by the sun or microorganisms, some of the benefit of plastic is lost. Since many of the products made from recycled plastic have to withstand the forces of nature, degradable plastic could make recycling *more* difficult. Fences and park benches, for example, can be made from recycled plastic, but if either contains photodegradable material, it won't last long in a sunny park.

Beardsley, Tim. "Disappearing Act: Can Degradable Plastics Ease the Landfill Crisis?" *Scientific American,* November 1988.

A Molecular Soccer Match

In 1827, botanist Robert Brown noticed tiny particles of plant pollen jiggling randomly around in a dish of water under his microscope. Brown knew that the particles weren't alive, but he couldn't explain their movement.

Nearly a century later, Einstein used Brown's observations as evidence in one of the major debates of his time—the question of whether or not molecules existed. One group, including Einstein, believed that matter was made up of smaller particles like sand on a beach. Other scientists claimed that matter was continuous like a smooth slab of rock. No one could see molecules, but Einstein argued that Brown's particles moved as they did because they were being hit by water molecules.

To see how, imagine a field of people, all pushing an enormous ball. Each time someone hits the ball, it moves a tiny bit. The ball moves this way and that, and gradually works its way around the field. A distant observer can't see individual people, and so the ball appears to move randomly on its own.

The tiny particles drifting in water are much bigger than the invisible water molecules, but the molecules push the particles around the way the crowd pushes the ball. Physicists have named this random jiggling motion "Brownian movement," after the botanist who was astute enough to observe the strange motion, even though he had no idea of its cause.

Little did Brown know that in 1905 a young physicist just starting his career would use those jiggling pollen particles to answer one of the biggest questions of physics at the turn of the century.

Feynman, Richard P. *The Feynman Lectures on Physics.* Reading, Mass.: Addison-Wesley, 1964.

14 *Conversation at a Crowded Party*

"I don't know what she sees in him."
"Beg your pardon?"
"I say, I DON'T KNOW WHAT SHE SEES IN HIM."

An article published in 1959 in the *Journal of the Acoustical Society of America* presented a rough theoretical analysis of sound levels at cocktail parties. The author, William MacLean, analyzed the problem of carrying on a conversation in the presence of background noise from other conversations, and he made a prediction that you can check for yourself.

At the beginning of a party, when few guests are present, quiet conversation is possible. As more guests arrive, you have to talk louder and louder to override the increasing background noise.

MacLean's calculations predicted that when the number of guests at a party exceeds a certain maximum determined by the size and other characteristics of the room, merely talking louder is of no avail in continuing your conversation. You just force everybody else to talk louder. The ensuing increase in background noise soon drowns you out unless you move closer to the person you're talking to—closer than you might get in another situation.

The acoustics of real rooms are so complex that it's practically impossible to say exactly when this need to get closer will set in—but MacLean predicted that that moment will occur at some point as more and more people arrive.

Someone may temporarily quiet a loud party, perhaps to introduce the guest of honor. But, MacLean found, even if everyone tries to talk quietly afterward, dialogues like the one we began with eventually drive the background noise back up to its earlier level. A crowded party remains loud until guests begin to leave.

Hall, Edward T., Jr. "The Anthropology of Manners." *Scientific American,* April 1955.
MacLean, William R. "On the Acoustics of Cocktail Parties." *Journal of the Acoustical Society of America,* January 1959.

Bloodletting 15

If you got sick 200 years ago, your doctor might well have drawn out some of your blood. Bloodletting hasn't been common in Western medicine for more than a hundred years, but some studies may have found medical evidence for the value of this practice.

All living cells, whether they are part of a person or of a bacterium, need iron to live. In order to meet this need for iron, everything from drink mixes to breakfast cereals is now fortified with iron. Lots of breakfast cereals advertise that one helping contains all the iron you need for that day. That means that if you eat any more iron that day, you'll be getting more than you need.

But the bacteria that make us sick also need iron, and one of the ways the body fights disease is to lower its own level of iron in order to starve the bacteria. After surgery, during the growth of cancer cells, or whenever there is a threat of disease or infection, the concentration of iron in the body goes down. And studies have shown that giving extra iron to people in these situations may actually increase the danger of disease or infection by making the bacteria healthier.

When the old-time doctors drew blood, the idea was to get rid of poisons in the blood. In fact, their method may have worked because they were getting rid of valuable nutrients that would otherwise have strengthened the microorganisms causing the disease. Most of the body's iron is in the blood, and so by getting rid of the iron, the doctors may have been slowing the growth of the disease.

Extremely low iron levels are just as dangerous, and no one yet is advocating a large-scale return to bloodletting. But it looks like we may be taking another look at one old medical practice, once chalked up to ignorance.

Kent, Susan; Eugene D. Weinberg; and Patricia Stuart-Macadam. "Dietary and Prophylactic Iron Supplements: Helpful or Harmful." *Human Nature* 1, no. 1 (1978).

Weinberg, Eugene D. "Iron Withholding: A Defense against Infection and Neoplasia." *Physiological Review* 64 (1984).

Weinberg, R. J.; S. R. Ell; and E. D. Weinberg. "Blood Letting, Iron Homeostasis, and Human Health." *Medical Hypotheses* 21 (1986).

16 *Looming on the Horizon*

When we say that distant mountains are looming on the horizon or, more figuratively, that an important event is looming, we are using an old sailor's term for a particular kind of mirage.

One way to see looming is to stand on the shore of a large lake or sound on a sunny afternoon and look at the horizon, preferably through binoculars. If you see the water surface at the horizon appearing to curve upward, giving you the impression that you are inside a shallow bowl, you are seeing the kind of mirage known as looming.

On a sunny afternoon, warm air is likely to be moving from the land out over the cool water, which cools that air from below. Looming arises from the bending of light rays as they leave the distant water surface and pass through that cool layer of air near the surface into warm air higher up.

Whenever light rays pass from a dense medium like cool air into a less dense medium like warm air, the rays are bent. In the case of looming, light rays leaving the distant water at a shallow angle that would otherwise cause them to pass over your head unseen are instead bent downward, toward the horizontal, as they travel from cool air into warm air.

When those light rays, now traveling horizontally, reach your eye, they give you an image of the distant water as you would see it if you were higher above the ground than you really are. In sailors' language, on a sunny afternoon the horizon looms: the water surface appears to curve upward like the inside of a shallow bowl.

Fraser, Alistair B., and William H. Mach. "Mirages." *Scientific American,* January 1976. Reprinted, with introductions by David K. Lynch, in the *Scientific American* anthology *Atmospheric Phenomena* (1980).

A Wet Paintbrush

Take an artist's watercolor brush, dip it in water, and pull it out again. The bristles cling together to form a smooth, pointed shape that artists and calligraphers use to paint lines of varying thickness. Something similar happens when a person with straight hair dives into water and climbs out again: that person's hair is slicked down.

We usually say that the bristles or hairs cling because they are wet. But that can't be the real explanation, as you can see if you look at the bristles of that brush while you hold it underwater. While immersed in water, the bristles do not cling, even though they are certainly wet. Wet bristles—and wet human hairs—cling together not if they are surrounded by water, but only if they are surrounded by a water *surface.*

The clinging of the bristles is really a manifestation of the clinging of individual water molecules. A water molecule at the surface of a body of water—say, on the outside of a wet brush—is pulled strongly toward that body of water, because that's where the other water molecules are. One result of this mutual attraction between water molecules is that a water surface is under tension, like an elastic skin.

That surface tension pulls water into beads on a well-waxed car. It also holds the bristles of a wet brush together—if the brush is surrounded by air. The bristles of a brush immersed in water don't cling because they are not surrounded by a water surface.

Boys, C. V. *Soap Bubbles and the Forces Which Mould Them.* Garden City, N.Y.: Doubleday Anchor Books, 1959.

Putting on the Brakes

A dog runs in front of your car, and your foot jumps to the brake. But for the quickest stop, should you lock the wheels and skid to a stop, or brake more gently so the wheels still turn? Either way, what stops the car is the friction of the tires on the road—the greater the friction, the quicker the stop. Part of the complexity of this problem is that there are two different kinds of friction: sliding and static.

First, let's take a different situation involving friction. Imagine that you are trying to push a heavy box down a wooden ramp. At first it won't move, because on a microscopic level the two surfaces are rough enough to catch on each other and resist your push. The rough surfaces conform like two open egg cartons stacked together. The force that the two rough surfaces exert to hold the box in place is called *static friction*.

But when the box does start to move, you need less work to keep it going. That's because when the surfaces slide they separate slightly, and the higher spots on one rough surface move across the higher spots on the other surface. The rough surfaces still exert some force, slowing the box down; this force is called *sliding friction*. And, as you can tell from your own efforts with the box, static friction can exert more force than sliding friction.

But how does this apply to the car? As long as the wheels turn, some part of the tire is always planted firmly on the road. As you brake, the momentum of the car forces the tires forward against the road surface, just as when you pushed on the box. The harder you brake, the more static friction develops between the road and the tires—until you start to slide. At that point, the sliding friction offers less resistance to the car's momentum than the static friction did just before you started to skid. You can stop the fastest, then, by not quite skidding, and that is the principle behind antilock brakes.

Walker, Jearl. "The Amateur Scientist." *Scientific American,* February 1989.

Good Science, Bad Results

In the nineteenth century, geology was a new science. And as geologists studied the earth's rocks and fossils, they began to suspect that the planet was far older than anyone had imagined. Until about the middle of the eighteenth century, scholars had set the beginning of the earth at between 4,000 and 5,000 B.C. But by the middle of the nineteenth century, a hundred years of geological discoveries had extended the age of the earth from a mere 6,000 years into the billions of years. Then, in 1868, the British physicist Lord Kelvin used the earth's temperature to calculate a much shorter age for our planet.

Most geologists accepted that the earth had started as a molten mass and had been cooling ever since. Kelvin calculated how long it would take the earth to cool to its current temperature from its original molten temperature. Volcanoes proved that the inside of the earth was extremely hot. And, he reasoned, for the earth still to be that hot, it could not be more than 100 million years old, and perhaps as young as 26 million. The age of the earth according to Kelvin's calculations was short enough to force major changes in the way nineteenth-century scientists imagined the world.

No one at the time could refute Kelvin's results because he accounted for all the known laws of physics, and he used evidence that any geologist could measure. Kelvin's calculations were so simple and straightforward that today some historians wonder why no one had presented them earlier.

Kelvin was wrong, but not because of his calculations. Early this century, physicists discovered that naturally occurring radioactivity in the earth was releasing enough heat to offset much of the earth's cooling. Taking into account this radioactivity, geologists now estimate the age of the earth at 5 billion years.

Bowler, Peter. *Evolution: The History of an Idea.* Berkeley: University of California Press, 1984.

Gould, Stephen Jay. *Time's Arrow, Time's Cycle.* Cambridge, Mass.: Harvard University Press, 1987.

Hawking, Stephen. *A Brief History of Time.* New York: Bantam Books, 1988.

Tickling the Funny Bone

Of all the parts of our body, the funny bone may have the least appropriate name. That sensitive point on the elbow is not a bone, and it certainly isn't funny.

Most of us have at some time banged an elbow on a sharp corner and felt that indescribable tingling—like an electric shock—up and down the arm. What we are hitting is not a bone but a bundle of nerves, causing them all to fire at once.

Thousands of nerves carry messages from every part of the arm to the brain. Some report on heat, others on cold, and others on pressure. One bundle of nerves passes through a channel in the elbow that we call the funny bone. If you could intercept some of the messages along the way, the messages would all look the same—a combined electrical and chemical impulse. Your brain recognizes heat, cold, and pain only because it knows which nerves sent the signal.

The nervous system is generally reliable, but sometimes it can fool us. Amputees, for example, who have lost a leg may feel pain in the missing foot. The foot is gone, but if the nerves that connected the foot to the brain fire, the brain interprets the signal as pain in the foot.

When you bang the nerves passing through your funny bone against the corner of a table, the shock causes all the nerves to send their messages at the same time. So the message the brain gets is a confused combination of cold, pain, heat, and everything else which it interprets as coming from all over the arm.

A jolt of electricity can also cause nerves to fire randomly, and that is why a bump on the funny bone feels like an electric shock. So banging the funny bone is not very funny, but the reason it feels the way it does is that your brain doesn't know *what* to think.

Putting South on Top

Maps of the world usually have north at the top and Greenwich, England, on a north-south line which runs through the center of the map. Not quite all world maps are laid out this way, however. In the mid-1980s an Australian cartographer by the name of McArthur published his so-called "McArthur's Universal Corrective Map of the World."

McArthur's map looks almost like one of the rectangular world maps we see all the time, but turned upside down. Also, Australia, not England, is at the horizontal center. The printed words on the map—the title and the names of oceans, countries, and a hundred or so major cities—are right side up only if you orient the map with south at the top. Looking at McArthur's world map is a strange experience. The United States occupies the lower left corner, with the Pacific Ocean to the right of North America and the Arctic Ocean below.

McArthur says that his map begins a crusade against "the perpetual onslaught of 'downunder' jokes—implications from Northern nations that the height of a country's prestige is determined by its equivalent spatial location on a conventional map of the world."

McArthur is only half joking. Cartographers remind us that any map is merely an interpretation of the world, that no single map can serve all purposes, and that maps shape and are shaped by the self-images of the people who make and use them.

"New Map Turns World Geography Upside Down." *Earth Science,* Fall 1985. (This article says that 35" x 23" laminated copies of McArthur's map can be bought [or could be bought in 1985] from Rex Publications, 413 Pacific Highway, Artarmon 2064, Australia.)

Phipps, William E. "Cartographic Ethnocentricity." *The Social Studies,* November–December 1987.

Porter, Phil, and Phil Voxland. "Distortion in Maps: The Peters Projection and Other Devilments." *Focus,* Summer 1986.

Mayonnaise Emulsions

When we say that two people are like oil and water, we usually mean that they don't get along together. Oil won't mix with water, or vinegar, and that's why you often have to shake salad dressing before you use it.

But there is a way of mixing oil and vinegar so they stay mixed. One such mixture is mayonnaise. To make mayonnaise, you need to make what's called an emulsion. An emulsion combines two liquids that ordinarily don't mix by breaking one of the liquids up into tiny droplets that stay suspended in the other liquid.

Try mixing oil and vinegar by shaking them in a jar. When you stop, you can see that the oil is broken up into tiny particles, swirling about in the vinegar. But if you want to use the mixture on a salad, you'd better hurry, because almost immediately the oil droplets float to the surface and separate from the vinegar.

An emulsion, such as mayonnaise, needs an emulsifying agent to keep the droplets in suspension. In mayonnaise, egg acts as the emulsifying agent. To make mayonnaise you beat egg yolks with a little lemon juice, then add oil very slowly as you continue beating the mixture. The beater not only breaks the oil into tiny droplets, just as you did when you shook the jar, but also coats the droplets with egg yolk. The yolk coating prevents the droplets from coming back together, and so is said to "emulsify" the oil.

When you finish making mayonnaise, you'll probably want to use soap to clean out the oily dishes. Soap is also an emulsifying agent. As you scrub the dishes, the soap wraps itself around the oil, drawing it into suspension in the dishwater so it can be washed away.

The Joy of Cooking has some easy recipes for mayonnaise. Try experimenting with different varieties and amounts of oils. You'll not only learn about emulsions, but make better sandwiches, too.

McGee, Harold. *On Food and Cooking: The Science and Lore of the Kitchen.* New York: Scribner, 1984.

Learning to Talk

Parents of young children are sometimes surprised when their preschoolers' grammar starts getting worse. When children begin using sentences, their grammar is reasonably correct. Then, as they get a little older, the same children start making more mistakes. A child who used the word "mice" might start saying "mouses," even though she had never heard anyone else make that mistake. If you see this pattern in your own child, don't worry; child development specialists say it's actually a good sign. By making these mistakes, children are showing a deeper understanding of grammar.

The early sentences are grammatically correct only because the child is imitating adults. When you say, "We went to the zoo," the child repeats, "We went to the zoo." But a year later, when you ask, "Did you go outside?" the same child might answer, "Yes, I goed outside." To say "I goed outside" may not be correct, but it does follow the common rule that the English past tense is usually formed by adding -ed. In this later stage of language learning, the child is breaking up phrases such as "We went outside" into words and trying to recombine them to mean different things. The collection of rules that we use to combine words in different ways is grammar.

We think we teach children grammar by correcting their mistakes, but a child learns about grammar mostly through listening to others, and by trial and error. No one told the child to say "mouses" for "mice," or "goed" for "went"; those words children figure out on their own based on the English grammar rules that form plurals by adding -s, and past tenses by adding -ed. And just as children learn the mistakes by themselves, they eventually learn the correct forms by themselves as well.

Baby's First Steps

Children don't learn to walk until about age one. But if you hold a newborn baby so its feet just touch the ground, an automatic response causes the baby to lift its legs as if walking. What is more puzzling, though, is that this automatic stepping response stops after a few months, and doesn't return until about six months later.

Scientists have offered several complicated explanations. One suggestion was that the newborn's stepping response was a primitive instinct which disappeared as the baby developed, and that the later stepping was a more conscious, human effort at real walking.

But the complicated, theoretical explanation is not always the correct one. Indiana University psychologist Esther Thelen used two simple experiments to demonstrate a much simpler answer. Thelen's explanation was this: The fat in a baby's legs increases faster than the baby's muscular strength. When the legs get too heavy, the baby stops trying to lift them. In other words, a six-month-old baby doesn't try to walk when its feet touch the ground because its legs are too fat.

Thelen's experiment involved a group of babies who had grown out of the automatic stepping stage. She held these babies in shallow baths of water so that the buoyancy of the water would take most of the weight off their legs. When their feet touched the bottom, the babies began stepping.

In the other experiment, Thelen tied tiny ankle weights to the legs of a group of newborn babies, and held them in the air so their feet just touched the ground. The weights acted like the added fat in older babies, and the newborns did not begin stepping.

The two experiments showed that whether or not a baby picks up its feet when they touch the ground depends on the weight of the baby's legs. Thelen's practical experiments solved a problem that had puzzled developmental biologists for a long time.

Whole-Wheat Bread Is a Mixed Bag

One of the ideas behind the interest in "whole" foods, including whole-wheat bread, is that if you eat more of the plant, you get more of the vitamins. When the outer layer is removed from whole wheat to make white flour, the flour does lose iron and some B vitamins, but by leaving that layer on you may be losing other nutrients.

Although it might seem improbable that by taking part of the grain away you would get more of some nutrients, calcium is one important mineral that is more available from white flour than from whole-wheat. Whole-wheat flour has just as much calcium as white flour, but whole-wheat also contains phytic acid, which binds up the calcium, making it harder for your body to absorb.

If you get enough calcium in other forms, such as milk, you don't need as much calcium from bread, but for people who already have inadequate diets—and especially for children with growing bones—the loss of calcium can be serious. When Dublin was put on a diet of whole-wheat bread during World War II, the result was a massive epidemic of the bone disease rickets.

In a healthy diet, the main advantage of whole-wheat bread is the fiber, which is undigestible but is still necessary for good digestion. By adding bulk, and speeding up the digestive process, the fiber from whole-wheat can help prevent appendicitis, gall-stones, hardening of the arteries, and some types of cancer.

But, like all food, whole-wheat bread is a mixed bag. For most of us, the benefits of the fiber probably outweigh the slight loss of nutrients, but the value of any food depends as much on the other things you eat as it does on the chemistry of that particular food.

McGee, Harold. *On Food and Cooking: The Science and Lore of the Kitchen*. New York: Scribner, 1984.

Packaging for the Birds

If you were manufacturing a highly perishable product, you might not want a porous container to pack it in. And yet that is exactly what hens have been doing for thousands of years. In order for a chick embryo to develop, the eggshell has to be slightly porous so that oxygen can pass through. But the danger of a porous shell is that bacteria can get through as well.

The catch is that for bacteria to get to the yolk and the unhatched chick, they have to pass through the white of the egg, where the chicken has set a chemical trap for unwanted cells. Bacteria, like all animals, need iron to survive, and the unhatched chick gets its iron from the yolk. But the white that separates the iron-rich yolk from the shell has virtually no iron. And not only is the white low in iron, it also contains a protein called con-albumin that is strongly attracted to iron. Because there is far more conalbumin than iron in egg white, the conalbumin kills any cells that come through the eggshell by stealing their iron. Eventually the conalbumin gets enough iron that it's no longer attracted to the iron in the bacteria, and the egg will spoil.

When the Earl of Gloucester in Shakespeare's *King Lear* is

injured, a servant shouts, "I'll fetch some flax and whites of eggs to apply to his bleeding face" (Act III, Scene 7). No one had heard of conalbumin in the seventeenth century, but the servant knew that egg white would prevent the infection of his master's eyes. Chickens probably don't know about conalbumin either, but their eggs demonstrate the efficiency of one natural immune system that scientists are just beginning to understand.

Kent, Susan; Eugene D. Weinberg; and Patricia Stuart-Macadam. "Dietary and Prophylactic Iron Supplements: Helpful or Harmful." *Human Nature* 1, no. 1 (1978).
Weinberg, Eugene D. "Iron Withholding: A Defense against Infection and Neoplasia." *Physiological Review* 64 (1984).

Look through Your Comb at the Mirror

26 Hold a pocket comb, with teeth vertical, between your eyes and a bathroom mirror. Look through the teeth of the real comb at the teeth of the reflected comb. Slowly move the comb toward the mirror, always keeping both the comb and its reflection in your line of sight. As the comb gets within a few inches of the mirror, you will see what appears to be a shimmering, magnified view of the comb's teeth, with the magnifying power steadily increasing as the comb approaches the mirror.

The shimmering image is a pattern of light and dark created by overlap of the teeth of the real comb and the reflected comb. In some places, you see the teeth of the reflected comb fill in gaps between the teeth of the real comb, and you see solid black. In other places, gaps between teeth on the real comb line up with gaps in the reflected comb. Those areas appear relatively light.

The eerie pattern of dark and light areas is an example of a so-called moiré pattern. Moiré patterns arise whenever two repetitive gridlike designs overlap. In this case, the repetitive design is the row of evenly spaced teeth on the comb. And moiré patterns often resemble a magnified view of the overlapping designs. For example, when you look at overlapping folds of sheer drapery fabric, you see a moiré pattern of crisscrossed dark lines that look like a magnified view of the fabric.

Returning to our comb example: Notice that the magnified teeth in the moiré image are even tapered, just like the real ones, and that if you point the teeth slightly toward or away from you, the moiré image appears to do the same thing. You have to see it to believe it.

Stecher, Milton. "The Moiré Phenomenon." *American Journal of Physics*, April 1964.

Opera Singers Cut through the Orchestra

First-class opera singers can make themselves heard distinctly even over a fairly loud orchestra. Acousticians have found that singers accomplish this at least partly by making extra sound at certain moderately high frequencies where the orchestra is not especially loud.

Recall that the sound of a singing voice or a musical instrument is really a complex mixture of vibrations at many different frequencies. Each instrument and each voice has its own peculiar mixture of frequencies that we perceive as its tone color.

Good opera singers learn, by one method or another, to produce a tone that contains an especially large amount of sound energy in the frequency range of 2,000 to 4,000 vibrations per second. The emphasis on frequencies in the 2,000-to-4,000-vibration-per-second range makes the operatic voice sound very different from the pop singer's voice and from ordinary speech.

The sound of a symphony orchestra, on the other hand, does not have any special emphasis on frequencies between 2,000 and 4,000 vibrations per second. So opera singers cut through the orchestra by emphasizing frequencies that the orchestra does not.

Pop singers, by the way, often don't emphasize those special high frequencies because they want to create a more conversational, speechlike sound than an opera singer. But at least one respected book on sound recording recommends that the pop recording engineer electronically amplify the frequencies between 2,000 and 4,000 vibrations per second on vocal tracks to keep the voices from being buried by the accompanying instruments!

Runstein, Robert E., and David Miles Huber. *Modern Recording Techniques*. Indianapolis: Howard W. Sams and Company, 1986.

Sundberg, Johan. "The Acoustics of the Singing Voice." *Scientific American*, March 1977. Reprinted in the *Scientific American* anthology *The Physics of Music*.

The Roots of "Algebra"

Our word "algebra" comes from one word in the long Arabic title of a mathematics book written about 1,150 years ago in Baghdad. The author was the Islamic mathematician and astronomer Abu Jafar Muhammad Ibn Musa al-Khwarizmi. The Arabic word in question, "al-jabr," was used by al-Khwarizmi to mean restoration or completion—one of the techniques he recommended for solving an equation.

In modern language, this is the technique of taking terms preceded by a minus sign on one side of an equation and moving them to the other side, where they can then have plus signs. Maybe you remember learning this trick in school.

The full title of al-Khwarizmi's *Algebra* has been translated as *The Compendious Book on Calculation by Completion and Balancing*. The book's stated purpose was to provide "what is easiest and most useful in arithmetic, such as men constantly require in cases of inheritance, legacies, . . . lawsuits, and trade." Al-Khwarizmi's *Algebra* was a standard text in the Middle East and Europe well into the Middle Ages.

Unlike modern algebra books, al-Khwarizmi's *Algebra* used neither x's nor y's, nor even numerals. All the problems were stated in words; for example: "A quantity: I multiplied a third of it and a dirham by a fourth of it and a dirham; it becomes twenty."

Al-Khwarizmi did use numerals in some of his other works, including a book explaining arithmetic with Hindu numerals. Those Hindu numerals were the ancestors of the numerals 1 through 9 and zero that we use today. But al-Khwarizmi's reputation was so great that those symbols later became known as Arabic numerals. And al-Khwarizmi's name is the root of the modern word "algorithm," meaning a step-by-step procedure for solving a mathematical problem.

"Al-Khwarizmi." In *Dictionary of Scientific Biography*, Charles Coulston Gillispie, Editor-in-Chief. New York: Scribner, 1971.

Morality and Nutrition

Health food is popular in this country—mostly for the sake of our physical health. A hundred years ago, around the end of the last century, the United States was in the middle of its first health-food craze, but back then physical health was only part of the reason. Refined foods, additives, and stimulants were considered immoral as well as unhealthy.

In a book called *Plain Facts for Old and Young*, Dr. John Harvey Kellogg wrote, "A man who lives on pork, fine-flour bread, rich pies and cakes, and condiments, drinks tea and coffee, and uses tobacco, might as well try to fly as to be chaste in thought." The message was that if you eat impure food, you'll have impure thoughts.

The center of the health-food movement in the nineteenth century was Battle Creek, Michigan, which was also the world headquarters of the Seventh-day Adventist church. In 1863, Ellen White, who was then the leader of the church, had a religious revelation telling her to eat only certain foods. As a result, meat and stimulants became forbidden by church doctrine, and White hired Dr. Kellogg to run the Seventh-day Adventists' sanatorium in Battle Creek. In order to make the diet more interesting, Dr. Kellogg developed a new breakfast cereal by baking oats, wheat, and cornmeal into hard biscuits and then crumbling the biscuits into small chunks. He named his new cereal "granola" because it was made from granules of whole-grain biscuits. So the next time you sit down to a bowl of granola, remember that it was invented not just for your physical health, but for your moral health as well.

McGee, Harold. *On Food and Cooking: The Science and Lore of the Kitchen.* New York: Scribner, 1984.

Moral Fiber in Whole-Wheat Bread

What do you say when the person behind the sandwich counter asks you, "Would you like that on white or whole-wheat?"

Actually, the interest in whole-wheat bread is relatively new.

For thousands of years, wheat has been ground and the non-digestible outer layer thrown away. Until the nineteenth century, when machinery made it easier to process flour, white flour was much more expensive than whole-wheat. The cost, along with the lighter color and texture, made white bread a status symbol.

But the first large movement to encourage the use of whole-wheat bread was not based solely on physical health. In 1837 a Presbyterian minister named Sylvester Graham wrote *A Treatise on Bread and Bread-Making*, in which he denounced white bread as unnatural, since he said God had made wheat with both a digestible and a non-digestible part.

Today, health experts recommend the non-digestible fiber of whole-wheat bread because it adds bulk and speeds up the digestive process. Nobody knows for certain how much dietary fiber really helps, but it is thought that as the food passes more quickly through the intestines, there is less time for the body to absorb toxic chemicals.

Although Graham didn't have the information that we have today, he recognized the importance of the non-digestible part of the wheat. Only according to Graham, the benefits of whole-wheat bread included not only physical health but also, in his words, the "intellectual, and moral, and religious, and social, and civil, and political interests of man."

Now, our reasons for eating whole-wheat bread may be a bit more modest, but Sylvester Graham was the first person known to have argued publicly for the benefits of dietary fiber. Even today, whole-wheat flour is sometimes called "graham flour," after Sylvester Graham. And graham crackers are another familiar food named after the Reverend Sylvester Graham.

McGee, Harold. *On Food and Cooking: The Science and Lore of the Kitchen.* New York: Scribner, 1984.

Blow Out Candles with an Oatmeal Box

To do this trick, you need an empty cylindrical cardboard oatmeal box with its lid. Cut a round hole the size of a penny in the center of one end of the box.

Now aim the box at a lighted candle, with the hole facing the candle. Tap sharply on the other end. If you have aimed the oatmeal box correctly, the candle will be suddenly blown out a moment after you strike the box. With some practice you can blow candles out from up to six feet away.

When you strike the box, a so-called vortex ring comes out of the hole. This vortex ring is a region shaped like a rubber O-ring constantly turning itself inside out. That turning-inside-out motion of the air enables the vortex ring to retain its shape as it travels toward the candle. That same motion, combined with the forward motion of the vortex ring, blows the flame out when the ring arrives at the candle.

You can make that vortex ring visible as a smoke ring. Fill the oatmeal box with cigarette smoke, then tap very gently on the end of the box. A smoke ring will emerge from the hole, travel relatively fast for a foot or two, then slow down and spread out. If you tap harder, the smoke ring will travel farther but will be harder to see.

Beeler, Nelson F., and Franklyn M. Branley. *Experiments in Science.* Revised enlarged edition. New York: Crowell, 1955.

Feynman, Richard P. *The Feynman Lectures on Physics.* Reading, Mass.: Addison-Wesley, 1963.

What Temperature Boils Down To

Water boils at 212 degrees and freezes at 32. The human body temperature is about 98.6 degrees, and a comfortable room is between 65 and 70. We take these kinds of numbers for granted, but have you ever wondered how such seemingly arbitrary numbers came to have such meaning?

Actually the numbers are arbitrary. If you wiped all the numbers off of a thermometer and replaced them with your own, you could still use that thermometer to compare the temperature in your house from one day to the next. But you wouldn't be able to compare the temperature of your house with the temperature of another house down the street.

The first widely accepted temperature scale—and the one most commonly used in the United States—is the Fahrenheit scale developed by the Dutch physicist and instrument-maker Gabriel Daniel Fahrenheit in the early 1700s. When Fahrenheit was working, there were at least 35 different temperature scales. So if someone at that time said the temperature was 65 degrees, you still wouldn't know whether it was hot or cold unless you knew what scale the temperature referred to.

Fahrenheit assigned the number zero to the lowest temperature that he could get by mixing salt and ice. He then assigned the number 96 to body temperature. Using his new scale, Fahrenheit found that pure water freezes at 32 degrees and boils at 212 degrees. As temperature measurements became more accurate, Fahrenheit's scale remained in place, even though physiologists figured out that typical human body temperature is about 98.6 degrees Fahrenheit and not 96, as Fahrenheit had calculated.

The United States is one of only a few countries that use the Fahrenheit scale. Most others use a scale developed by the Swedish astronomer Anders Celsius about a decade after Fahrenheit developed his. The Celsius scale was created by assigning the number zero to the temperature at which water freezes, and 100 to the temperature at which it boils. Speaking in Celsius, a healthy body temperature is around 37 degrees, and an average room is about 20 degrees.

On the Fahrenheit scale, there are 180 degrees between the freezing point—32—and the boiling point—212. On the Celsius scale, there are only 100 degrees between the freezing and boiling points of water. That means that each Celsius degree is 1.8 times the size of a Fahrenheit degree. So a temperature change of 10 degrees Celsius is the same as a change of 18 degrees Fahrenheit.

Normally Americans don't have too many occasions to convert between Fahrenheit and Celsius, but if you can think of 20 degrees as a comfortable room temperature, and 40 degrees as a very hot day, then when someone tells you it's a balmy 24 degrees out, you'll know what they mean without converting at all.

Both the Fahrenheit and Celsius scales are *relative* scales because they tell us the temperature relative to some other temperature. But for most other measurements we use *absolute* scales. If you start with a 25-pound sack of flour and take out 10 pounds, you'll be left with 15. If you take away another 15 pounds, you will have zero pounds of flour—in other words there will be no flour left. If this seems obvious, think how different it is from temperature measurements. You can have minus 5 degrees Fahrenheit or Celsius, but you can't have minus 5 pounds of flour.

In order to avoid the relativity of these two temperature scales, most scientists use an absolute temperature scale introduced by the British scientist Lord Kelvin near the end of the nineteenth century. On the Kelvin scale, zero degrees is the point where there is absolutely no heat. Zero degrees Kelvin is very cold—close to minus 460 degrees Fahrenheit—and is referred to as absolute zero. Nothing can get colder than absolute zero; in fact, it is a temperature that cannot actually be reached. On the Kelvin scale water freezes at 273 degrees, a comfortable room is about 293 degrees, and your body temperature is about 310 degrees.

Ahrens, C. Donald. *Meteorology Today: An Introduction to the Weather, Climate, and the Environment.* St. Paul: West Publishing Company, 1991.

"Fahrenheit, Gabriel Daniel," and "Thompson, Sir William." In *Dictionary of Scientific Biography,* Charles Coulston Gillispie, Editor-in-Chief. New York: Scribner, 1971.

The Fable of Centrifugal Force

If you tie a rock to the end of a piece of string and whirl the rock in a circle over your head, you feel tension in the string. Most of us would say that the tension comes from centrifugal force, a force pulling toward the outside of the circle, away from the center. But look more closely and you can see why centrifugal force is really a fable—a useful idea in some situations, but basically fictitious.

Imagine that while you're whirling the rock around, you let go of the string. If there really were such a thing as "centrifugal force" pulling the rock away from the center of the circle, that force would make the rock fly off in a direction straight away from the center of the circle. But the rock doesn't do that. Instead, it continues in the same direction it was going at the moment you released the string. The rock flies off along a tangent to the circle.

Obviously, whirling rocks on strings is dangerous unless you are alone in the middle of a very large open field. But you can safely observe how, according to the same principle, a baseball leaves a pitcher's hand along a tangent to the curved path of the hand. Both the rock and the baseball illustrate one of the laws of motion stated 300 years ago by Isaac Newton: Objects go in straight lines at steady speeds unless acted on by some force.

When you were holding on to the string, you were exerting a force on the rock, constantly pulling it toward you, keeping it from going in a straight line as it would, so to speak, prefer to do, and making it go in a circle instead. The tension in the string was caused not by "centrifugal force" but by you, pulling on the rock!

The same principle applies when you are in a car that makes a turn. Say you're steering to the right, and as you do you feel a mysterious force pushing you against the left side of the car, against the seat belt and the door. Souvenirs hanging from your rearview mirror swing to the left as if pushed by an invisible hand. Again, you might conclude that what we all call "centrifugal force" is pushing you away from the center of the turn. Centrifugal literally means flying away from the center. But why should a force appear out of nowhere just because you decided to turn right? What's really happening?

Consider another point of view—looking down on your car from a balloon hovering over the freeway interchange. You look down and see your car going along part of a circle as it rounds the corner. Remember Isaac Newton's law of motion. Some force must be acting on that car to make it go in a curve. The force in this case is friction between the road and the tires, pushing the car toward the center of the circle because the front tires are turned. Then, the car, its door, and its seat belts push the driver toward the center of the circle. If the friction were to disappear—say, because of ice on the road—the car would continue in a straight line, in accordance with Newton's law, in whatever direction it was moving at the moment it encountered the ice.

So in a tight right turn, the driver feels a push from the left side of the car and blames the sensation on "centrifugal force." But the big picture shows what's really happening: Friction between road and tires pushes on the car, and the car pushes on the driver, forcing them away from the straight path they would follow if there were no friction.

Abell, George O. "The Fable of 'Centrifugal Force.'" In *Exploration of the Universe*. New York: Holt, Rinehart and Winston, 1969.

The Storm Surge of a Hurricane

Many of us associate tornadoes and hurricanes with high winds and rain, but the most damaging force of a hurricane comes from the unusually high waves as the storm hits the coast. High winds create high waves, but in the case of a hurricane, the low pressure at its center also creates what meteorologists call a "storm surge."

When you suck water up through a straw, the water rises because the pressure in the straw is lower than the pressure above the water in the rest of the glass. Just like the suction that you create in the straw, the extremely low pressure at the eye of the hurricane can suck up the ocean into something like a hill of water. This is a "storm surge," and it can rise to as much as several yards above the water outside the stormy area.

The high winds that circle around the eye of the hurricane build up huge waves as much as 30 to 50 feet high that move off in all directions. As the hurricane reaches land, the storm surge, accompanied by the abnormally high waves, can flood areas far inland of where ocean water normally goes. When a hurricane coincides with a normal high tide, the water level—and the waves—are even higher.

In 1969, Hurricane Camille hit the coast of Mississippi. Camille's storm surge was more than 22 feet high. Combined with a normal high tide and winds of close to 200 miles per hour, the damage from Camille was estimated at $1.5 billion, and more than 200 people were killed.

Ahrens, C. Donald. *Meteorology Today: An Introduction to Weather, Climate, and the Environment.* St. Paul: West Publishing Company, 1991.

Savoring the Aroma

The nineteenth-century French chef Brillat-Savarin once wrote that "smell and taste form a single sense, of which the mouth is the laboratory and the nose is the chimney." Taste and smell are closely related in that they discriminate between different chemicals—unlike hearing and sight, which detect different frequencies of sound and light, or touch, which detects pressure or temperature.

When you smell coffee, receptor cells in your nose are correctly identifying molecules of coffee vapor drifting in the air. Taste buds are the receptor cells on your tongue that identify specific molecules in your mouth. Although taste and smell don't always detect the same chemicals, they work closely with each other and in similar ways. For a short distance, the mouth and nose share a common air passage called the pharynx. As the food passes through your mouth, vapors drift through the pharynx to your nose, so what your mind registers as the "flavor" of food is really a combination of its taste and its smell. When you exhale through your nose while eating, you get a stronger sense of what the food tastes like. And food tastes especially strong when it is heated because the warm food gives off more vapors.

When you have a cold, you can't taste your food as well for two reasons, both having to do with smell. When your nose is blocked, the vapors from the food don't drift through the pharynx so you don't get the smell. And some cold viruses can kill smell receptor cells so that even the vapors that do get through the pharynx won't have as much of an effect.

McGee, Harold. *On Food and Cooking: The Science and Lore of the Kitchen.* New York: Scribner, 1984.

Salting Your Food

Maybe you like salt on your food, but your doctor says it causes high blood pressure. Well, humans aren't the only animals with a taste for salt. Porcupines will chew through wooden outhouses for the salt left in the wood from human urine. Deer and other animals will search out natural salt deposits. A study by two psychologists in 1940 described a three-year-old boy whose damaged adrenal glands prevented his body from retaining sodium—the more important of the two elements in table salt. The boy recognized salt and ate it as another child might eat sugar. When he was put on a hospital diet with a normal amount of salt, the boy died. People, like all other animals, need the right balance of sodium in order to regulate nearly every system in the body. If they lose too much sodium, they crave the taste of salt.

And yet you can also develop a taste for higher or lower levels of salt in your food by using more or less of it. To figure out why *eating* more salt would cause you to *want* more salt, a team of scientists asked two groups of people to increase their salt intake. Members of one group added 10 grams of salt to their food each day, while members of the other group swallowed 10 grams of salt tablets. The group that added the salt to their food came to prefer highly salted food, while there was no change in the preferences of the group that took the tablets.

The conclusion the researchers drew was that among people with adequate salt levels in their bodies, the preference for salty food comes from acquiring a taste for salt, and is not a result of the increased sodium level in the body. So, although there is good biological reason for our enjoyment of salt, it appears we can still cut down on the amount of salt we eat and enjoy our food all the same.

Beauchamp, Gary K. "The Human Preference for Excess Salt." *American Scientist,* January–February 1987.

McGee, Harold. *On Food and Cooking: The Science and Lore of the Kitchen.* New York: Scribner, 1984.

Why Human Milk Is Low in Iron

A baby gets its first immunity from its mother. As the baby's own immune system gradually takes over, another change occurs to help fight off disease: the concentration of iron in the baby's body drops dramatically during the first few months.

All living cells need some iron, and so we normally think of iron as beneficial. But the bacteria that cause disease also depend on the iron in the baby's body. The baby has to maintain enough iron for its own body without developing an excess that could encourage disease-causing microorganisms.

So how does milk fit into this picture? Human milk helps starve the microorganisms of their iron in two ways. First, human milk is lower in iron than milk from most other mammals. Also, human milk contains a chemical called lactoferrin that is strongly attracted to iron. Lactoferrin binds up iron and prevents cells—including disease-causing bacteria—from using it. The relatively large quantity of lactoferrin and the low concentration of iron in human milk may be two of the reasons that breast-fed infants are less prone to infections than infants fed only on cow's milk or iron-fortified milk formula.

Anemia from lack of iron is a serious problem in many developing countries, but in more affluent societies, babies and adults may be getting so much iron that they are losing some of their natural immunity.

Kent, Susan; Eugene D. Weinberg; and Patricia Stuart-Macadam. "Dietary and Pro-
    phylactic Iron Supplements: Helpful or Harmful." *Human Nature* 1, no. 1 (1978).
Weinberg, Eugene D. "Iron Withholding: A Defense against Infection and Neoplasia."
    Physiological Review 64 (1984).

Floating

We've all heard that floating objects are held up by a so-called buoyant force. But it's a challenge to explain to yourself where this force comes from. You might think of it this way: Suppose you take a plastic bag whose volume is one cubic foot, fold it up and put it in your pocket, and jump in a lake. Underwater, you open the bag, fill it with water, tie it shut, and let go of it. The bag neither floats nor sinks. It neither floats nor sinks because it merely encloses a cubic foot of water that was already there in the lake to begin with.

But a cubic foot of water is heavy—about 64 pounds. Take that bag of water out of the lake, and it's hard to lift. What this experience tells you is that while that water-filled bag was immersed, the water in the lake was supporting it, pushing up on it with a force of 64 pounds.

Now here's the crucial point: The lake had, so to speak, no way of knowing what was in the bag. The lake water will push up with a force of 64 pounds on *any* immersed object whose volume is one cubic foot. Substitute a block of wood for the bag of water, and suppose you're underwater with a one-cubic-foot block of wood weighing 40 pounds. The wood's weight pushes it down with a force of 40 pounds, but the water pushes it up with a force of 64 pounds, because the block's volume is one cubic foot. The result: a net buoyant force of 24 pounds pushing the wood up toward the surface.

So the essence of this approach to understanding the subtle phenomenon of buoyant force is to imagine replacing a cubic foot of water with a cubic foot of something else. That something else will be supported as if it were a cubic foot of water!

Epstein, Lewis Carroll. *Thinking Physics.* San Francisco: Insight Press, 1989.

39

Radiation, a Word of Many Meanings

If someone says, "There's radiation in this area," you will probably stay out. The word "radiation," used in this sense, usually refers to what is technically known as ionizing radiation. Ionizing means taking electrons away from atoms or adding electrons to atoms. Where atoms are ionized, chemical changes are likely to take place. So ionizing radiation is radiation capable of causing chemical changes in material it strikes, including the cells of living organisms.

Ionizing radiation usually comes from decaying atomic nuclei. Decaying in this sense means spontaneously breaking into smaller pieces. A material made of atoms whose nuclei tend to decay is said to be radioactive. When the nucleus of an atom decays, most of the radiation that comes out is composed of some combination of three ingredients. First are the so-called alpha particles, each made of two protons and two neutrons stuck together. Second are beta particles, which are electrons. Third are gamma rays, which are high-energy photons—elementary particles of high-energy light. (The names alpha, beta, and gamma were given to the different components of nuclear radiation almost a hundred years ago, before anyone understood the particles involved.)

So when we hear about radiation as a dangerous phenomenon, we're usually hearing about ionizing radiation from the decay of radioactive nuclei. But the word "radiation" has many other uses in science and engineering, some with sinister connotations and some without.

In a wider sense, radiation means the propagation of energy through space. The light we see with our eyes is a form of electromagnetic radiation. The word "electromagnetic" is added because light is made of electric and magnetic fields vibrating from side to side as the light travels forward. Radio waves are another form of electromagnetic radiation.

 You may hear a meteorologist talk about the radiation of heat from the ground to the sky. That process involves the type of electromagnetic radiation known as infrared rays. Infrared rays also give you a sensation of heat when you stand near a hot radiator. Microwave radiation is a form of electromagnetic radiation used to transmit telephone conversations and to cook food. Sound is described as radiation that carries energy through air and other materials, whereas electromagnetic radiation can travel through empty space. Recording engineers talk about the radiation of sound from a musical instrument or a loudspeaker. Using the word in an even broader sense, biologists may talk about the radiation of a species of living organism from one area into surrounding areas.

So the word "radiation" often refers to a dangerous emission of particles from decaying atomic nuclei. But radiation may refer to almost any kind of propagation of energy through space, or any process of divergence from a central point. Radiation is one of the most broadly defined and widely used words in science.

"Radiation." In *McGraw-Hill Encyclopedia of Science and Technology*, 6th ed. New York, 1987.

"Radiation." In *Oxford English Dictionary*, 2nd ed. New York: Oxford University Press, 1989.

Strict Rules for Sloppy Speech

Elocution is the study of the rules of proper speech. But what about the rules for sloppy speech? In fact, even sloppy speech has rules that native speakers know without ever being taught. Here's one example. When a four-year-old child asks, "Do I *hafta* go to bed?" you might call the word "hafta" a sloppy contraction of "have to." And yet by changing the *v* sound in "have" to an *f* sound in "hafta," the child is unconsciously following a complex rule of English that many non-native speakers never learn.

In speech, we have what are called "voiced" and "unvoiced" consonants. Hold your fingers against your throat so you can feel the vibration of your vocal cords. If you pronounce the sound of the letter *v*, you can feel your vocal cords working, and so *v* is what is called a voiced consonant. Next try the letter *f*. As long as you don't add any vowel sounds after the *f*, you can make that sound without the vibration, and so *f* is an unvoiced consonant.

Now, one rule of English is that, within a word, an unvoiced consonant—such as *f* or *t*—can't follow a voiced consonant, such as *v*. Or, conversely, a voiced consonant can't precede an unvoiced. That's why when a word ends in a voiced consonant, as in "bug," we pronounce the plural as if it were formed with a *z*-also a voiced consonant—instead of *s*, which is unvoiced.

It's not that we can't put an unvoiced consonant after a voiced; in a sentence such as "I have two cars," the *t* of "two" follows the *v* of "have" with no difficulty. It's only that within a single word, it isn't done. So when English speakers turn two words, such as "have to," into one word, "hafta," the *v* becomes an *f* so the word will seem natural to native speakers.

The Random Walk

The phrase "random walk" is a modern buzzword in book titles and party conversations. It actually refers to one of the most useful ideas in science. First, an example of a normal, non-random walk: You decide to walk to a point 10 steps in front of you. So you take 10 steps forward. That's a non-random walk.

Now, the simplest version of the random walk: Flip a coin. If the coin comes up heads, take one step forward. Tails, take one step backward. As you randomly step backward and forward, you gradually drift away from your starting point. There's no way to predict whether you'll end up ahead of or behind your starting point. But the theory of probability can predict about how many random steps it will take to carry you a certain distance either ahead of or behind your starting point.

If you want to get to a distance of 10 normal steps from your starting point, you'll probably have to take about 100 random steps. If you want to get 100 normal steps away, you'll have to take about 10,000 random steps—that's a lot more steps. In mathematical language, the number of random steps you'll need to take is roughly proportional to the square of the distance you want to cover.

This is scientifically important because your back-and-forth walk is a lot like the random motion of molecules and other small particles. Perfume molecules escaping from a bottle, salt molecules dissolving in water, and photons inside the sun all take random walks because they are constantly jostled by the particles around them. The theory of the random walk explains how fast the perfume smell travels, how long the salt takes to dissolve, and how long light takes to travel from the center of the sun to the surface.

Feynman, Richard P. "Probability." In *The Feynman Lectures on Physics*. Reading, Mass.: Addison-Wesley, 1963.
Gamow, George. "The Law of Disorder." In *One, Two, Three . . . Infinity*. New York: Viking Press, 1947.

Common Birthdays, Classic of Probability

Consider a class of 30 children. What is the probability that at least 2 of them have the same birthday? The surprising answer is that the probability is better than 70 percent that at least 2 children in a class of 30 have the same birthday.

The secret to understanding this amazing 70 percent figure is to think about the likelihood of all the children's birthdays being different. Imagine asking the children, one at a time, to announce their birthdays. The first child can have any one of 365 different birthdays, of course. The second child can have any one of 364 different birthdays that will not match the first child's birthday. In other words, the chance that the first two children's birthdays will not match is 364 out of 365.

Now the question becomes, what is the chance of getting 29 non-matches in a row? The third child can have any one of 363 different birthdays that won't match the first two. So the third child's chance of not matching is 363 out of 365. The fourth child's chance of not matching is 362 out of 365, and so on. With each new child, the chance of not matching birthdays with at least one of the previous children gets smaller and smaller. To find the probability of getting 29 non-matches in a row, you have to multiply all those chances together. A calculator makes it easy. And it turns out that the chance of getting 29 non-matching birthdays in a row is less than 30 percent. That's why the probability is better than 70 percent that at least 2 children in a class of 30 will indeed have the same birthday.

Gamow, George. "The Law of Disorder." In *One, Two, Three . . . Infinity*. New York: Viking Press, 1947.

Peters, William Stanley. *Counting for Something: Statistical Principles and Personalities.* New York: Springer-Verlag, 1987.

Note: The probability of a common birthday in a group of 30 is about 0.7304.

Babies on Treadmills

When your baby takes its first steps, it's on its way to mastering an act of balance and coordination so complex that scientists haven't yet been able to build a two-legged robot. But where does a baby, who couldn't even crawl a few months earlier, get such a complicated set of skills? In fact, babies are probably born with some of what it takes to walk.

To test babies' innate walking abilities, psychologist Esther Thelen at Indiana University held a group of infants so that their feet just touched a moving treadmill—something like a miniature conveyor belt. As the belt pulled their feet backward, the babies brought their feet forward one at a time. They could have brought their feet forward together or just let them drag behind, but for some reason the babies moved their legs as if they were walking.

Next, Thelen used a double treadmill with one belt under each foot. Even when the two belts traveled at different speeds, the babies kept on walking with regular, alternating steps, even though they had to move one foot much faster than the other to keep up.

Some babies walk more easily than others on the treadmill, but by around four months, most babies walk in a regular, alternating step. And seven-month-old babies walk on the treadmill as easily as older children walk by themselves. Babies begin walking around the age of one not because they learn how at that age, but because they have finally developed the strength, coordination, and balance to do what they have been partially capable of since birth.

A Ticklish Question

When someone else tickles the bottom of your foot, the nerves in your foot send messages to the brain which send you into convulsions of laughter. But tickle yourself and nothing happens. Very little is known about tickling—including why we laugh—but a group of British psychologists built a tickling machine to help explain why we can't tickle ourselves. They proposed two reasons why tickling ourselves doesn't work: first, we have control over the hand that is doing the tickling; and second, our brain gets information from our hand that changes the way it interprets the nerve impulses coming from the foot. This added information going to and from the brain somehow counteracts the tickle impulse from the foot.

To test their hypothesis, the psychologists used the tickling machine in three different ways. To operate the machine, someone stands on a box with a movable pointer sticking out of the top. By moving a handle on the side of the box, either the experimenter or the subject can drag the pointer around and tickle the foot.

When the experimenter operated the machine, the tickling worked. When the subject operated the machine, there was very little effect—just like tickling yourself. But when the experimenter moved the handle while the subject's hand rested passively on it, the level of tickling was in between self-tickling and being tickled by someone else. This method was still somewhat ticklish because the subject couldn't control the handle, but not as ticklish as the first method because the subject's hand still provided information about the movement of the pointer.

So, apparently tickling needs at least two other conditions to make us laugh: a lack of knowledge about what's going on, and a lack of control.

Bicycles, Footballs, and Space Shuttles

To steer a bicycle at high speed, you don't turn the handlebars, you just lean the way you want to go and the wheel turns slightly by itself. If you try to steer with the handlebars alone, you may fall over in the opposite direction.

The reason for this strange relationship between steering and leaning has to do with what physicists call "angular momentum." Any moving object—such as your bike—has momentum. Changing its momentum requires a force. You increase the momentum by pedaling; the wind decreases it by pushing in the opposite direction. But spinning objects—such as your bike's wheels—also have angular momentum. Like your forward momentum, the angular momentum of the wheel has a specific direction which is perpendicular to the ground as long as you're traveling upright in a straight line. By leaning the bike to one side or by turning the handlebars, you change the direction of the wheel's angular momentum, but the wheel reacts in a very surprising way. As you lean to one side, the wheel turns to the same side. If you steer to one side, the wheel wants to lean in the opposite direction.

Take the wheel from a bicycle and, holding it vertically with one hand on each end of the axle, give it a good spin. Tilt the wheel to the right as if you were leaning into a turn, and you'll find the wheel steers itself to the right. Turn the wheel as if you were steering, and you'll feel it lean the other way. The antics of the wheel are due to the changes in angular momentum you produce by twisting it in one direction.

The spinning bicycle wheel is very much like the device used to navigate the space shuttle—a gyroscope. A gyroscope is any object—but usually a wheel—spinning inside a stationary framework. The gyroscope's spin gives it angular momentum, as did the bicycle wheel's spin. Just as a moving object continues in the same direction because of its forward momentum, a gyroscope stays at the same angle because of its angular momentum.

Another way to feel the angular momentum of a gyroscope is to hold the base of a blender minus the bowl and blade in both hands and, without turning it on, tilt it to the right and left. Now tilt it with the motor on. You'll find that the spinning motor acts as a gyroscope with angular momentum and resists your efforts to change its angle. You may not feel a very strong resistance because the mass that is turning in this case is fairly small. But larger gyroscopes, mounted in the space shuttle, take the place of a compass for navigating in space. A navigational gyroscope sits in a framework that allows it to turn freely in any direction. When the space shuttle turns, the gyroscope's angular momentum causes the gyroscope to stay pointing in the same direction.

Navigators on land rely on the needle of a compass which always points in the same direction. In space, where there is no north, south, up, or down, astronauts use gyroscopes to tell which way they're heading.

When a quarterback throws a football, he spins the ball to give it angular momentum just like a gyroscope. The angular momentum stops the ball from wobbling and keeps it traveling point-first so as to offer the least wind resistance. Keeping the ball straight helps it go farther and also makes it easier to catch.

The Shape of a Raindrop

Ask a friend to draw you a picture of a raindrop and you'll probably get something the shape of a tear—heavy at the bottom with a long point on top. And if you look at a drop of water coming out of the faucet, it does have that shape. The water drop coming out of the faucet is shaped like that because of the attraction water molecules exert on each other. As the drop leaves the faucet, the last part to come out clings to the moisture inside the faucet, and so the drop is pulled out into a tear shape.

But the same attractive force of water molecules gives raindrops an entirely different shape. Actually the shape of a raindrop depends on the size of the drop. Smaller raindrops are spherical because as the water molecules cling together, a sphere is the most compact shape. Larger raindrops, however, have another shape. Drops with a diameter of more than about two millimeters—or the diameter of the wire in a coat hanger—are shaped more like the top half of a hamburger bun. As the drop is falling downward, there's more air pressure on the bottom than on the sides. The mutual attraction between the water molecules still keeps the drop mostly round, but the air pressure on the bottom causes the drop to become flattened underneath.

If you're an artist, you may want to go on drawing raindrops in the shape of teardrops, since most people wouldn't recognize little circles or tiny hamburger buns as rain. But you might still want to know that, according to meteorologists, raindrops and tears have very different shapes.

Ahrens, C. Donald. *Meteorology Today: An Introduction to Weather, Climate, and the Environment.* St. Paul: West Publishing Company, 1991.

What Good Is Snow?

Any skier can tell you what good snow is, but when you're out shoveling your driveway in the winter, you may feel hard-pressed to find any good words for the white nuisance.

Actually, in cold climates, snow is far more useful than even most skiers might imagine. When the temperature drops below freezing, snow forms a blanket over the ground. Snow may be cold, but it's an excellent insulator against the colder air above. The snow protects plants and animals that can survive under the snow at temperatures slightly below freezing but would die in the outside air.

The winter snow blanket also keeps the ground from freezing too deeply. When a cold climate doesn't get enough snow and the ground freezes, spring rains and snow runoff from higher up can't seep into the ground. As a result, the plants on the hillside don't get enough water and the streams below become dangerous, raging torrents from the excess water.

Snow is a good insulator because the intricate crystalline flakes trap large amounts of air. Light, dry snow is the best because it contains the most air. Wet snow or old snow that is more compact is not as good an insulator. Human activities such as snowmobiling can also pack down the snow, reducing its insulation value and causing it to last later into the spring without melting.

A year without snow can affect warmer areas as well if they rely on water from rivers such as the Mississippi or the Colorado that start in northern mountains. Without spring floods from melting snow, lots of ordinarily active rivers are dry or low.

So if you live in a cold climate, try to remember this winter as you're out shoveling that you're working with nature's own quilt.

Ahrens, C. Donald. *Meteorology Today: An Introduction to Weather, Climate, and the Environment.* St. Paul: West Publishing Company, 1991.

A Fan of Sunbeams

The sun is setting behind broken clouds. The air is hazy. Sunlight shining through rifts in the clouds illuminates the haze and creates the appearance of a fan of sunbeams emanating from the sun. Even if both the sun and the clouds are below the horizon, out of sight, the effect is often visible. The fan-of-sunbeams effect can be produced not only by clouds but also by mountains on the horizon, blocking the sun's rays in some places and allowing them to pass in others.

After a moment's thought, you realize that the way those sunbeams appear to radiate in all directions from one point is really a perspective effect. It's true that the sunbeams all originate in one place—the sun—but the particular sunbeams you see lighting up the haze in the air do not actually radiate in all directions.

Because the sun is so far away—93 million miles—those

sunbeams are essentially parallel. They appear to radiate in all directions for the same reason that the rails of a straight railroad track appear to radiate from a vanishing point on the horizon. As the rails get farther and farther from you, they occupy a smaller and smaller portion of your entire field of view, so they appear closer and closer together.

Knowing this explanation for the fan-of-sunbeams effect, you can watch for related effects. For example, if the sunbeams are brilliant enough, you may see them not only diverging from the sun, but converging on the opposite side of the sky, just as railroad tracks appear to converge on the horizon behind you.

Finally, if you look down from an airplane at sunset, you may see sunbeams shining through rifts in the clouds. While people on the ground below you see those sunbeams appearing to radiate in all directions, you will see that they are actually parallel.

Humphreys, W. J. *Physics of the Air.* New York: Dover Publications, 1964.
Minnaert, Marcel. *The Nature of Light and Color in the Open Air.* New York: Dover Publications, 1954.

Making Water in the Desert

When Norwegian physiologist Knut Schmidt-Nielsen visited the Arizona desert, he was especially impressed by the number of small rodents. How, he asked, did these animals get enough water to survive? Kangaroo rats, like other desert rodents, rarely drink water, and they eat mainly dried seeds with almost no water. The answer, Schmidt-Nielsen found, lies in what's called "metabolic water," which is created when the body extracts energy from, or metabolizes, food.

If you hold a glass jar over a candle or the gas burner of a stove, you'll see moisture form on the inside of the glass. And yet there's no water in wax or natural gas. When the gas molecules burn, they separate into carbon and hydrogen. The hydrogen then joins with the oxygen in the air to form water, which condenses on the inside of the glass.

All organic matter, including the dried seeds of a kangaroo rat's dinner, includes carbon and hydrogen. When that food is broken down, the hydrogen from the food combines with oxygen that the animal has breathed. The result is metabolic water. Even though there's almost no water in the dried seeds, the body creates water when it metabolizes the seeds to get energy. A kangaroo rat gets about 90 percent of its water in this way, and the rest comes from the small amount of water already absorbed in its food.

Humans get about 10 percent of their water from metabolism, but our bodies are nowhere near as efficient as the body of the kangaroo rat when it comes to using water. In the desert, using water efficiently is a life-or-death matter, as is conserving water.

Conservation of water brings us to another interesting comparison between our bodies and the kangaroo rat's. When our noses drip in the winter, one reason is that the moisture from our warm breath condenses on the inside of our cold noses. The same process is at work when you breathe on a window pane on a cold day and mist appears on the glass from the moisture in your breath. But where does the moisture come from?

When you inhale a breath of air at 32 degrees Fahrenheit, it may contain as much water vapor as it can at that temperature. But as the air warms to body temperature, its ability to hold water increases tenfold. As a result, the warmed air immediately begins to absorb moisture from your lungs and throat. When your nose drips in the winter, one reason is that all that moisture in your breath is now condensing on the inside of your cold nose—just as it does when you breathe on a window pane.

But what does this have to do with desert rodents? Most people don't need to conserve body moisture because they can always drink water. And the fact that our bodies aren't adapted to conserve moisture suggests that humans evolved where water was plentiful. But in the desert a cold nose helps many animals conserve the moisture they need to survive.

Because the kangaroo rat's nasal passage is much longer, almost all of the water evaporated in the animal's lungs is condensed in its nose on the way out. That moisture is then reabsorbed instead of being exhaled into the dry desert air. Unfortunately for us, our noses don't reabsorb moisture. And that's why, unlike the kangaroo rat, we have to carry handkerchiefs to deal with a dripping nose.

Schmidt-Nielsen, Knut. *Desert Animals: Physiological Problems of Heat and Water.* London: Oxford University Press, 1964.
Schmidt-Nielsen, Knut. *How Animals Work.* London: Cambridge University Press, 1972.

Human on a Bicycle

A human on a bicycle is one of the most efficient machines on earth. In this case we are using the word "efficient" to mean the amount of energy needed to transport a kilogram of mass over a distance of one kilometer. Specialists in the field of biomechanics have found that in this sense a human on a bicycle is more efficient than a horse, a locust, a salmon, or any other running, flying, or swimming animal. A human on a bicycle is more efficient than a car or a jet airliner, although less efficient than a truck or a train. A human traveling one kilometer on a bicycle uses only about one-fifth as much energy as that same human traveling that same kilometer on foot, and goes about three times faster.

There are several reasons why bicycling consumes less energy than walking the same distance. In walking, our leg muscles must raise and lower our entire body with each step, as well as moving our legs repeatedly backward and forward. Walking also involves a lot of friction—with each step some of our energy goes into wearing out our shoes and socks.

On a bicycle only our legs go up and down, and the leg going up is lifted partly by the other leg pushing down on the other pedal. On a bicycle we sit at a constant height above the ground and do not need to put any effort into raising or lowering our entire body. Friction is kept to a minimum in bicycles through the use of ball bearings and pneumatic tires, both of which, incidentally, saw their first widespread use in bicycles a century ago, and were later incorporated into automobiles and other machines.

The main obstacle faced by a cyclist is wind resistance, which increases dramatically with increasing speed. But at moderate speeds a human on a bicycle is the most efficient moving creature we know.

Hunt, Robert G. "Bicycles in the Physics Lab." *The Physics Teacher,* March 1989.
Vogel, Steven. *Life's Devices: The Physical World of Animals and Plants.* Princeton, N.J.: Princeton University Press, 1988.
Wilson, S. S. "Bicycle Technology." *Scientific American,* March 1973.

Using Purple Cabbage as a pH Indicator

Maybe your shampoo advertises that it's "acid-balanced" or that it has a low pH. But how do you know? When chemists talk about the "pH" of a substance, they are referring to acidity and alkalinity on a pH scale ranging from 1 to 14. Anything above 7 is said to be alkaline. Anything below 7 is said to be acid. And 7 is the neutral point that isn't acid or alkaline.

One way to tell whether your shampoo is acid or alkaline is by using what's called pH paper. When you put a drop of shampoo on the paper, the paper changes to some new color depending on the pH. A chart usually comes with the pH paper indicating which colors refer to which pH value.

But if you don't have pH paper, you can use the broth left over from cooking purple cabbage. Straight out of the pot, the cabbage broth is slightly acid—a pH of about 6—and purple. If you slowly add acid, such as vinegar, the pH goes down and the color becomes red at a pH of around 3. If you add alkali, such as baking soda, the pH goes up and the color turns blue at a pH of around 8. A strong alkali, such as some scouring powder, will turn the broth green at around 11.

So, going from strong acid to strong alkali, purple cabbage broth goes through bright red, purple, blue, and green. The color changes look like magic tricks because the colors of the ingredients don't match the colors of the results, but what you're really seeing is the relationship between color and pH. Try using cabbage broth to measure the pH of other household chemicals, or you can even try using it to test the soil in your garden.

Tocci, Salvatore. *Chemistry around You: Experiments and Projects with Everyday Products.* New York: Arco Publishing, 1985.

Cooking with Alloys

Anyone who has used aluminum cookware knows that eventually the aluminum gets pitted and discolored. That happens as the aluminum reacts with the air and with the food that's cooked in it. And there's some possibility that aluminum absorbed from cookware may be harmful over a long period of time.

Many pots and pans as well as parts for boats are made of stainless steel because, unlike most metals, stainless steel won't rust. All steel is a combination—or "alloy"—of iron and other metals. Stainless steel doesn't rust because it contains about 15 percent chromium, which is much less reactive than iron. The chromium is also why stainless steel is often shiny, like a chrome bumper on a car.

But even with this benefit, stainless steel also has its drawbacks. One drawback to steel made with chromium—besides its high price—is that chromium doesn't conduct heat as well as iron. As a result, stainless steel pans tend to develop "hot spots" instead of spreading the heat out evenly like a cast iron pan. To make up for this problem, the best stainless steel pans have copper bottoms. Because copper is an excellent conductor, the heat spreads out more evenly.

So next time you're heating tomato sauce in a stainless steel pan, remember that the chromium alloy in the metal will keep the pan shiny, but may cause the sauce to burn.

McGee, Harold. *On Food and Cooking: The Science and Lore of the Kitchen.* New York: Scribner, 1984.

The Legacy of the Dodo

The last dodo bird died in the late 1600s, probably as food for sailors. On the island of Mauritius in the Indian Ocean, where they lived, the large, flightless dodoes had been shot and eaten for years by sailors. Today we think of the dodo as the classic example of a peculiar anachronism, but in its own habitat the dodo played a critical role.

Also on the island of Mauritius was the Calvaria Major tree, which had evolved seeds so hard that they couldn't germinate by themselves. Instead, the seeds had to be cracked somehow before they could grow into young trees. Dodoes ate these seeds and digested the outer layer. But by cracking the seeds and removing their outer layer, the dodo's gizzard also prepared the seeds for sprouting, and when they left the bird's body they were ready to grow. When the last dodo died, there were no animals left on the island that could perform the necessary service for the Calvaria seeds. Today there are only about a dozen of these trees left on the island, all more than 300 years old.

The relationship between the dodo and the Calvaria is one example of what biologists call "coevolution"—when two or more species evolve in ways that make them mutually dependent on each other. The dodo depended on the Calvaria for food, and the Calvaria depended on the dodo to make its seeds viable. Coevolution means that all species are part of a complex web, and that for every species that goes extinct, several more extinctions may result. Sometimes species adapt to life without their coevolved partners, but often, as in the case of the Calvaria, the dependent species die off as well.

Temple, Stanley A. "Plant-Animal Mutualism: Coevolution with Dodo Leads to Near Extinction of Plant." *Science,* August 26, 1977.

The Musical Bean

As more people look for substitutes for red meat, many of them are finding that beans, especially dried beans, don't digest very well. The result may be benign but disagreeable embarrassments at inopportune moments.

In recent decades, there's been an increase in research on flatulence, but the phenomenon itself is hardly new. In the Middle Ages, Saint Augustine saw flatulence as one more indication of man's fall from grace. For a long time it was believed that flatulence increased sexual appetite by tickling the genitals, and so Saint Jerome prohibited beans for the nuns under his charge.

In the 1950s, chemists identified the offending ingredient in beans as a group of chemicals called oligosaccharides, a term from Greek meaning "a few sugars." As the name implies, oligosaccharides are complex sugars made of a few simple sugars, but unlike some other complex sugars, they can't be broken down by the chemicals produced in the human digestive tract. As the undigested oligosaccharides move on to the lower intestines, bacteria do the work that our own bodies can't. In the process of breaking down the complex molecules, the bacteria produce a variety of gases, but mainly carbon dioxide—the same gas that we, and other animals, exhale all the time. In the 1960s, researchers estimated that the average adult produces about a pint of gas a day. Fortunately only a very small percentage of that has an offensive smell.

Not all beans contain equal amounts of oligosaccharides. Lima beans and navy beans are the worst offenders, and botanists are working on ways to grow beans with fewer oligosaccharides.

McGee, Harold. *On Food and Cooking: The Science and Lore of the Kitchen*. New York: Scribner, 1984.

Keeping a Cool Head

When we get hot, we sweat, and evaporation cools our body. When your dog gets hot, it pants. Air traveling rapidly through the dog's wet nose and across its tongue causes evaporation and cools its head. For a dog's body to get rid of excess heat, its blood has to carry the heat to the dog's head before the heat can be eliminated. So, while we cool down all over by sweating, a dog's cooling system works almost entirely from its head.

You might assume that cooling the whole body directly would be more efficient than cooling the head and letting the head cool the rest of the body. But in some ways, panting is more efficient than sweating. Warm-blooded animals maintain fairly constant body temperatures regardless of the temperature outside. But even warm-blooded animals get warmer from exercise, heat, or illness. Under these conditions, the increase in temperature may benefit the animal but not the brain. Even a small increase in the brain's temperature can cause serious damage.

How then do you let your body warm up while still keeping a cool head? One solution is in the way the head is separated from the body by a relatively thin neck. Just as the handle of a frying pan cools off faster than the rest of the pan, the head of an animal cools off faster than its body. The horns of some animals and the ears of the jackrabbit work like extensions on the frying pan handle and help get rid of heat even more efficiently. Like horns or jackrabbit ears, panting also helps get rid of head heat first. That doesn't mean that on a hot day your shaggy sheep dog is cooler than you are, but by panting, he's at least keeping a cool head.

Schmidt-Nielsen, Knut. *How Animals Work.* London: Cambridge University Press, 1972.

Benjamin Franklin Drops a Dollar

In 1757 Benjamin Franklin made some astute observations about heat and cold. Franklin noticed that if he touched the metal lock on his desk, then the wood of the desk, the lock felt colder, even though both were exposed to the same temperature in the room. He concluded that the metal lock felt colder because metal is a better conductor of heat than wood, and drew heat from his hand more than the wood did.

In 1757 Franklin could not have known the real nature of heat. Only in the last century has heat been revealed as random vibration of the atoms that make up all the objects around us. Faster vibration means hotter temperature. Those vibrations are conveyed from hot to cold objects when they touch. On a large scale, however, heat behaves very much like a fluid passed from object to object.

Benjamin Franklin's desk observations demonstrated that metal conducts heat faster than wood. Franklin demonstrated that fact even more dramatically with a silver dollar and a candle. He wrote: "If you take a dollar between your fingers with one hand, and a piece of wood, of the same dimensions, with the other, and bring both at the same time to the flame of a candle, you will find yourself obliged to drop the dollar before you drop the wood."

Franklin, Benjamin. Letter to John Lining, April 14, 1757. In *The Ingenious Dr. Franklin: Selected Scientific Letters of Benjamin Franklin,* ed. Nathan Goodman. Philadelphia: University of Pennsylvania Press, 1974.

From One Cell to Many

Some living things, like bacteria, are made of only one cell. Others, like human beings and trees, are made of many cells—maybe billions of them—each cell doing a special job, all cells cooperating. But some living things are right on the borderline between those two categories.

For instance, there's the whole order of green algae known as the volvocines. The microscope reveals that the basic cell of these algae is egg-shaped, with a couple of whiplike tails that it uses to swim around in water. The simplest volvocine algae are collections of just four of these cells, stuck together with a kind of jelly and arranged so their whiplike tails are all on the same side. The whole colony of four cells swims as a unit. There are other volvocines, with pretty names like Pandorina and Eudorina, made of 16, 32, or 64 cells that swim together as a unit, cooperating for the common good.

The next step up in complexity is to add specialization to cooperation. There are colonies of 64 or 128 cells—the so-called Pleodorina, for instance—in which only the cells on one side of the colony are capable of reproducing. The other cells help with swimming, but they can't reproduce.

And most complex of all are the so-called Volvox colonies, made of thousands of cells connected to make a beautiful emerald-green hollow sphere that swims as a unit. Inside each Volvox sphere are a few large cells whose only function is to reproduce. Those special reproductive cells aren't even capable of swimming.

The different kinds of volvocine algae, ranging from extreme simplicity to the beginnings of complexity, may be giving us a glimpse of how the first living things made of more than one cell evolved.

Curtis, Helena. *Biology.* 4th ed. New York: Worth Publishers, 1983.
Gilbert, Scott F. *Developmental Biology.* 4th ed. Sunderland, Mass.: Sinauer Associates, 1994.

Cologne and the Blue Sky

About a hundred years ago, the English physicist John Tyndall wrote an article about why the sky is blue. He wrote: "Eau-de-Cologne is prepared by dissolving aromatic gums or resins in alcohol. Dropped into liquid water, the scented liquid immediately produces a white cloudiness, due to the precipitation of the substances previously held in solution."

By "precipitation" Tyndall meant the formation of extremely small solid particles as the alcohol in the cologne mixed with the water.

Tyndall went on, "Against a dark background—black velvet, for example—the water . . . shows a distinctly blue color."

You can repeat Tyndall's experiment, using some of your own cologne. Put some tap water in a clear drinking glass, allow a few minutes for all the fine bubbles to rise to the top and disappear, then let a few drops of cologne fall into the water. The combination of cologne and water will make what looks like smoke—the precipitation Tyndall mentioned.

When you hold the glass up to a window, that smoky precipitate will look reddish in color. But when you view the glass against a dark background with light entering from one side, the same smoky stuff in the water will look blue, more or less like the sky.

Molecules of air act on sunlight in the same way that particles in the cologne mixture do. Extremely small objects like molecules tend to scatter blue light sideways while letting red light proceed straight through. Sunlight is a mixture of all the colors of the rainbow. Some of the blue part of sunlight is scattered every which way by air molecules, giving the clear sky its blue glow.

When the sun is low in the sky, its light passes through a lot of air on its way to us. Much of the blue is scattered out of sunlight by air along the way, leaving mostly reddish light for us to see.

Tyndall, John. "The Sky." *The Forum*, February 1888. Reprinted in *Fragments of Science*, 6th ed. New York: P. F. Collier, 1905.

Walker, Jearl. "The Colors Seen in the Sky Offer Lessons in Optical Scattering." *Scientific American*, January 1989.

Father Determines Sex

The microscope has revealed that every human cell contains 46 so-called chromosomes, which have been discovered in this century to be the carriers of genetic information. By genetic information we mean the instructions that determine superficial characteristics such as eye color and more basic characteristics such as sex. These 46 chromosomes come in 23 pairs. In each pair, one chromosome is inherited from the father and one from the mother. In every pair but one, the two chromosomes have basically the same structure and size.

One pair, however, may not match. This is the pair that determines sex. No matter what your gender, you have a so-called X chromosome, inherited from your mother, as one of the members of this pair. If you're male, you have a so-called Y chromosome inherited from your father accompanying that X from your mother. If you're female, the chromosome inherited from your father was an X, not a Y, giving you two X chromosomes in that last pair.

By the way, the word "chromosomes" literally means colored bodies. About a century ago, biologists found that things inside cells become visible through the microscope when the cells are stained with dyes. Chromosomes take certain dyes especially well, and appear as sausage-shaped objects in the cell.

So females have the combination XX in that sex-determining twenty-third chromosome pair; males have the combination XY. Your mother could have given you only an X chromosome, because human egg cells contain only X's; your father, on the other hand, could have given you either an X or a Y, because sperm cells can have either type. Your sex was ultimately determined by whether you received an X or a Y chromosome from your father.

Curtis, Helena. *Biology.* 4th ed. New York: Worth Publishers, 1983.

The Monarch Butterfly's Poison Pill

Milkweed plants defend themselves against being eaten by making a bitter-tasting poison of chemicals technically known as cardiac glycosides. Most insects and other animals who try to eat milkweed never try again, if they're lucky enough to survive the first attempt.

However, the larva of the monarch butterfly is special: it has evolved the ability to handle the toxins in milkweed, but not by digesting them and not by excreting them as waste products. Instead, the monarch butterfly larva stores up milkweed toxins in its body. Even after the larva has turned into a full-fledged orange-and-black adult monarch butterfly, its body still contains the milkweed toxins it ate early in life. Most creatures get sick or die after eating milkweed. But neither larva nor adult monarch suffers any harm.

Among the animals that like to eat butterflies are bluejays. However, a naive bluejay who tries eating a monarch butterfly may be in for the unpleasant surprise of a mouthful of bitter, nauseating milkweed toxin. The bluejay learns a lesson: don't eat orange-and-black butterflies. This is too late to help the individual butterfly attacked by the bluejay, of course, but it has obvious long-term benefits for monarch butterflies as a species.

So the monarch butterfly has evolved a sort of poison-pill defense. The butterfly uses the milkweed's defense system to make itself repulsive to its potential enemies. And if you're a butterfly living among hungry bluejays, it is to your advantage to be orange and black, to look like a monarch butterfly—even if you've never eaten milkweed in your life. You don't have to be toxic as long as you look toxic. That's the strategy of viceroy butterflies. They don't store milkweed toxin, but they look a lot like monarchs and are generally left alone by bluejays.

We've seen how this relationship with the milkweed plant benefits the monarch butterfly, and even butterflies that look like monarchs. But what's in this for the milkweed plant? After all, the monarch larvae do eat some of the plant. Why hasn't the milkweed evolved a toxin that repels monarch larvae as effectively as it repels most other animals? One possible answer is that monarch larvae concentrate the odor of the toxin by storing up the toxin and staying on the milkweed. That odor repels other potential enemies of the plant.

The story of the milkweed plant and the butterflies is fascinating. But there is no reason to think it's unusual. Among the plants and animals of the world there must be millions of other ingenious chemical defense strategies—most of them still unknown to us.

Harborne, J. B. *Introduction to Ecological Biochemistry.* 2nd ed. New York: Academic Press, 1982.

Cabbage Wars

Here's another true story about an insect, a plant, and a chemical made by the plant.

Cabbages and their relatives make an acrid-smelling mustard oil. This oil is the cabbage's way of defending itself. Actually the mustard oil is created in the cabbage from another chemical called sinigrin, which is toxic to most insects. Sinigrin will kill a black swallowtail butterfly larva. Most insects won't touch a plant containing sinigrin.

But experiments have shown that larvae of another butterfly— the so-called cabbage butterfly—won't eat plants that *don't* contain sinigrin. They'd rather starve. Adult female cabbage butterflies can be fooled into laying eggs on a piece of paper soaked in sinigrin. Sinigrin attracts cabbage butterflies and repels almost everything else. How did this arrangement come about?

It seems likely that cabbages, like most plants, evolved the ability to make toxins in order to repel animals that might eat them. But before long, in evolutionary terms, one particular insect, the cabbage butterfly, evolved the ability to eat the toxins without getting sick. That gave the insect a monopoly on the cabbage supply and freed it from having to compete for food with other insects. Now cabbage butterflies have evolved a taste for sinigrin. The aroma of the toxin serves as a signal that good food is nearby.

This leads to another question: Why haven't all the cabbages in the world been devoured by cabbage butterflies? Obviously it's in the interest of cabbage butterflies not to eliminate their entire food supply. But the individual butterfly doesn't know that.

61

Fortunately for the butterflies, there are other toxins and parasites that will cut down their population if it gets too large.

Harborne, J. B. *Introduction to Ecological Biochemistry.* 2nd ed. New York: Academic Press, 1982.

The Strangeness of Ice

Ice floats on water. We all know this and think nothing of it because water and ice are so common on the surface of the earth. Chemists tell us, however, that the buoyancy of ice is unusual.

Most liquids get denser when they freeze. This makes sense when you think about the nature of heat as revealed by twentieth-century physics. Heat is the tiny random jiggling motion of atoms. Faster motion means hotter temperature; slower motion means colder temperature. An atom in a cold object—that is, an atom that's jiggling slower—tends to take up less room than a fast-jiggling atom in a hot object. So most objects contract as they cool. And most substances weigh more per cubic inch when they're cold and solid than when they're hot and liquid.

Not so for ice. Water molecules can't link together to make an ice crystal unless the molecules are, so to speak, at arm's length from each other. Imagine everyone in a crowded elevator pushing everyone else out to arm's length and you get the idea. Water expands as it turns to ice. Ice weighs less per cubic inch than liquid water, so it floats.

Fish and other things living in water survive winter because ice floats. Lakes and oceans freeze from the top down. Ice on top protects liquid water below from the cold. Imagine the alternative: Suppose ice sank rather than floating. Ice would pile up on the bottom of every lake, where it would be protected from the sun and might never thaw. Soon every body of water would be permanently frozen, except for a thin liquid layer on top in the summer. Fortunately for life on earth, water is strange: when it's frozen solid, it's less dense than when it's liquid.

Atkins, P. W. "Molecules." In *Scientific American Library.* New York: Scientific American Library, 1987.

Animal or Plant?

Often the answer is neither. Before the twentieth century, animals included things that move, eat, and grow to a certain adult size and stop growing. Plants included things that don't move or eat and which grow indefinitely. Plants don't eat because they use the process of photosynthesis to make their own food from carbon dioxide, water, minerals, and sunlight.

Improvement in microscopes in the last century has undermined this simple scheme. Microscopes reveal that mushrooms, for instance, have a cell structure so distinctive that they can't rightly be called plants or animals. Some one-celled organisms make their own food by photosynthesis like plants, yet swim around like animals.

While the microscope was dissolving the old animal-versus-plant distinction, it was revealing another profound division among all living things. Some living cells have a nucleus, a separate body inside the cell that divides whenever the cell divides, and which contains most of the cell's genetic information. Other cells don't have a nucleus—the molecules with genetic information are distributed around the inside of the cell.

A cell with a nucleus is said to be eukaryotic; a cell without a nucleus is prokaryotic. We humans are eukaryotic—our cells have nuclei. So do the cells of all the other animals and plants we see every day. Bacteria are prokaryotic—they don't have nuclei. Animal or plant? That old distinction has been replaced. Now we might ask, prokaryote or eukaryote?

Many biologists favor a scheme of not two but five kingdoms of life. Here's a common everyday way of distinguishing between the kingdoms: think about a trip to the supermarket.

First stop: the dairy section. Obviously all these milk products ultimately come from animals.

Next: meats and seafood. Again, obviously animals.

Then produce. Celery, tomatoes, apples—all from plants. But what about mushrooms? Mushrooms grow out of the ground like plants, but there the resemblance ends. Mushrooms get nourishment from decaying matter on the forest floor, not from carbon dioxide and sunlight. Their cell walls are made of chitin, a substance that also makes up the outer armor of insects but which is not characteristic in plants. Mushrooms are neither plant nor animal—they are members of a distinct kingdom, the fungi. Other fungi at the supermarket include yeasts in the bakery and the molds in some cheeses.

Speaking of cheeses, the acids that help coagulate milk proteins to make cheese and yogurt usually come from bacteria, which are neither plants, nor animals, nor fungi—they are members of yet a fourth kingdom, the prokaryotes. Recall that prokaryotes are cells without a nucleus. The greatest value of this distinction has to do with history. Prokaryotes are relatively simple; that suggests that in the history of life on earth, prokaryotes came first.

Finally, it's over to the health and beauty shelf for a tube of toothpaste. The abrasive in that toothpaste is probably made from the mineral skeletons of diatoms, one-celled organisms completely different from bacteria. Diatoms live in the sea and are included in a fifth kingdom, the protozoa. Today's plants and animals probably evolved from protozoa of long ago.

Curtis, Helena. *Biology*. 4th ed. New York: Worth Publishers, 1983.

More Than an Ordinary Sauna

In 1775 a Dr. Blagden, then secretary of the British scientific organization known as the Royal Society, conducted a dramatic demonstration of the ability of the human body to maintain a constant internal temperature. Dr. Blagden and some friends stepped into a room that had been heated to a temperature of 260 degrees Fahrenheit. That's well above the 212-degree boiling temperature of water. *Don't try this.* They stayed in the 260-degree room for 45 minutes and emerged unharmed. A steak Dr. Blagden took with him, however, was cooked.

Unlike the steak, Dr. Blagden sweated profusely in the hot room, and that is why he was not cooked. Evaporation of water—sweat—takes energy—energy from heat brought to the skin by the bloodstream. Every molecule of water driven away from Dr. Blagden's damp skin carried heat with it, and that's why he survived in an environment far hotter than his body temperature.

Dr. Blagden demonstrated this principle in another way, with two buckets of water also taken into the hot room. One bucket had a layer of oil poured on top of the water, preventing evaporation of the water. The oil-covered water soon began to boil.

Another bucket contained water with no oil covering. That uncovered water stayed much cooler, because evaporation from the surface carried heat away from the water, just as evaporation of sweat from Dr. Blagden's skin carried heat away from his body.

You can see now that Dr. Blagden's survival in his 260-degree room depended on the air being dry. In fact, Dr. Blagden tried pouring water on the floor of the hot room to make the air humid. This reduced evaporation of sweat. Dr. Blagden had to get out of the hot room, fast.

Schmidt-Nielsen, Knut. *Desert Animals: Physiological Problems of Heat and Water*. London: Oxford University Press, 1964.

See Milk Protein

Put a teaspoonful of milk in the bottom of a glass. A teaspoonful is enough, because you're not going to want to drink this. Then add a teaspoonful of vinegar, wait a few seconds, and watch the milk curdle. The curd is mostly casein, the main protein in milk. What you've just done is not to change the chemical composition of the milk protein, but to make it behave differently by changing its environment.

Normally, small bundles of milk protein molecules are dispersed throughout the milk. They scatter light and contribute to milk's white color. When the environment becomes acid—when you add vinegar—electrical forces between proteins change. In an acid environment, milk proteins clump together and make the curd you see on the bottom of the glass after adding the vinegar. Tilt the glass to see the curd better.

Our demonstration mixture of milk and vinegar is basically useless, but curdling with acid under more carefully controlled conditions is one of the steps in changing milk into cheese. In cheesemaking the acid often comes from a carefully cultured strain of bacteria.

A completely different application of basically the same process is the mechanism that plugs small injuries in our skin. Proteins normally dispersed in our blood meet enzymes at the site of an injury. In the presence of those enzymes, the proteins link up into a web—a clot—that seals the wound and draws the injured skin back together.

McGee, Harold. *On Food and Cooking: The Science and Lore of the Kitchen.* New York: Scribner, 1984.

"Protein" and "Casein." In *McGraw-Hill Encyclopedia of Science and Technology*, 6th ed. New York, 1987.

66 *A Couple of Desk Tricks*

All you need for this experiment is a 25-cent piece and a small postage stamp. Put the stamp on the desk and hold the quarter horizontally about half an inch above the stamp. Now blow hard down onto the quarter. The stamp immediately rises from the desk and seems to stick to the back of the quarter until you stop blowing.

This is a quick and easy demonstration of the same principle that holds airplanes up in flight. A stream of air—or any fluid—has lower pressure than the atmosphere around it. The faster the stream, the lower the pressure. This is generally referred to as Bernoulli's principle, after the eighteenth-century Swiss physicist Daniel Bernoulli. The fast-moving air flowing past the edges of the quarter makes relatively low air pressure around the edge of the coin. Atmospheric pressure beneath the stamp then pushes the stamp against the quarter.

The wings of birds and airplanes exploit the same effect. The top surface of a wing is curved, the bottom relatively flat. As the wing moves through the air, that special shape forces air to move faster over the top of the wing than along the bottom. The faster-moving air on top of the wing has lower pressure than the slower-moving air on the bottom. The result is a force pushing up on the wing. If the wing is big enough and the air speed fast enough, that force can help carry a bird or an airplane through the air.

Here's another way to demonstrate the same principle. You need a candle, and a card such as a business card or playing card. Hold the card between your mouth and the candle, about two inches from the candle flame. Now blow against the center of the card. The candle flame will lean toward the card, not away from it, to the astonishment of all the guests.

In this candle trick, fast-moving air around the edges of the card makes low air pressure on the other side of the card. Atmospheric pressure on the far side of the candle pushes air toward the card, and the flame moves in response to that air.

Now pick up the wine bottle—or the soft-drink bottle or the ketchup bottle, depending on what kind of dinner it is—and hold it between you and the candle. Blow against the side of the bottle. The round shape of the bottle is streamlined—the shape makes it easy for air currents from your breath to rejoin on the other side of the bottle and continue toward the flame. The candle will be blown out as if the bottle weren't there at all.

Gardner, Martin. *Entertaining Science Experiments with Everyday Objects.* New York: Dover Publications, 1981.

Lynde, C. J. *Science Experiences with Home Equipment.* Princeton, N.J.: Van Nostrand, 1949.

Wine without Legs

Put some wine or some other alcoholic liquor in a glass, swirl the glass to wet the inside surfaces with liquid, set the glass down on the table, and wait. You are likely to see a ring of liquid clinging to the inside of the glass half an inch or so above the liquid surface. This liquid ring gets gradually thicker, until liquid begins to run down the side of the glass in streams sometimes called legs or tears.

More than 140 years ago, James Thomson, little-known brother of a famous English physicist named William Thomson, gave a lecture on this subject. His explanation involved surface tension—the attractive force between liquid molecules that pulls water into droplets on a well-waxed car, among other effects.

Thomson pointed out two important differences between alcohol and water: alcohol evaporates faster than water, and alcohol has less surface tension—weaker attraction between molecules—than water.

Thomson explained legs in a wine glass by saying that alcohol evaporates fastest from the liquid film on the glass. That leaves a watery film on the glass with less alcohol and stronger attraction between molecules than the wine below. Now the attractive force between water molecules pulls more wine up the side of the glass until the ring forms. When the ring gets too heavy, liquid runs out and makes legs.

A nice explanation, but can it be checked? In 1855 Thomson tested the idea by putting wine in a vial and sealing it with a cork to prevent evaporation of alcohol. No legs appeared. When the vial was uncorked and fresh air was allowed to reach the wine again, the legs reappeared. Wine in a corked vial has no legs. The experiment worked in 1855. Does it work in your kitchen?

McGee, Harold. *On Food and Cooking: The Science and Lore of the Kitchen.* New York: Scribner, 1984.

Thomson, James. "On Certain Curious Motions Observable on the Surfaces of Wine and Other Alcoholic Liquors." 1855. In *Popular Lectures and Addresses,* ed. William Thomson. New York: Macmillan and Company, 1891-94.

Unseen Reflection

In 1901 Guglielmo Marconi sent a radio signal across the Atlantic, from England to Newfoundland. How this happened was a great mystery to Marconi and everyone else. Radio signals were known to travel in straight lines, just as light rays do. Radio and light are really two forms of the same thing. So how did Marconi's signal get over the curve of the earth?

Two British engineers, Arthur Kennelly and Oliver Heaviside, independently proposed in about 1902 that there might be some unseen layer in the upper atmosphere that bends or reflects radio waves over the horizon. A British physicist, Edward Victor Appleton, looked for the so-called Kennelly-Heaviside layer, and found it in 1924. Appleton's technique was to send a signal from the English city of Bournemouth to Oxford. Appleton found that he could make the received signal stronger or weaker merely by changing the wavelength of the signal at the transmitter.

Part of the signal received at Oxford was coming straight from Bournemouth, and part was coming by way of the Kennelly-Heaviside layer—a longer path. If the two parts of the signal arrived at the receiver with their waves in step with each other, the received signal would be strong. If Appleton changed the wavelength, the received signal would be weak, because then a high point of one wave might arrive with a low point of another. The two waves, arriving out of step, would cancel each other out.

Edward Victor Appleton in 1924 not only showed the existence of the first known reflecting layer of what is now called the ionosphere, but calculated its height: about 50 miles above the ground.

By the way, this Appleton is no relation to the Victor Appleton who wrote the Tom Swift science-fiction novels. That Appleton was a pen name used by a syndicate.

"Appleton." In *Dictionary of Scientific Biography,* Charles Coulston Gillispie, Editor-in-Chief. New York: Scribner, 1971.
Appleton, E. V. "The Ionosphere." Nobel lecture, 1947.

Approaching the Dew Point

Take all the air in the lower atmosphere over the county you live in. That air contains a certain amount of water vapor. You can get an idea of how much water vapor by listening for the relative humidity measurement in a weather report. The relative humidity tells you how much water vapor the air holds, compared to the amount it's capable of holding. If the air over your county contains only 50 percent of the water vapor it's capable of holding, then the relative humidity is 50 percent.

The relative humidity will almost certainly change as the day goes on. More water vapor may be added to the air, possibly by evaporation from the ocean. But the biggest cause of change of relative humidity will probably be change of temperature.

This evening, as the air gets cooler, the relative humidity will increase. Cool air cannot hold as much water vapor as warm air. As the air cools, the amount of water vapor it already contains will get closer and closer to the maximum the air can hold. At some temperature the air will become saturated; the relative humidity will reach 100 percent; the air will become unable to hold any more water vapor. Fog may form. That temperature is the so-called dew point, another number sometimes included in weather reports. As air temperature approaches the dew point, relative humidity approaches 100 percent.

Any object whose temperature is at or cooler than the dew point will cause water to condense from the air. Water condenses on a glass of iced tea in summertime because the temperature of the glass is not only cooler than the air temperature, but cooler than the dew point.

During the night a blade of grass loses heat to the sky, like a radiator. A blade of grass can't hold much heat to begin with, so it quickly becomes cool enough to cause water to condense—in other words, its temperature drops below the dew point.

Ruffner, James A., and Frank E. Beri. *The Weather Almanac.* 5th ed. Detroit: Gale Research, 1987.

Note: For more on relative humidity, see "Humidity, Relative to What?" on p. 80.

Interpret Oil Stains

Imagine that your car has a very small engine oil leak. Sooner or later enough oil will leak out to make an oil drop hanging from the bottom of the engine like a water drop hanging from a leaky faucet. Soon the oil drop will be almost but not quite heavy enough to fall from the engine under its own weight.

Now suppose you drive the car through a dip in the road. As you climb the up side of the dip, you feel pressed down into your seat because the car is being accelerated upward by the slope. Meanwhile, the same upward acceleration throws that hanging oil drop from your engine. The oil drop falls to the concrete and makes a little stain.

Now imagine hundreds, thousands of cars with leaky engines

going through the same dip in the road. All those little oil stains add up to one big stain that says, "Here's a place in the road where cars accelerate upward." Of course, deep dips in the road are easy to see even without oil stains. But even a very gentle dip should, according to this line of reasoning, have a bigger, darker oil stain than a level part of the same road.

In fact, any part of a road where a car is made to accelerate upward or sideways is likely to have a bigger-than-average, darker-than-average oil stain. For instance, a car going down a hill will be accelerated upward when it encounters level road at the bottom of the hill. The driver will feel momentarily pressed down into the seat. And at the same time an oil drop may be thrown from the bottom of the engine onto the concrete. Oil drops may also be thrown from the engine when a car takes a curve at high speed.

So be an oil stain interpreter: see whether stains on highways near you reveal the shape of the road surface.

Bartlett, A. A.; D. F. Kirwan; and J. Willis. "External Manifestation of the Variation of Free-Fall Acceleration inside Moving Cars." *The Physics Teacher*, November 1980.

You Can't Heat an Ice Cube

More precisely, you can't heat an ice cube past a temperature of 32 degrees Fahrenheit. Put some ice cubes in a saucepan, put the pan on the stove, turn on the heat. The ice will melt, but it won't get warmer than 32 degrees.

This strange fact troubled the eighteenth-century Scottish physicist Joseph Black. What really bothered him was, why do ice and snow melt so *slowly?* If you warm an ice cube to 32 degrees and then add just a little more heat, the ice doesn't melt all at once. You have to keep adding heat for a long time to melt the whole cube. Joseph Black concluded that adding heat does not always make things warmer. He wrote, "Melting ice receives heat very fast, but the only effect of this heat is to change it into water, which is not in the least sensibly warmer than the ice was before. . . . A great quantity . . . of the heat . . . which enters into the melting ice, produces no other effect but to give it fluidity . . . ;

[the heat] appears to be absorbed and concealed within the water, so as not to be discoverable by the application of a thermometer."

Joseph Black's observations of the 1750s made sense when the real nature of heat was revealed early in the twentieth century. Heat is the random jiggling motion of atoms; hotter temperature means faster motion.

Ice is water molecules linked up as a rigid crystal that can take a certain amount of molecular shaking without coming apart. But when the shaking is violent enough—when the temperature gets to 32 degrees—water molecules are shaken loose from the ice to form liquid water. As long as you continue to add heat to an ice cube, that heat is used exclusively to shake water molecules loose until no more ice is left. That takes time, so ice melts slowly— fortunately for people who live below snowy mountains.

Black, Joseph. "Lectures on the Elements of Chemistry." In William Francis Magie, *A Source Book in Physics.* New York: McGraw-Hill Book Company, 1935.

Wolf, Abraham. *A History of Science, Technology, and Philosophy in the Eighteenth Century.* 2nd ed. Gloucester, Mass.: Peter Smith, 1968.

Howling Wind

When wind blows over pine needles, the needles break up the smooth flow of air. Behind each pine needle is a wake in the air, something like the swirling water trailing a canoe paddle. This wake in the air is made of eddies—technically, vortices—that form just behind the pine needle, then detach themselves from it and move downwind.

These vortices form on alternate sides of the pine needle dozens or hundreds of times per second in a regular rhythm that creates a sound with a definite musical pitch. The pitch becomes higher if the wind blows harder—that is, if the air moves faster. The pitch is also higher if the diameter of the pine needles is smaller.

In the early 1900s, the Hungarian physicist Theodore von Karman mathematically analyzed the vortices that form behind cylindrical obstructions. It was a tough job, but von Karman developed a simple formula that allows you to predict what the pitch will be—in other words, how fast the vortices will form—if you know the diameter of the cylinder and the speed of the wind.

As the vortices, the eddies, move downwind from a cylindrical object, they take up alternating positions along the wake like lamps on opposite sides of a street. The vortices are now usually said to form a "von Karman vortex street" behind a cylindrical object. Decades ago, people often noticed a humming sound coming from telegraph wires strung between poles. The sound was caused not by electricity but by vortices forming in regular rhythm in the air downwind of each wire. Nowadays there are fewer aboveground wires to listen to, but we can still hear the weird sound of the von Karman vortex street when wind blows through a pine tree.

Humphreys, W. J. *Physics of the Air*. 3rd ed. New York: Dover Publications, 1964.
"Von Karman." In *Dictionary of Scientific Biography*, Charles Coulston Gillispie, Editor-in-Chief. New York: Scribner, 1971.

Measuring Altitude with a Thermometer

It takes longer to hard-boil an egg in Denver than in New York. The reason is that water boils at about 203 degrees Fahrenheit in Denver, and at about 212 degrees in New York. At Denver's altitude of about 5,000 feet above sea level, the atmospheric pressure is lower—fewer air molecules strike the surface of liquid water than at New York's altitude near sea level. So a pan of boiling water in Denver is slightly cooler than a pan of boiling water in New York because the altitude is higher, and the atmospheric pressure is slightly less. The boiling point of water drops about 2 degrees Fahrenheit with every thousand feet of altitude.

Once you heat water to its boiling point, you can't make the liquid any hotter. New heat energy added to boiling water goes into making water evaporate as steam, not into heating the liquid. Even if you turn up the gas all the way under a saucepan of boiling water in Denver, the water temperature will remain at 203 degrees—unless you seal the top of the pan so the pressure inside will increase. Then you have a pressure cooker.

If boiling temperature depends on atmospheric pressure, then why not measure atmospheric pressure by measuring boiling temperature? This clever idea occurred to Gabriel Daniel Fahrenheit himself in the 1720s. Fahrenheit marked one of his thermometers not with degrees but with a scale indicating atmospheric pressure. Just dip the instrument in boiling water, and you could read off the atmospheric pressure.

A Colombian geographer, Francisco José de Caldas, took the idea a step further around the year 1800. Knowing that atmospheric pressure decreases as you go higher, Caldas used the boiling point of water to measure the height of mountains in South America.

McGee, Harold. *On Food and Cooking: The Science and Lore of the Kitchen.* New York: Scribner, 1984.

Negret, Juan P. "Boiling Water and the Height of Mountains." *The Physics Teacher,* May 1986.

Rombauer, Irma S., and Marion Rombauer Becker. *The Joy of Cooking.* Indianapolis: Bobbs-Merrill, 1975.

Wolf, Abraham. *A History of Science, Technology, and Philosophy in the Eighteenth Century.* 2nd ed. Gloucester, Mass.: Peter Smith, 1968.

Relying on Bacteria

All protein molecules include nitrogen atoms. All living organisms need proteins, so they all need nitrogen. The air around us is 78 percent nitrogen gas, but our bodies cannot use nitrogen in that form. We must get nitrogen for our proteins either by eating plants or by eating animals that have eaten plants. Plants, in turn, get their nitrogen—some of it, at least—from so-called nitrates, nitrogen compounds dissolved in water in the soil. Those nitrates are made by bacteria when they decompose dead plant and animal tissue. So there is a nitrogen cycle: animals and plants die; their tissues are decomposed by bacteria to make nitrates; those nitrates are taken up from the soil by plants, which are eaten by animals, and so on.

But that's not all. Some soil bacteria break down nitrates and release the nitrogen to the atmosphere. These bacteria take usable nitrogen out of the biological cycle. If this lost nitrogen were not continually replenished, life on earth would soon disappear.

Fortunately, most of the lost nitrogen is replenished by so-called nitrogen-fixing bacteria. These bacteria provide a vital service: they capture nitrogen from the air and incorporate it into molecules plants can use—but not just any plants. Nitrogen-fixing bacteria live in the roots of the plants known as legumes—beans and alfalfa, for example. Farmers alternate corn and beans in the same field partly because nitrogen-fixing bacteria in the roots of the beans return nitrogen to the soil.

Nowadays usable nitrogen can also be added to soil in the form of chemical fertilizers. But most nitrogen fixation is still done by bacteria. Every living thing that relies on plants for food ultimately relies on nitrogen-fixing bacteria.

Curtis, Helena. *Biology*. 4th ed. New York: Worth Publishers, 1983.
"Nitrogen Cycle." In *McGraw-Hill Encyclopedia of Science and Technology*, 6th ed. New York, 1987.

Invention of the Vacuum Cleaner

According to the imposing eight-volume *History of Technology* edited by Charles Singer and Trevor Williams, an English civil engineer, H. Cecil Booth, got the idea for the vacuum cleaner about the year 1900. Booth went to a London hotel to see a demonstration of a new machine designed to clean the seats of railway cars. This American machine blew compressed air onto the seats to drive out dust.

Booth had the idea that this seat-cleaning device might work better if it sucked rather than blew air. He went back to his office, put a handkerchief on the carpet, knelt down on the floor, and sucked through the handkerchief. Sure enough, the other side of the handkerchief was covered with dust. Inspired by this experiment, Booth built a device in which an electric pump sucked air through a cloth bag, and the vacuum cleaner was born.

Soon H. Cecil Booth had created the British Vacuum Cleaner Company. The company's horse-drawn cart would visit people's homes, where uniformed workers would pass long suction tubes through windows into rooms to be cleaned. One of the company's most prestigious early jobs was cleaning Westminster Abbey for the coronation of King Edward VII in 1902. In 1904 Booth's company came out with a small domestic vacuum cleaner in which the electric air pump and cloth bag were mounted on a little wagon. The operator swept the carpet with a long suction hose plugged into the wagon.

In 1908 an American, James Spangler, developed a new compact design: an electric suction pump mounted vertically over a set of wheels. The pump sucked air and dust from the carpet and blew it into a cloth bag, rather than sucking through the dust bag as in Booth's version. Spangler sold the patent to the Hoover Company, which got out of its original business—leather processing—to make vacuum cleaners full-time.

Singer, Charles Joseph. "The Twentieth Century, c. 1900 to c. 1950, Part II." In *A History of Technology*, vol. 7, ed. Trevor I. Williams. Oxford: Clarendon Press, 1978.

A Stubborn Business Card

Take an ordinary business card—a calling card—and fold the two ends down at right angles, so the card makes a little bridge about half an inch high. Put the card on a table so it stands on the two folded edges. Now challenge someone to turn the card over by blowing air through the space underneath it. The card will not flip over. Instead it will cling to the table. The harder you blow, the tighter it clings.

This is another desk trick based on the principle that a fast-moving stream of air has lower pressure than the still air around it—a principle named after the eighteenth-century physicist Daniel Bernoulli, who discovered it. The fast-moving air under the folded card has lower pressure than the still air above. Atmospheric pressure above the card presses it onto the table.

Bernoulli's principle is the basis of flight. Airplane wings, like bird wings, are curved on top and relatively flat on the bottom. That forces air to flow faster over the top of the wing than across the bottom. That, in turn, makes lower air pressure on the top of the wing than on the bottom. The result is a force due to atmospheric pressure pushing up on the bottom of the wing.

Bernoulli's principle suggests that you might be able to flip the card over by blowing hard horizontally over the top of the card, so the fast-moving low-pressure air is above the card rather than below. It can be done, but it takes practice and luck.

Lynde, C. J. *Science Experiences with Home Equipment.* Princeton, N.J.: Van Nostrand, 1949.
Swezey, Kenneth. *Science Magic.* New York: McGraw-Hill, 1952.

Bent Out of Shape

Bend a paper clip slightly, and it springs back. Bend it too far and it stays bent, although it still has its springiness. These facts may not seem remarkable until you try to explain them. The French physicist Charles-Augustin Coulomb pondered the behavior of springy metals more than 200 years ago. Coulomb hung a weight at the end of a long metal wire, twisted the weight around the axis of the wire, and let go. If he twisted the weight only slightly, it would rotate back and forth, like a rotating clock pendulum or a rope climber spinning at the end of a rope, and eventually stop in its original position. But if he twisted the weight too far, it would eventually stop not in its original position, but in some new position.

Charles-Augustin Coulomb concluded that when he twisted the weight hanging at the end of the wire, he was working against two different kinds of resistance. First there was elasticity, or springiness, which returned the weight to its original position after a slight twist. Second, there was cohesion, which held the metal itself together and maintained the basic shape of the wire. Coulomb guessed that when the wire took on a permanent twist—that is, when it had been bent out of shape—it was because small component parts of the metal in the wire had slid over one another. The force of cohesion had been overcome.

That was more than 200 years ago. Much later, when the atomic structure of metals was revealed, Coulomb's hunch turned out to be right. When the atoms that make up a metal are pulled apart slightly, forces between atoms will pull them back toward their original positions. But if the force on the metal is great enough, whole layers of atoms will slide past each other. You can never get those layers back to their original arrangement. The metal is permanently bent out of shape.

Bronowski, Jacob. "The Hidden Structure." In *The Ascent of Man*. Boston: Little, Brown, 1974.

Wolf, Abraham. "Coulomb's Theory of Torsion." In *A History of Science, Technology, and Philosophy in the Eighteenth Century*, 2nd ed., revised by D. McKie. Gloucester, Mass.: Peter Smith, 1968.

Diving Raisins

Fill a drinking glass with some fresh carbonated beverage—any kind will do. Wait for the foam to settle. Now toss in a few raisins and wait. At first the raisins go straight to the bottom. Soon, however, they rise to the surface. After floating just beneath the liquid surface for a few seconds, each raisin appears to dive suddenly back to the bottom. Before long, each raisin rises again, dives again, and so on.

The raisins are actually carrying carbon dioxide out of the liquid in the form of bubbles stuck to their wrinkled skins. As the carbonated drink sits in the glass, it slowly loses carbon dioxide to the air anyway—that's why the drink goes flat after a couple of hours. Bubbles of carbon dioxide forming below the surface and rising to the top simply speed up the process.

But bubbles won't form spontaneously in the middle of a clean, quiet liquid. Bubbles form where the liquid touches some solid object. That object might be a small particle of dust or the surface of a raisin. Once a bubble begins to form, it tends to grow. The carbon dioxide dissolved in the liquid will, so to speak, take advantage of the chance to leave the liquid and become gas. So the bubbles on a submerged raisin grow until they lift the raisin to the surface. When the raisin reaches the surface, the bubbles eventually pop, although surface tension in the liquid may keep them just under the surface for a while. When the raisin has lost enough bubbles, it loses its buoyancy and sinks.

You might try cutting the raisins into small pieces before tossing them into the carbonated drink. Smaller pieces are lighter and therefore easier for the bubbles to lift. Some books recommend doing the same trick with coffee grounds or small shirt buttons.

Gardner, Martin. *Entertaining Science Experiments with Everyday Objects.* New York: Dover Publications, 1981.

Lynde, C. J. *Science Experiences with Home Equipment.* Princeton, N.J.: Van Nostrand, 1949.

Water Is Hard to Heat

Water is by far the most abundant liquid on the surface of the earth. Also, anywhere from 50 to 95 percent of the weight of any living thing is water. Water is familiar, but it's chemically peculiar.

One of water's peculiarities is that it is, so to speak, reluctant to change temperature, compared to other materials. You have to burn almost twice as much gas in a stove to raise the temperature of an ounce of water one degree as to raise the temperature of an ounce of ethyl alcohol one degree, for example. In chemists' language, water has a high specific heat compared to almost every other material.

The explanation takes us down into the molecular world. Recall that heat is the random jiggling motion of molecules. Faster motion means hotter temperature. Water molecules attract each other very strongly compared to molecules of most other materials. When you add energy to water in the form of heat, a lot of that energy goes into breaking the strong attraction between molecules rather than into making those molecules move faster. The result is that you have to burn a lot of gas under a saucepan to get the temperature of water in the pan to change even a little.

This reluctance of water to change temperature means that living things in the oceans don't have to contend with rapid variations in temperature. The sea is slow to cool at night and slow to warm in the morning, slow to cool in autumn and slow to warm in spring. The oceans are heat reservoirs; they provide a relatively constant environment for marine life and exert a moderating influence on the weather.

Curtis, Helena. *Biology.* 4th ed. New York: Worth Publishers, 1983.

Humidity, Relative to What?

Relative humidity compares the amount of water vapor the air actually holds at the moment to the maximum amount of water vapor the air is capable of holding. If the relative humidity is 100 percent, the air cannot hold any more water vapor—the air is said to be saturated. Wet laundry will not dry in saturated air.

On the other hand, if the air is not saturated—if the relative humidity is less than 100 percent—the air contains less water vapor than it's capable of holding. If the relative humidity is, say, 50 percent, then the air contains only half the water vapor it's capable of holding; if it's 75 percent, then three-quarters, and so on. Wet laundry will dry if the relative humidity is less than 100 percent because the air, so to speak, has room for more water vapor.

How much water are we talking about? Here's an example. Take some warm, humid summer air: temperature 86 degrees Fahrenheit, relative humidity 100 percent. Take enough of that warm, humid air to fill a phone booth. (The volume of a phone booth is assumed to be two cubic meters.) The water in that phone booth full of saturated summer air weighs about two ounces.

For contrast, imagine now a sample of humid winter air: relative humidity still 100 percent, temperature now minus 4 degrees Fahrenheit. Again, take enough to fill a phone booth. The water in that sample of saturated winter air weighs only about a fifteenth of an ounce. Cold air has a much smaller capacity for water vapor than warm air does. Relative humidity is a measure of how close the air is to saturation. It takes only a little water vapor to saturate cold air; it takes a lot to saturate warm air.

We now know that warm air can hold a lot more moisture than cold air. So why, when you turn on your furnace in the winter, does the heated air often feel so dry? How dry the air *feels* is a measure of how quickly moisture is being evaporated from your skin. As the relative humidity drops—in other words, gets farther below the saturation point—the air feels drier because it is taking more moisture from your skin.

On a cold winter day, there is probably much less moisture in the outside air than on a typical summer day in the same area. But the relative humidity may still be near 100 percent because at the lower temperature the saturation point is much lower. When that cold, saturated air goes from below freezing outside to room temperature inside, it doesn't lose any of its moisture, but it feels much drier because it is now capable of absorbing more than three times as much moisture from your skin. If the relative humidity outside is 100 percent, the relative humidity inside will be less than one-third of that—or only about 30 percent.

On a cold day in Milwaukee, there's less moisture in the air than on a hot day in the Sahara Desert, even though the relative humidity is higher in the colder climate. If you heat the air in Milwaukee to room temperature without adding any moisture, the relative humidity in your house will drop to less than what it is in the Sahara Desert.

Ahrens, C. Donald. *Meteorology Today: An Introduction to the Weather, Climate, and the Environment.* St. Paul: West Publishing Company, 1991.
Encyclopedia Britannica. 16th ed. Chicago, 1991.
Handbook of Chemistry and Physics. Cleveland, Ohio: Chemical Rubber Company, 1988-89.

Colors on Metal

Metal pots and pans often have patches of rainbow color on their surfaces after they've been used for a while. The colors are made by thin films of metal oxides—chemicals formed in a reaction between metal and air at high temperature. The colors look like the colors in oil floating on a puddle, or the colors in a soap bubble. In fact, all those colors are caused by the same mechanism: the reflection of light from both surfaces of a thin film.

Wherever the metal oxide film is exactly thick enough to accommodate a whole number of waves of, say, red light, red light will be reflected to your eye, because red-light waves bouncing off the back side of the film will be exactly in step with red-light waves bouncing off the front of the film. The same goes for other colors. Wherever the film's thickness varies, so do the colors.

Variations in time and temperature of heating make variations in the color of the metal oxide film. Toolmakers and metallurgists examine those colors to judge the temperature of a piece of metal during the process of tempering.

Around the turn of the twentieth century, the American glassmaker Louis Comfort Tiffany developed a way to apply a thin coat of metal oxide to glass to make iridescent colors. Lusterware and other Tiffany glasses now command good prices on the antique market.

Most metal oxide films stick tightly to the surface and protect the metal beneath. That prevents further reaction between metal and oxygen in the air. One big exception to this rule is iron. Rust, which is made of iron oxides, flakes off and exposes fresh metal, which rusts, flakes off, and so on until the iron is gone.

Brill, Thomas B. "Why Objects Appear as They Do." *Journal of Chemical Education*, April 1980.

"Corrosion." In *McGraw-Hill Encyclopedia of Science and Technology*. New York, 1987.

Hall of Mirrors

Hold two rectangular flat mirrors so their edges touch and so they meet at a shallow angle, like the covers of an open book. Now slowly bring the mirrors together as if you were closing the book. Watch the reflections. At some point the reflection of the right-hand mirror will appear in the left-hand mirror. At about the same time, the reflection of the left-hand mirror will appear in the right-hand mirror. Keep closing the angle between the mirrors. Soon the left-hand mirror will show not only a reflection of the right-hand mirror, but also what is reflected in that right-hand mirror, that is, the left-hand mirror.

And so it goes. As the angle between mirrors gets smaller, you see more reflected mirrors. Just before the two mirrors meet, you can peek into the space between them and see many reflections—dozens, perhaps. The more distant-looking reflections are dark because the glass absorbs some light with each reflection.

Now separate the two mirrors and hold them parallel and

facing each other. Better yet, prop the mirrors up on a table so you don't have to struggle with holding them steady. You have made a miniature hall of mirrors. Peek over the top of one mirror and you will see into what looks like a tunnel. If the two real mirrors are 6 inches apart, each reflected mirror will appear 6 inches behind the last one. In general, the reflection of any object 6 inches in front of a mirror appears 6 inches behind that same mirror. If you can see 10 reflections in your miniature hall of mirrors, then the tenth reflection will appear 60 inches behind the mirror; in other words, that tunnel will appear 5 feet deep.

Now, here's another mirror demonstration you can try. Turn off the lights and hold a candle about an inch in front of an ordinary bathroom mirror. Don't let the glass get hot. You'll see several reflections of the candle flame, apparently lined up behind the mirror. It's the hall-of-mirrors effect again. One of the two mirrors is the reflecting surface on the *back* of the glass. The other mirror is inside the *front* surface of the glass, which reflects some light back into the glass rather than letting it emerge into the air.

The general rule is: Put any object a certain distance in front of a mirror, and the reflection will look like a copy of that object exactly the same distance behind the mirror. Put an object between two mirrors, and the image of that object in one mirror becomes the object reflected in the other mirror.

If you open up a toy kaleidoscope, you'll see two mirrors joined at one edge like the covers of an open book. When you look through the eyepiece of the kaleidoscope, you look into those mirrors at a glancing angle and see multiple reflections of scattered pieces of colored plastic at the other end. Each mirror shows you not only a reflection of the colored plastic, but also a reflection of the other mirror—which shows you a reflection of the plastic and of the first mirror, and so on.

For this last demonstration, get a third rectangular hand mirror, and set the three mirrors in a triangle, facing each other, edges touching, like walls of a miniature triangular room. Drop a penny into the space between the mirrors. Peek over the edge of one wall and you'll see dozens and dozens of pennies. The Paris

Exhibition of 1889 had a room like this, big enough for people to walk into. Two or three people could become a crowd!

Greenslade, Thomas B., Jr. "Multiple Images in Plane Mirrors." *The Physics Teacher,* January 1982.

Take Bets on a Leaky Milk Carton

(Note: Be sure to do this experiment where it won't hurt if things get wet.)

Get an empty half-gallon milk carton. Take a sharp pencil and poke three small round holes in the side of the carton, one above the other: one hole about a quarter of an inch up from the bottom of the carton, a second hole about two inches higher, and a third hole about two inches higher still. Put this milk carton on a flat surface, fill it with water, and watch the water squirt out of the three holes. Take bets on this: Which of the three streams will hit the surface farthest from the carton?

You might guess that water will squirt fastest from the bottom hole—and rightly so, because the pressure is greater the deeper you go into a container full of water. Dive to the bottom of a swimming pool and feel the increasing pressure on your ears. So, because the water pressure is greatest behind the bottom hole, the water will squirt fastest from that hole. Therefore, you might guess, the bottom stream will hit the surface farther from the punctured milk carton than either of the other two streams. Try it. You may be surprised to see the bottom stream land *closest* to the milk carton. Either the middle or the top stream will hit farthest away.

What's wrong? We considered horizontal velocity, but we failed to consider the *time* needed for the water to fall from the height of each hole. Yes, the water coming out of the bottom hole is moving faster, horizontally, than water from the upper holes. But the bottom stream has less time to fall before it hits the flat surface. During that time the water can travel only a short horizontal distance.

But there is a way to make the demonstration come out as you might think it should. Try this: Move that same leaky milk carton to the edge of the table, so the three water streams hit the floor. Now the bottom stream wins; it hits the floor farther from the table than either of the other two.

The distances from the three holes to the surface of impact are now much more nearly the same. Now the difference in time of fall is small between the top hole and the bottom hole, but the difference in horizontal velocity is still large. Now difference in horizontal velocity is the crucial factor, and the demonstration comes out as you might expect—the bottom stream wins.

Grimvall, Göran. "Questionable Physics Tricks for Children." *The Physics Teacher,* September 1987.
Paldy, Lester G. "The Water Can Paradox." *The Physics Teacher,* September 1963.

Bacteria, Corn, Cars, and Terre Haute

In the early 1900s the Russian-born chemist Chaim Weizmann, working in England at the University of Manchester, developed a process in which a certain strain of bacteria fermented corn into a useful chemical and an apparently useless by-product. The useful chemical was butyl alcohol—not the kind you drink. Weizmann expected that it would be useful in making synthetic rubber. The apparently useless by-product was acetone, now known to most of us as nail-polish remover. But that came much later.

Back to the early 1900s. World War I began. The Allies needed acetone to make the explosive cordite. Now the Weizmann process was used for a new purpose. The U.S. government took over distilleries in Peoria, Illinois, and Terre Haute, Indiana, and turned them into acetone factories using the Weizmann process. Butyl alcohol was the useless by-product now.

World War I ended. There was no longer much need for acetone. But butyl alcohol had been piling up during the war, and people in the paint business came up with a use for it. Before 1920 the bottleneck in car manufacturing was the paint shop. Automobile varnishes took up to three weeks to dry. Paint experts knew that the so-called nitrocellulose lacquers would dry much faster, but they needed a cheap solvent, among other things. Butyl alcohol filled the bill. A private company bought the distilleries in Peoria and Terre Haute and went into the business of supplying solvent for lacquer for new cars of the twenties—using the same chemical process Chaim Weizmann had developed because of his interest in synthetic rubber.

If there's a moral to this story, it might be that you can't predict the ultimate results of basic research.

Gabriel, C. L. "Butanol Fermentation Process." *Industrial and Engineering Chemistry*, October 1928.
———. "Development of the Butyl-Acetonic Fermentation Industry." *Industrial and Engineering Chemistry*, November 1930.
Haynes, Williams. *American Chemical Industry*. New York: Van Nostrand, 1945.
Ihde, Aaron J. *The Development of Modern Chemistry*. New York: Harper and Row, 1964.

86 *Big Shadows*

Try this after a candlelight dinner: Blow out all the candles but one, then turn off all the other lights in the room. Look at the walls. The candle throws frighteningly huge shadows of you and your friends onto the walls. The bigger the room, the bigger the shadows.

Being careful not to get burned, hold your hand about two feet from the candle and notice the size of the shadow your hand casts on the wall. Now move your hand to a position one foot from the candle; notice how much larger the shadow becomes. There's a mathematical proportion in this situation. If your hand is five times closer to the candle than to the wall, then the shadow of your hand will be five times bigger than your hand itself. If your hand is ten times closer to the candle than to the wall, the shadow will be ten times as big as your hand. And so on.

Why doesn't an ordinary living-room electric lamp cast huge, dark shadows? The answer is that electric lamps and most electric light bulbs are designed to cast soft shadows, unlike a bare candle flame. The candle on the dining-room table is a small light source; the flame is usually less than an inch high. A frosted light bulb, on the other hand, is several inches high and gives off light from all over its surface—it's a bigger light source than a candle. A lampshade makes the effective size of the light source even bigger. The larger the light source, the more diffuse the shadow.

If you put your hand a foot away from a candle, you block a large amount of light that would otherwise reach the walls; put your hand a foot away from an electric lamp with a frosted bulb and a big shade, and you block much less light, so the shadow on the wall is much less noticeable.

Lynde, C. J. *Science Experiences with Ten-cent Store Equipment.* 2nd ed. Princeton, N.J.: Van Nostrand, 1950.

The "Weightlessness of Space"

Actually space is not the only place weightlessness can occur. You can see weightlessness anyplace, anytime. Toss a bunch of keys on a key ring into the air. Toss the keys so they don't tumble end over end. After the keys leave your hand, while they travel through the air, they seem to float around just like weightless objects we've seen in television pictures taken aboard orbiting spacecraft. You can hear the keys strike each other gently as they float around. While they travel through the air, the keys don't hang down from the key ring anymore. The keys are weightless.

If you are in orbit in a space shuttle, you don't have to throw your keys to see this effect; you only have to let go of them. You, the spacecraft, and the keys have already been thrown—at about 18,000 miles an hour—by the rocket engines that fired for a few minutes after lift-off. You, the spacecraft, and your keys are in a continuous free fall, just as the keys were after you tossed them into the air at home.

Unlike the keys at home, you won't hit the ground if you're in orbit. True, your path constantly curves toward the center of the earth, because the earth's gravity constantly pulls you toward the center of the earth. But you're also going sideways at 18,000 miles an hour—about 180 times as fast as the fastest pitch in a major-league baseball game. Since you're above the atmosphere—in other words, in space—there's practically no air to slow you down.

So your path curves downward very gently—as gently as the curved surface of the earth below you. You keep falling, but you never get closer to the ground. Your orbiting spaceship and your keys fall at exactly the same rate as you do. So you and your keys can float inside the ship without hitting the walls. You and your keys are weightless.

"Weightlessness." In *McGraw-Hill Encyclopedia of Science and Technology*, 6th ed. New York, 1987.

The Mystery of Proteins

In the late 1700s, chemists observed that many materials change from solid to liquid when they are heated. Ice is an example. But a few materials change from liquid to solid when they are heated. Milk and eggs, for instance—and blood. Beginning in the 1700s, chemists called these unusual materials albuminous substances—the name was borrowed from albumen, another name for egg white.

At first, albuminous substances seemed to come mostly from animals. The watery juice left behind after any animal tissue was cooked in a pressure cooker would congeal. Later, albuminous substances were found in wheat and beans. By the mid-1800s a Dutch chemist, Gerardus Mulder, suspected that albuminous substances were basic materials of all living things. The Swedish chemist Jöns Jacob Berzelius suggested calling them proteins, from Greek words meaning "primary substance."

Not till the mid-twentieth century did anyone discover why proteins congeal. A protein molecule, it turns out, is made up of hundreds of smaller molecules, the so-called amino acids, hooked up to make a chain. The chain is coiled into a very specific shape for each type of protein. Heating uncoils protein molecules so that they can link together in new ways and make a relatively rigid structure. That's what happens when you cook an egg. The protein molecules act something like little balls of sticky string unrolling and then sticking together in a new, open mesh.

Incidentally, finding out the exact shapes of protein molecules is one of the biggest problems in modern chemistry, and one of the most important. How a protein functions in a living organism depends on its shape.

Ihde, Aaron J. *The Development of Modern Chemistry*. New York: Harper and Row, 1964.
McCollum, Elmer V. *A History of Nutrition: The Sequence of Ideas in Nutrition Investigations*. Boston: Houghton Mifflin, 1957.
McPherson, Alexander. "Macromolecular Crystals." *Scientific American*, March 1989.

Who Can Drink Milk?

Milk contains a particular kind of sugar technically called lactose. A molecule of lactose is made up of two simpler sugar molecules—glucose and galactose—hooked together. In that hooked-together form, the sugar is useless to the human body.

Infants and some adults make an enzyme in their small intestines that cuts the lactose molecule apart. This enzyme has the technical name of lactase.

Once the milk sugar molecule has been separated into glucose and galactose, the body can use it. That's how milk sugar—lactose—is digested. People whose small intestines don't make that lactase enzyme can't digest milk sugar. The undigested lactose passes into the large intestine, where it draws water from body tissues. It also ferments. That produces gas. The result is diarrhea, a symptom of lactose intolerance.

Normal human infants make the lactase enzyme until they're two or three years old. They need it to digest their mothers' milk. After that, most people don't make lactase anymore, and can't drink milk because they can't digest the milk sugar, lactose; they are lactose-intolerant.

But people who have studied diets around the world tell us that lactose intolerance is normal—if by normal you mean the situation that applies to most people in the world. Most adults in the world cannot drink milk—at least not more than about a pint a day. Adults who can drink milk tend to be descended from cultures with a long-standing tradition of raising dairy cattle; their ancestors come either from northern Europe or from certain areas of Africa. Exactly how the genetic trait of adult tolerance for milk sugar became concentrated in those areas of the world is still unknown.

89

Kretchmer, Norman. "Lactose and Lactase." *Scientific American*, October 1972. Reprinted in the anthology *Nutrition*, with introductions by Norman Kretchmer and William van B. Robertson. San Francisco: W. H. Freeman, 1978.

McGee, Harold. *On Food and Cooking: The Science and Lore of the Kitchen*. New York: Scribner, 1984.

Reflections in the Water

Springtime: Magazines run vacation advertisements, illustrated with beautiful photographs of faraway places. Often these photographs show some landscape reflected in a quiet lake, with water smooth as glass. Maybe you've taken pictures like this yourself. The water is so smooth that the upside-down reflection is indistinguishable from the real scene.

Or is it? When you look at the reflection of a house in the water, you actually see the house from a slightly different point of view than when you look directly at the real house.

Imagine following your line of sight as you look at a reflection in a smooth lake. Draw an imaginary straight line to the point on the lake where you see the reflection of some particular feature on the house. Now draw another straight line from that point on the lake to the corresponding point on the real house. That second straight line goes *up* from the water to the house.

Those imaginary straight lines are the paths followed by light on its way from the house to your eye.

So when you look at the reflected image of a house, you are in effect looking *up* at the house. Any object in front of the house—a person standing in the front yard, for instance—will look a little taller, compared to the house, in the reflection than in reality, because that person is being viewed from a slightly lower vantage point.

So you may be able to distinguish the reflected scene from the real one. The reflected landscape shows everything from a lower point of view.

Easton, D. "On Reflections in Ponds." *The Physics Teacher,* March 1987.

Half Heads, Half Tails

Flip an honest coin, and you expect a head just as much as you expect a tail. Flip a coin 10 times, and you expect to get about half heads and half tails. But here's an interesting question: Should you expect to get exactly 5 heads and 5 tails?

The answer is no. It is very likely that 10 flips will give

approximately half heads and half tails. But it is much less likely that 10 flips will give *exactly* half heads and half tails.

Here are some more precise numbers, calculated from the laws of probability. If you flip a coin 10 times, there is less than a 25 percent chance of getting exactly 5 heads and 5 tails. However, there is almost a 66 percent chance that you'll be close to 5 heads and 5 tails; in other words, there's almost a 66 percent chance that you'll get either 4 heads and 6 tails, 5 heads and 5 tails, or 6 heads and 4 tails.

The more times you flip the coin, the more likely it is that you will get *approximately* half heads and half tails; but the more times you flip the coin, the less likely it is that you will get *exactly* half heads and half tails. If you flip a coin 20 times, your chance of getting exactly 10 heads is only about 18 percent, but your chance of getting something between 8 and 12 heads is about 74 percent.

If you flip a coin a million times, your chance of getting exactly 500,000 heads is infinitesimally small; but your chance of getting between 499,000 and 501,000 heads is extremely large.

Feynman, Richard P. "Probability." In *The Feynman Lectures on Physics*. Reading, Mass.: Addison-Wesley, 1963.

Huff, Darrell. *How to Lie with Statistics*. New York: Norton, 1954.

Note: The numbers come from the binomial distribution tables in the Handbook of Chemistry and Physics.

Spiders Don't Get Caught in Their Own Webs

Spiders have an oily secretion on their feet that keeps them from sticking to their webs. But there's more to the story than that. Not all the threads made by a spider are sticky. A spider can make more than one kind of silk. Spiders use their silk not only to make the sticky parts of their webs, but to line their burrows, to wrap their eggs, and as parachutes enabling them to travel on the wind.

Even in a web whose function is to trap insects, not all the threads are sticky. Take, for example, the so-called orb web—the kind that probably comes to mind first when we think of a spider web. An orb web has one set of threads emanating from the center, and another thread applied over those radial threads in a spiral pattern something like the groove on a phonograph record. Generally, only the spiral thread is sticky, not the radial threads.

But even the sticky threads in a web are not sticky over their entire length. A spider makes a sticky thread by applying glue to the silk as it is spun. The spider applies glue continuously to the new thread as it emerges from the end of the spider's abdomen. This glue doesn't form a continuous coat on the silk thread, however. Surface tension comes into play.

Surface tension is the same attraction between molecules that makes water gather into beads on a well-waxed car. Surface tension in the spider's glue gathers that glue into beads, arranged along the thread like beads on a string. Those beads of glue on the spiral threads of an orb web may be just barely visible through a good magnifying glass.

Bristowe, W. S. *The World of Spiders*. London: Collins, 1971.
Grzimek's Animal Life Encyclopedia. New York: Van Nostrand Reinhold Company, 1984.
Zim, H. S. *Spiders and Their Kin*. New York: Golden Press, 1990.

Ice in Oil

Fill a small drinking glass with vegetable oil at room temperature, add an ice cube, and watch what happens. The ice cube will probably float. But as the ice melts, water gathers in a large drop on the bottom of the floating ice cube. Soon this drop of water becomes heavy enough to separate from the ice cube and fall slowly to the bottom of the glass. The water drop sinks because water is denser than vegetable oil. The weight of a sphere of water half an inch in diameter is greater than the weight of a sphere of vegetable oil of the same size.

You can see liquid water coming off an ice cube in oil because oil and water don't mix. The reason for that has to do with a basic difference in the structure of oil molecules and water molecules. A molecule of water has a slight positive electrical charge on one side and a slight negative charge on the other side. The charge here is a very tiny amount of the same kind of charge that everybody knows as static electricity. In the world of electricity, opposite charges attract. So the positive side of one water molecule is strongly attracted to the negative sides of other water molecules; in general, water molecules attract each other strongly. Molecules of oil, on the other hand, don't have these electrical charges. So water molecules won't get into intimate contact with oil molecules.

Incidentally, this demonstration doesn't really show how fast ice melts in liquids other than oil, such as water. Speed of melting depends on other factors such as how water molecules from the ice interact with molecules in the surrounding liquid and how quickly the liquid conducts heat to the ice.

Webster, David. *More Brain-Boosters*. Garden City, N.Y.: Doubleday, 1975.

The Fuzzy Edge of a Shadow

Walk outside on a sunny day, hold your hand out in front of you, and look at the shadow of your hand on the sidewalk. The edges of the shadow are not sharp but fuzzy. The sun cannot cast a perfectly sharp shadow because the sun is not an infinitesimally tiny point of light. The sun appears as a disk, about one-half a degree of angle in diameter.

93

To see why a disk of light cannot cast a sharp shadow, imagine yourself as some kind of tiny bug walking on the sidewalk through the shadow of someone's hand, looking up toward the sun as you go. At first you walk in full sunlight. Soon, however, you enter a region where the hand overhead blocks out part of the sun's disk—but not all of it. In that region, you, the little bug, get something less than full sunlight. You are in the fuzzy gray edge of the shadow, the region technically called the penumbra.

You, as the little bug, continue walking. You enter regions where more and more of the sun's disk is blocked by the hand above. Eventually you progress from the penumbra to the so-called umbra, the dark central part of the shadow, the region in which the sun's disk is completely blocked by the hand above.

Keep going and you soon emerge into the penumbra on the other side. From there you eventually return to full sunlight.

Not all shadows have an umbra, a dark central part. Imagine yourself as a bug on the sidewalk again, but this time imagine the person whose hand is casting the shadow to be standing on a balcony, high above the sidewalk. From your bug's vantage point on the sidewalk, the hand appears smaller than the sun's disk, so you can never see the sun completely blocked by the hand. You are always illuminated by at least part of the sun's disk. The person whose hand is casting the shadow looks down at the sidewalk and sees only a penumbra, a fuzzy gray shadow of the hand.

Minnaert, Marcel. *The Nature of Light and Color in the Open Air.* New York: Dover Publications, 1954.

Brighter Colors from the Air?

When we look at a distant mountain, we see not only light reflected from the surface of the mountain but light added by the intervening air. The light added by the air is bluish, just like the blue of a clear sky. So distant mountains look blue.

The sun's light is a mixture of all the colors of the rainbow—it's white. But the portion of sunlight scattered sideways by air is bluish. It happens that very small particles like air molecules tend to scatter blue light sideways while allowing red light to pass straight through. So as a beam of sunlight passes through air, some of the blue is removed from the beam and sent out to the side. It is that blue light that we see when the sun shines down through the air between us and a distant mountain. The more air between us and the mountain, the more blue is added to what we see when we look at the mountain.

Now suppose we fly over this mountain in an airplane. If we are, say, 2 miles above the mountain, we look through much less air to see it than if we are on the ground, 50 miles from the mountain. Therefore, less blue is added to what we see; if the air is clean, the mountain is likely to look more vividly colored from the air than from the ground.

The book *The Nature of Light and Color in the Open Air* by Marcel Minnaert suggests that a landscape seen from an airplane at low altitude has more vivid colors than that same landscape seen from the ground. Professor Minnaert writes: "The haze hiding all colours as long as we were on firm ground, has practically disappeared altogether, and the hues are now displayed for the first time in their full warmth and saturation. This explains the charm of the scenery experienced by everyone who has had the opportunity of making a trip by air."

Minnaert, Marcel. *The Nature of Light and Color in the Open Air.* New York: Dover Publications, 1954.
Some of the complexity of atmospheric color is discussed by Jearl Walker in his "Amateur Scientist" column in the January 1989 *Scientific American.*

Find the Center of Your State

Once in a while we hear the name of a Midwestern town that is said to occupy the geographical center of the continental United States. What this statement usually means or implies is that if you go to that town, as many square miles of the continental U.S. will be north of you as south of you, and as many square miles of the continental U.S. will be east of you as west of you.

Where's the geographical center of your own state? Here's a way to get a good idea. Cut out a piece of cardboard in the shape of your state. Get the shape by tracing a good map. Now stick a pin perpendicularly through the cardboard somewhere near the edge. Tie a thread to this pin. Attach a small weight to the other end of the thread—a paper clip, for instance. Now hold the pin horizontally so the cardboard and the weighted thread hang straight down from the pin.

The so-called center of gravity of the vertically hanging cardboard—the point at which it will balance—is somewhere directly below the pin, somewhere along the line marked by the vertically hanging thread. So you want to draw a pencil line on the cardboard exactly where the thread is now. Hold the thread against the cardboard and draw a line exactly where the thread lies.

Now stick the pin through the cardboard in some other place near the edge, so that the thread crosses the line you have drawn. Again, let the cardboard and thread hang freely, then hold the thread against the cardboard and trace its position with the pencil.

The two lines you've drawn should intersect at the center of gravity, the point at which the cardboard will balance on the end of a pencil eraser. That point corresponds to the geographical center of the state. Now refer back to your map and see which town is closest to that point.

Gardner, Martin. *Entertaining Science Experiments with Everyday Objects*. New York: Dover Publications, 1981.
Goldstein-Jackson, Kevin. *Experiments with Everyday Objects*. Englewood Cliffs, N.J.: Prentice-Hall, 1978.

More Than One Way to Make a Frog

Most frogs in North America lay eggs in water. Then the eggs hatch into tadpoles, which have tails for swimming and gills to gather oxygen from the water. Eventually the tail and the gills disappear as the tadpole develops into an adult frog. But some frog species, especially in Central and South America, have a different life history: they skip the tadpole stage. In many tropical species, the eggs are laid in burrows in the ground, not in the water. The newly hatched frogs already look something like miniature adults. They never develop gills or even the circulatory system that would supply blood to gills. This so-called direct development, without a tadpole stage, seems to be well suited to tropical environments, where tadpoles swimming in open water would be in greater danger of being eaten than in colder climates like those in North America.

So different types of frogs have different ways of developing from embryos into adults. The difference in life histories is due not so much to a difference in basic body plan but to a difference in timing of development. For example, one type of tropical frog that skips the tadpole stage begins to develop legs very early— long before it hatches. In North American frogs, on the other hand, the development of legs is delayed until long after hatching. So tadpoles have no legs. But the end results—the legs of the adult frog—are basically the same in tropical frogs and in North American frogs. This is a case in which the schedule of development from egg to adult has been modified by evolution to suit different environments.

Raff, Rudolf A., and Thomas C. Kaufman. *Embryos, Genes, and Evolution*. New York: Macmillan, 1983.

96

Dappled Shade

As new leaves grow on the trees, the forest floor becomes dark in the middle of the day—except for small circular patches of sunlight here and there on the ground. Those patches of light are circular because they are images of the circular disk of the sun itself, projected on the ground by small openings between the leaves overhead. The principle of a pinhole camera is involved.

Since light travels in straight lines, a small hole can project an image on a flat surface. Each point in the projected image of the sun is formed by a ray of light coming through the opening in the leaves from one point on the disk of the real sun.

Although you can't usually tell, the images of the sun cast on the forest floor are upside down. Light from the north side of the sun passes through the opening in the leaves and ends up on the south side of the projected image; light from the south side of the sun ends up on the north side of the image. More than a thousand years ago, a Chinese philosopher, Shen Kua, explained this by pointing out that light rays going through a small hole are constrained like an oar in a rowlock: when the handle is down, the paddle is up, and vice versa.

Occasionally you may get a chance to verify that those little circles of sunlight really are upside-down images of the sun. If a cloud drifts across the face of the sun, moving, say, from west to east, then the shadow of that cloud in each little circle of light on the ground will move the opposite direction—from east to west.

The sun appears as a half-circular disk when it is either half risen or half set over the ocean or behind any other smooth, flat distant horizon. Suppose that, during such a sunrise or sunset, the sun's light shines through a tree onto a smooth wall. The patches of light on the wall will be not circles but half-circles, with the flat side up—upside-down images of the sun's half-disk.

Minnaert, Marcel. *The Nature of Light and Color in the Open Air.* New York: Dover Publications, 1954.

The Chinese analogy comes from J. H. Hammond, *The Camera Obscura: A Chronicle.* Bristol: Adam Hilger Ltd., 1981.

The First Elementary Particle

In the 1890s, physicists all over Europe were experimenting with electric currents flowing between two metal plates inside a sealed glass bulb with almost all the air pumped out.

In one variation on this scheme, electricity emanated from a metal plate connected to the negative terminal of a battery, passed through a metal tube connected to the positive terminal of the battery, and hit the other end of the glass bulb, where it made a glowing green spot. A TV picture tube is basically a fancy version of the same gadget. But in the 1890s people wondered: What was that beam of electricity in the glass bulb made of?

The English physicist Joseph John Thomson investigated the beam by carefully measuring how much it was deflected by static electricity and by a magnet. Thomson's method was something like watching someone throw ping-pong balls and golf balls in a high wind. Even from a distance, you can distinguish ping-pong balls from golf balls, because ping-pong balls, being light in weight, are deflected by wind much more than golf balls. Watch the deflection, and you can distinguish light balls from heavy ones.

By watching how much the mysterious beam in the glass bulb was deflected not by wind but by electric and magnetic forces, J. J. Thomson concluded, after some calculation, that the beam was made of particles almost 2,000 times lighter than the lightest atom. Today those particles are called electrons. All atoms, of every kind, contain electrons.

In 1897 J. J. Thomson concluded that he had found "matter in a new state, . . . in which the subdivision of matter is carried very much further than in the ordinary gaseous state: a state in which all matter . . . is of one and the same kind; this matter being the substance from which all the chemical elements are built up." Today J. J. Thomson is remembered for discovering the first elementary particle, the electron, in 1897.

Thomson, Joseph John. "Cathode Rays." 1897. Reprinted in *The World of the Atom*, ed. H. Boorse and L. Motz. New York: Basic Books, 1966.

Toulmin, Stephen E., and June Goodfield. *The Architecture of Matter*. New York: Harper and Row, 1962.

Pillbugs Live in Damp Places

Pillbugs, woodlice, and sowbugs live in damp places because they have gills, and gills won't function unless they are wet. Pillbugs, woodlice, and sowbugs are all members of a suborder—technically called the land isopods—within the class of crustaceans. Other familiar crustaceans include lobsters, crabs, shrimp, prawns, and crayfish. Almost all crustaceans live in water—either seawater or fresh water. Pillbugs are an exception. In other words, those pillbugs, woodlice, or sowbugs you see in the damp soil under rocks are land-dwelling relatives of lobsters, crabs, and crayfish, and they get most or all of their oxygen in the same way as those aquatic animals—through gills.

A gill is a special surface exposed to the environment on one side and to the animal's circulatory system on the other. The gill surface allows oxygen dissolved in water to pass from the environment into the circulatory system. That oxygen must be dissolved in water for the gill to work. Gills must be kept wet. Aquatic crustaceans always have water on their gills anyway. But land crustaceans such as pillbugs must make a special effort to keep their gills wet. So most pillbugs prefer damp places.

Pillbugs have gills on their legs, and they have water tubes on their undersides that replenish the water film on those gills. They get water from their food, but they can also drink liquid water if they encounter it. Pillbugs have gills just like their aquatic relatives the lobsters. Incidentally, we humans also use wet surfaces to transfer oxygen into our circulatory system. But our wet surfaces are protected deep inside our bodies, in our lungs.

Curtis, Helena. *Biology.* 4th ed. New York: Worth Publishers, 1983.
Grzimek's Animal Life Encyclopedia. New York: Van Nostrand Reinhold Company, 1984.

Sleet, Hail, and Snow

Here is a very quick lesson on the differences between sleet, hail, and snow. All three have one thing in common: they are various forms of frozen water. Sleet and hail have several similarities, but snow is very different from them.

Sleet is transparent, solid grains of ice that are smaller than two-tenths of an inch in diameter, and spherical or irregular in shape. Sleet is formed when raindrops or melted snowflakes fall from warm air through a lower layer of below-freezing air, where the raindrops freeze and the melted snowflakes refreeze.

In many respects hail is a lot like sleet, but larger. Hailstones range from the size of a pea to the size of an orange, and there have been some recorded even larger than that. On average, though, they are smaller than one inch in diameter. The way hail forms is a good bit different from the process by which sleet forms. Hailstones form in thunderclouds, and begin as frozen raindrops or snow pellets called "hail embryos." The embryos come in contact with super-cooled water droplets, that is, water which has remained unfrozen at below-freezing temperatures.

As the embryos move through the droplets, the water freezes to them, and a hailstone forms as this freezing water accumulates on its surface. Strong updrafts in the thundercloud keep the developing hailstone moving around the cloud until the stone becomes too heavy and falls to the ground. How large a hailstone becomes depends on how long it remains in the cloud.

Snow is tiny ice crystals that grow from water vapor in cold clouds. For the most part snow crystals form in clouds with below-freezing temperatures. Snow crystals always have six sides, and they come in two forms: platelike crystals, which are the familiar star-shaped snowflakes, and columnar crystals, which resemble six-sided needles of ice.

"Hail," "Sleet," and "Snow." In *New Britannica,* 15th ed. Chicago, 1991.
"Hail," "Sleet," and "Snow." In *The World Book Encyclopedia,* vols. 9 and 17. Chicago, 1994.

Radar

What comes to mind when someone mentions radar? Tracking down enemy missiles, navigating a plane or ship, a speed trap, a character in *M*A*S*H?* Well, radar is involved in all these things. It has been around as long as most of us can remember, and has been invested with almost magical powers, as with the character in *M*A*S*H* who could almost see into the future. But basically radar is straightforward and simple, and considerably more limited than the myths about it.

The word "radar" is an acronym for Radio Detecting and Ranging. It works pretty much like an echo we hear, but instead of sound waves it uses radio waves. You can illustrate for yourself how radar works by using the echo analogy. All you need is a stopwatch and a friend to make a sharp, loud noise, a handclap, for instance. Stand several hundred feet from a reflecting surface, such as a wall. Have your friend clap her hands, and at the same time you start the watch. When you hear the sound echo back, stop the watch. Now multiply the time on the watch by the speed of sound, which is 1,200 feet per second, and divide by two. The result tells you about how far you are from the reflecting surface.

Radar works the same way, except radio waves are transmitted and received instead of sound waves. A radio transmitter beams waves at a distant object, and the time it takes for the waves to be reflected back to the receiver tells how far away the object is—just as with the echo. It all takes place a lot faster, though, since radio waves travel at the speed of light—186,000 miles per second.

So radar can tell you how far you are from something, such as another airplane, but it cannot tell you *where* you are. There are devices which can do that, and one such system is called LO-RAN, which is the acronym for Long Range Navigation.

LORAN is similar to radar, but instead of using the echo principle, it beams a precisely timed signal from a transmitter to a receiver, and rather than just one transmitter there are three. The transmitters are land-based and spaced some distance apart so that their signals will be received by, say, a plane or a ship at different times. A computer calculates the difference in the time it takes the signals to reach the receiver on the plane or ship, and pinpoints its location.

To see how this works, let's put ourselves on a ship equipped with a special receiver and computer. We're sailing up the East Coast, and want to know where we are. You'll be the navigator. We'll use hypothetical LORAN transmitters in New York City, Trenton, New Jersey, and Boston to guide us. Our receiver gets the signals from the three stations and computes the distance we are from each of them. When we take our readings, we find we are 94 miles from New York City, 127 miles from Trenton, and 133 miles from Boston.

As navigator you take down the distances. Now, using New York, Trenton, and Boston as centers, you draw circles on your map representing those distances. When you have drawn all three circles, there will be one spot where they all intersect at the same point, and that is where you are—in this case, 27 miles off the coast of Long Island, New York. In actual use, the electronic navigation system draws the circles, so to speak, but the principle is the same.

Gutleben, Glenn. "High Tech on the High Seas." *Exploratorium Quarterly,* Spring 1991. *McGraw-Hill Encyclopedia of Science and Technology.* 6th ed. New York, 1982.

Blinking

On average we blink about 14,440 times a day. Since each blink takes about a quarter of a second, about an hour of our waking hours is spent with our eyes partly or completely closed. It has been only in recent years that scientists have really begun to understand blinking. Probably most of us think that the main purpose of blinking is to clean and lubricate our eyes, but it's not. We blink about 15 times a minute, but only one or two of those blinks are needed to keep the surfaces of our eyes rinsed and moistened. We also blink a few times a day because of dust or smoke in our eyes, or being startled. But for the most part blinking is an indication of what's going on in our brains.

Generally speaking, the harder we concentrate, the less we blink. Car drivers blink less in city traffic than on the open road; they probably won't blink at all while passing a truck at high speed.

Further insights into blinking have been gained from studying subjects who were reading. They blinked most often at a punctuation mark, or the end of a page. It was sort of like a signal that the brain was taking a break, a mental punctuation mark, as it were.

The concentration connection wasn't evident just in visual activities. Someone who is anxious tends to blink more than one who is calm. A steady gaze is associated with confidence and self-assuredness; TV anchors are instructed not to blink much, so as to give the impression of being in control.

If blinking is a sort of mental punctuation, this might explain why people solving mental arithmetic blink at different rates. Some do not blink until they have mentally solved the problem, while others blink with each step in the process of solving it. If you want to test this, watch people on the sly so they don't become conscious of blinking, and although you won't be able to see *what* they are thinking, you might get a glimpse into *how* they are thinking.

Ingram, Jay. *The Science of Everyday Life.* New York: Penguin Books, 1989.
Stern, John A. "What's behind Blinking." *The Sciences,* November–December 1988.

Coriolis Effect

If you were to try to fly a plane in a *straight line* from Chicago to Atlanta, you would never get there because you would fly to the right of Atlanta. That doesn't seem logical, but it's true. This sideways drifting is called the Coriolis effect, and it's caused by the rotation of the earth. Although those of us who are earth-bound don't really have to be concerned about it, airplane pilots have to make adjustments.

To understand how the Coriolis drift affects planes, you need to be aware that if you're standing on the equator, the earth's rotation is carrying you eastward at about 1,000 miles per hour. As you move away from the equator, your speed decreases. For example, Boston is traveling at about 700 miles per hour.

Now back to our attempt to fly from Chicago to Atlanta in a straight line. As our plane sits in Chicago, it is spinning with the earth, of course, and when it takes off it continues to do so. However, our destination, Atlanta, being closer to the equator, is moving *faster* to the east. So if we do not correct for the faster eastward movement, we will end up to the right of Atlanta.

(Incidentally, because Atlanta is moving eastward faster than Chicago, if you try to fly northward in a straight line from Atlanta to Chicago you will still end up to the right of your destination.)

This sideways drifting does not occur just with airplanes, it applies to everything that moves on earth. Were it not for the friction of the tires on the road, a car traveling down a highway at 60 miles per hour would be carried off the road to the right at the rate of about 15 feet per mile.

This Moment of Science has dealt only with how the Coriolis effect applies to navigation, but, among other things, it affects weather and ocean currents as well. But as the saying goes, that's another story.

Ingram, Jay. *The Science of Everyday Life*. New York: Penguin Books, 1989.
McDonald, James E. "The Coriolis Effect." *Scientific American*, May 1952.

Illusion in a Coffee Cup

Things are not always as they seem, and this little demonstration will prove it. All you need is a cup of black coffee and an overhead light. A single incandescent bulb works best. Position the coffee cup so that the light is reflected in it. Look into the cup from a distance that allows the reflected light to just about fill the cup.

Now move your head quickly and smoothly toward the cup. The light appears to get smaller and farther away! The change is dramatic. The light seems to shrink to a quarter or a fifth of its original size, and to move away 10 times more than you moved.

This is obviously an illusion, since you know the light hasn't changed size or moved. However, as you move closer to the cup, the cup fills more of your field of vision than the light, so the cup seems larger, and the light smaller.

In trying to interpret the information being sent to it, your brain correlates smaller with farther away, and you perceive that the light has moved. Your brain cannot make an adjustment either; you can do this over and over again and the result will be the same.

Ingram, Jay. *The Science of Everyday Life*. New York: Penguin Books, 1989.
Senders, John. "The Coffee Cup Illusion." *American Journal of Psychology* 79 (1966).

Knuckle Cracking

How many of us have derived impish delight from annoying our mothers by cracking our knuckles? It's not something I did a lot, but I do recall my mother trying to discourage me by telling me it would cause my joints to swell. But then again, she also told me my hair would fall out if I wore my hat indoors.

While the annoyance factor related to knuckle cracking is indisputable, the actual cause of the noise was a puzzle until the early '70s. The most common explanations for the noises were bones snapping against each other, or tendons moving over bony projections in the joints. It kind of gives you goose bumps just thinking about it, doesn't it? Well, this Moment of Science is going to tell you what really makes the sound of cracking knuckles.

The sounds come from tiny explosions. Now, if the thought of your joints exploding doesn't make you feel any better, let me clarify. The sounds are not your joints exploding, but the popping of gas bubbles which are in the lubricating fluid that fills the joint.

In order to crack your knuckles you stretch the joints, causing an increase in the space between the finger bones. This increase in space reduces the pressure on the fluid that lubricates the joints. This reduction in pressure causes tiny gas bubbles to form in the fluid. As the pressure continues to go down, the bubbles burst, making the popping noise you hear.

After the bubbles burst, the gas does not escape the area, but is reabsorbed into the fluid as the joint returns to its original position. It takes about 15 minutes for the fluid to be reabsorbed, and that's why once you crack your knuckles, you can't do it again for a while.

So, even though the evidence indicates that you will not suffer disfigurement from cracking your knuckles, for the sake of mothers past, present, and future, if you feel the need to pop your knuckles, don't do it around your mother—or anyone else's.

Time, August 16, 1971.

Walker, Jearl. *The Flying Circus of Physics with Answers.* New York: John Wiley and Sons, 1977.

You're Not Holding Your Tongue Right

How many times have you noticed someone's tongue peeking out from between the teeth or lips when he or she was concentrating hard? You know, the classic tongue-in-the-corner-of-the-mouth look. Scientists have given this form of expression the unimaginative name of "tongue-showing," and it is a common and powerful form of non-verbal expression.

Tongue-showing is an unconscious act, so it does not include sticking your tongue out at someone. Tongue-showing comes in many forms, such as sticking it slightly between your teeth or lips, curling it inside your mouth and holding it there, etc. Whatever form it takes, it conveys one message: "Leave me alone." The fascinating thing about this is that psychologists have found that neither the tongue-shower nor the tongue-showee is aware that this message is being sent or received.

One interesting experiment which demonstrated that the "leave me alone" message was being sent involved 50 students who were given a test with one page missing from the test booklet. When they discovered the missing page, they approached the instructor to ask him about it. The teacher was ostensibly absorbed in his work, and when the students approached, he did not acknowledge them right away, but did show his tongue to half of them but not the other half.

A hidden observer timed how long it took each student to make a move to get the instructor's attention. The researchers found that the students to whom the tongue was shown took an average of *two and one-half times longer* to interrupt the teacher. Even more intriguing is that not one student had realized that the teacher's tongue had been shown, although each one sensed that the teacher did not want to be interrupted. In contrast, those to whom the tongue was not shown felt no reluctance at interrupting the teacher.

So, next time you're concentrating hard on a task and you get interrupted, maybe you aren't holding your tongue right!

Ingram, Jay. *The Science of Everyday Life.* New York: Penguin Books, 1989.

Smith, John W.; Julia Chase; and Anna K. Leiblich. "Tongue-Showing: A Facial Display of Humans and Other Primate Species." *Semiotica* 11, no. 3 (1974).

Why Are Clouds White?

We've all noticed the color of clouds, which ranges from brilliant white to almost black. Before we consider why clouds have such a range of color, we need to think about the nature of light. When all visible wavelengths of light reach our eyes, we see white. When only certain wavelengths reach us, we see the corresponding colors. When no visible wavelengths strike our eyes, we see black. For most of the day the sun radiates all visible wavelengths of light, and it appears white.

When the sunlight reaches a cloud, some of it is reflected away from the earth. The light which passes through the cloud gets scattered by tiny cloud droplets in all directions more or less equally. This scattering is something like a pinball being bounced off the pins and bumpers; when the light from the sun hits small particles in the atmosphere, it's knocked around. Since the sunlight is scattered fairly evenly by the cloud, allowing all wavelengths to reach us, the cloud looks white.

As a cloud grows larger and taller, more light is reflected from it, and less light is able to penetrate it. When a cloud gets a little over 3,000 feet thick, very little light is able to pass through it, and the base of it looks dark. At the same time the water droplets at the base of the cloud get larger, and as they do they absorb more light than they reflect. Now even less light gets through the cloud, and it appears almost black. These large, light-absorbing droplets often get heavy enough to fall from the cloud as rain. Just from casual observation we know that these dark, ominous clouds often bring rain. Now we know why they look so dark.

Ahrens, C. Donald. *Meteorology Today: An Introduction to the Weather, Climate, and the Environment.* St. Paul: West Publishing Company, 1991.

Oak Trees Outwit Mice

In a mythical Virginia newspaper we might call the *Acorn Times,* the banner headline reads "Oak Trees Outwit Mice." In the Appalachian Mountains of Virginia, it seems that the oak trees synchronize their production of acorns in a way that lets them stay one step ahead of the mice. In years when the white-footed mouse population is low, acorn production is high. Then in years when there are a lot of mice, the oak trees produce very few acorns. It looks as if the trees are pulling a fast one on the mice to keep the rodents from eating all their seeds.

It works like this: When the mouse population is low, the trees produce lots of acorns, many times more than the mice could possibly eat. With the help of this bountiful food supply, there is a mouse population explosion. Then for the next three or four years the trees produce very few acorns, if any. This lack of food causes a marked decline in the mouse population. The drop in the number of mice is followed by an increase in acorn production. And so the cycle goes. This strategy, if that is what it is, results in the survival of more seeds to germinate.

It is not clear how the trees synchronize. It could be an as yet unknown chemical which passes from tree to tree triggering acorn production, or a group response to climate fluctuations. It's more likely that the process evolved by chance: Trees with more acorns in one year than the next produced more offspring over time than those with smaller but consistent crops each year which fell prey to predators. It could just be coincidence, but it sure is to the oak trees' advantage.

"Confounding the Rodents." *Discover,* November 1992.

Let Me Sleep on It

Research has given new meaning to the phrase "Let me sleep on it." Students have sometimes found that after a good night's sleep they are able to remember very well material they studied the night before. Although this often is the case, you can't count on it. Some scientists think that sleep does indeed have an effect on memory, and to try to get a handle on these effects they have done experiments involving different stages of sleep.

Sleep is divided into five stages, including the one called the rapid eye movement, or REM, stage. In the course of a night's sleep, you go through the various stages several times, but it is only during REM sleep that dreaming occurs, and it is this stage which has the most profound effect on memory. You can recognize when someone is in REM sleep, because you can see their eyeballs moving underneath their closed eyelids.

In one study subjects were trained to recognize several patterns of lines a few hours before they went to bed. The experiment found that the volunteers could perform the tasks faster the next morning if they had had a good night's sleep. If they were awakened each time they entered REM sleep, they did no better than the night before. If instead they were awakened during non-REM sleep, they performed just as well as when they slept undisturbed.

The researchers concluded that REM sleep, and perhaps even dreaming itself, helps cement things in memory. The catch is that your REM sleep must not be disturbed, and controlling that is not as simple as hanging a "do not disturb" sign on your door. You can be awakened from REM sleep by dreams as well as a knock at the door.

At any rate, it could well be that if you want to increase your chances of remembering something, study it before you go to bed.

Ezzell, Carol. "For a Good Memory, Dream On." *Science News*, November 14, 1992.

Dimples in Golfballs

You're out on the golf course one pleasant afternoon. Your ball is set on the tee. You lean over the ball. You grip the club just right. Your arms are straight. Your stance is perfect. Whoosh! You swing, and the ball takes off toward the green, sailing in a beautiful arc. Your impeccable technique certainly has a lot to do with the success of that drive, but you got a major assist from the little dimples on the golf ball. Combined with the proper spin, the dimples help keep the ball in the air longer, and here's how.

Your picture-perfect swing puts backspin on the ball. The dimples trap a layer of air next to the ball, and this layer spins with the ball. The air being dragged across the top of the spinning ball moves in the same direction as the air that's rushing past. As the air spinning with the ball comes around the bottom, it is moving in the opposite direction from the air on top, and therefore against the onrushing air. Consequently it's slower than the air on top. Once again we encounter Bernoulli's principle: A slow-moving air stream has higher pressure than a fast-moving air stream. So the higher pressure on the bottom of the ball is going to hold the ball up longer. The effect of the dimples is so significant that a drive of 200 yards hit with a dimpled golf ball would be shortened with a non-dimpled ball to about 100 yards.

Incidentally, with top spin, which is the reverse of backspin, the principle is the same, but the effect is just the opposite—and disastrous for the golfer: with top spin the high pressure is on the top of the ball, so after a short flight the ball takes a nosedive into the ground.

Flatow, Ira. *Rainbows, Curve Balls and Other Wonders of the Natural World Explained.* New York: William Morrow and Company, 1988.

Where's the Plane?

How many times have you heard a jet plane going over, looked up to see it, but not been able to find it even though you were looking toward where the sound was coming from? Sometime during your life you might have been told that the plane wasn't with the sound because it was traveling faster than the speed of sound. It might have been, but it didn't have to be going that fast in order to appear to be separated from the sound.

The reason the jet appeared to be apart from the noise it was making was simply that sound travels a lot slower than light—about a million times slower. For quick review, at sea level sound travels about 750 miles per hour, while light travels at 186,000 miles per *second*.

Commercial jets normally fly at about 30,000 feet. From that height it takes sound about 30 seconds to reach earth. Light gets here in only about four one-hundred-thousandths of a second, or for practical purposes, instantaneously. A plane traveling at 600 miles an hour goes 5 miles in the 30 seconds it takes for the sound to reach you. By the time the sound from the plane reaches your ears, the plane is 5 miles from where that sound originated. So when you look toward the sound, the plane is not there anymore.

Vergara, William C. *Science in Everyday Life.* New York: Harper and Row, 1980.

Tiny Bubbles

In soft drinks, champagne, or other carbonated drinks, we've all seen the little rows of bubbles streaming from the sides of the glass. The sequence of events leading to the streams of bubbles starts with the glass itself. The sides of the glass look smooth, but actually there are tiny nicks and imperfections in the surface. As you pour the drink, a tiny bubble of air is trapped in a nick. Molecules of air attract molecules of carbon dioxide, commonly known as CO_2 (the gas which makes the drink fizzy). The air molecules sort of say "come hold hands with me," and the CO_2 can't resist the invitation.

However, soon so many CO_2 molecules gather in the nick that they form a bubble which is too buoyant to be held there, and it floats to the top. As in life, there is always somebody waiting to take its place, so more bubbles form in the same way, resulting in a continuous stream coming from the nick in the side of the glass. Even the smoothest glasses are covered with tiny nicks, and this explains why there are lots of streams of tiny bubbles.

Flatow, Ira. *Rainbows, Curve Balls and Other Wonders of the Natural World Explained.* New York: William Morrow and Company, 1988.

Night Vision

When we are in a fairly dark room, or outside at night away from lights, we can still see, but we can't see the colors of things very well. Why is that? To find out, let's take a "look" at night vision.

There are two kinds of light-sensitive organs located in the backs of our eyes: rod-shaped and cone-shaped. Both rods and cones are sensitive to light. The difference between them is that the rods allow us to see in very dim light but don't permit detection of color, while the cones let us see color, but they don't work well in dim light.

When it gets dark, the cones lose their ability to respond to light. The rods continue to respond to available light, but since they cannot see color, so to speak, everything appears to be various shades of black and white and gray.

A curious thing is that in dim light you can see more clearly out of the side of your eye, because the light-sensitive rods are more highly concentrated off to the side in the back of your eye. So next time you're out on a clear night, notice how little color you can see, and how you can see objects like dim stars better out of the corner of your eye than from the center.

Flatow, Ira. *Rainbows, Curve Balls and Other Wonders of the Natural World Explained.* New York: William Morrow and Company, 1988.

112 *Alcohol as an Antiseptic*

Alcohol is such a good germ killer because it has the ability to coagulate a germ's protein. The coagulation of the protein is somewhat like the coagulation of your blood on a cut. You can see how if all your blood became hard like that you would not be a very effective living specimen. Alcohol has the same effect on germ cells, and the cells die, too.

Oddly enough, a solution of 70 percent alcohol, that is, rubbing alcohol, is a more effective antiseptic than 100 percent alcohol—another case where more is not better. Pure alcohol doesn't work as well because when it contacts a germ cell it coagulates the cell's outer wall immediately. This forms a protective shell around the cell, which keeps the alcohol from getting through to the protein inside. So even though the bacterium becomes ineffective, it's not dead, and under the right circumstances it can function again.

Rubbing alcohol is not as concentrated as pure alcohol, so even though it coagulates protein just as well, it acts more slowly. This slower action gives the alcohol time to soak into the complete bacterial cell before coagulation takes place. Consequently all of the cell's protein is coagulated, and the bacterium dies.

So when you want to disinfect something, reach for the

rubbing alcohol, because by taking just a little more time to work, it does the job better.

Vergara, William C. *Science in Everyday Life*. New York: Harper and Row, 1980.

What Our Pupils Tell Us

The pupils in our eyes do more than control the amount of light entering them. The size of our pupils can give clues to our interest, emotions, attitudes, and thought processes.

If you've seen a magician tell which card someone picked from a deck, you've probably been amazed. Well, the pupils often open up when the magician picks the right card, so one of the tricks he or she can use is to look at the person's eyes.

The pupils tend to close in response to unpleasantness, and open in response to pleasure. For example, for those who find snakes loathsome, a picture of one will cause their pupils to close. For someone who likes snakes, the same picture will cause the pupils to open.

The same thing happens to people with strong political preferences. A conservative's pupils will close when shown a picture of a liberal. The liberal has the same reaction when shown a picture of a conservative. Their pupils open when looking at a picture of someone of their own persuasion.

When you are concentrating hard on something like a math problem, your pupils will remain open until the problem is solved.

What these and other studies have shown is that our pupils are very sensitive to our emotions and thought processes, often revealing things which we choose not to verbalize.

Vergara, William C. *Science in Everyday Life*. New York: Harper and Row, 1980.

Lightning Fertilizer

We don't usually think of lightning as having anything to do with nutrition, but it does. Our bodies need protein, and proteins contain nitrogen. The air we breathe has plenty of nitrogen to satisfy our needs, but that nitrogen is not available to us directly from the air. The only way we can get nitrogen is from the plants we eat, or from the animals we eat that eat the plants.

But there's a problem. A nitrogen molecule in the air consists of two atoms which are held together very tightly. In order for us to absorb nitrogen, the two atoms must be separated. But the two atoms are held together so tightly that our body chemistry does not have enough energy to process them.

This is where lightning comes in. Obviously we don't have to be struck by lightning in order to satisfy our need for nitrogen! However, in a thunderstorm there is enough electrical energy in lightning to separate the nitrogen atoms in the air. Once the atoms are separated, they can fall to earth with rainwater and combine with minerals in the soil to form nitrates, a type of fertilizer.

The nitrogen-containing nitrates in the soil are absorbed by the plants, and when we eat the plants or the animals that eat the plants, we get the nitrogen in a form which our bodies can use. So, in addition to providing a spectacular light show, and scaring us to death, lightning also helps fertilize the soil.

Vergara, William C. *Science in Everyday Life.* New York: Harper and Row, 1980.

Seeing Stars

At some point in your life you might have bumped your head so hard that you saw stars. Little lights didn't actually flash at the moment of impact, but your brain was tricked into thinking they did.

To understand how the brain gets fooled, it helps to know how we normally see. In the back of the eye there are about a hundred million nerve cells. When light strikes these nerves, they react by sending impulses to the brain. So vision really takes place in the brain as the result of nerve impulses from the eye interacting with signals produced in the brain.

A sharp blow to the head can cause the nerves in the eye to fire off messages to the brain, just as they do in response to light. Since the signals are coming from the eye, the brain interprets them as quick flashes of light, and that's what we see. So the stars we see when bumping our heads are an illusion caused by our brains' being confused by the signals coming from the nerves in our eyes.

Vergara, William C. *Science in Everyday Life*. New York: Harper and Row, 1980.

Where Do All Those Calories Go?

While part of the answer to the title question is "to our hips, thighs, and midsections," that's not where most of them go. In an average day we burn more than 2,000 calories. Surprisingly, most of them are *not* used up in physical activities such as walking or exercising. Most of the calories we take in are used to maintain our body temperature at a fairly constant level. So we and other mammals need frequent meals in order to keep our furnaces stoked, so to speak.

Our temperature varies only about one degree over the course of a day, so why is it so important to keep our temperature so consistent? It's partly because of the effect that temperature has on chemical reactions in our bodies. Although the rate of all chemical reactions speeds up as the temperature rises, the reaction rates for different chemicals do not always increase equally. These unequal increases in reaction rates could result in harmful chemicals building up in our bodies. Maintaining a consistent temperature has allowed the evolution of precise coordinations of different chemical reactions in our bodies.

You're probably aware that internal body temperatures that are too cool or too warm can be harmful or even fatal. Our internal systems have evolved to function in a very narrow temperature range, and if that range is exceeded there can be malfunctions. For example, if you get severely overheated you can suffer from heat stroke, a potentially fatal condition if you are not cooled off quickly.

So the calories from the "three square meals" we are advised to have each day provide a regular source of fuel for keeping our temperature constant.

Kalat, James W. *Biological Psychology*. 4th ed. Belmont, Calif.: Wadsworth Publishing Company, 1992.

Diamonds

You walk into a fancy party. What is the oldest thing there? No, not your in-laws, or even your grandparents. It will be a diamond someone is wearing. More on the age of diamonds later, but first some more amazing mysteries and facts about diamonds.

It's not completely clear how natural diamonds are formed, and although it is known that they are made from carbon, scientists are not sure how carbon gets to the extreme depths at which diamonds are made.

Diamonds are formed very deep in the earth. The optimum depth for their formation is about 120 miles beneath the surface, in the molten mantle. The temperature and pressure necessary for diamonds to crystallize are mind-boggling: the temperature must be over 2,000 degrees Fahrenheit, and the pressure must be at least 690,000 pounds per square inch. To put that pressure in perspective, a 150-pound person exerts only about 3 pounds per square inch. We would never know about diamonds were it not for volcanic activity, for that's what delivers diamonds from deep inside the earth to where we can get to them.

Theoretically, diamonds can remain diamonds only at high temperature and pressure. In theory, at atmospheric pressure and lower temperature, chemical changes are liable to take place that change diamond into graphite, similar to the stuff pencil leads are made of. However, it has been calculated that even if this change were to take place, it would take more than 10 billion years to happen.

Now back to the diamond's age. Scientists think that diamonds may have been forming throughout earth's history. Many have been found that are 3.3 billion years old. And the young ones are a mere 1 billion years old.

Kirkley, M. B.; J. J. Gurney; and A. A. Levinson. "Age, Origin and Emplacement of Diamonds: A Review of Scientific Advances in the Last Decade." *CIM Bulletin,* January 1992.

Legrand, Jacques. *Diamonds Myth, Magic, and Reality.* New York: Crown Publishers, 1980.

Wilson, A. N. *Diamonds from Birth to Eternity.* Santa Monica, Calif.: Gemological Institute of America, 1982.

As the Vine Twines

A vine twined around a tree limb or a trellis is a familiar sight, but did you ever wonder why and how it gets that way? The purpose of the twining is to anchor the vine. In some cases the vines themselves do the twining, while in others the vines have small appendages called tendrils that coil around twigs or trellises.

How does the vine know to twine, and in what direction? The fact is, the vine doesn't know anything; its coiling is a blind reaction, so to speak, caused by chemical changes inside it. When the growing tip of the vine touches an obstacle, such as a twig, this stimulates the cells of the vine on the side opposite the twig to grow faster than those next to the twig. As the side of the vine opposite the twig gets longer, and the side touching the twig grows very little, the vine is pushed around the twig.

Most vines are not particular about which way they twine. If the outside of an already twining vine's tip touches an obstacle, the vine will change direction.

For This You Need a Doctor?

Chicken soup is a time-honored treatment for fevers and coughs, recommended since ancient times by physicians and grandmothers. At least one modern scientist daring to investigate the validity of this ancient advice has found it to be correct.

Stephen Rennard at the University of Nebraska Medical Center wanted to see if there was a scientific basis for the chicken soup remedy. He knew that when the body is invaded by a virus or harmful bacteria, it sends certain white blood cells to release enzymes to help fight the infection. Unfortunately the enzymes that fight the infection also irritate our tissue, and give us the sore throats that so often come with the flu.

Rennard devised an experiment in which he could observe the movement of white blood cells toward bacteria, similar to the movement that takes place in the human body. He hoped to test what effect, if any, chicken soup had on this movement.

Using a recipe from his wife's grandmother, he added the various ingredients of the soup in stages to a container that held white blood cells and bacteria. Plain water had no effect on the movement of the white cells toward the bacteria, but when he added the vegetables, the cells moved distinctly slower. Unfortunately, the vegetable broth also killed some of the body's white cells.

However, when he added chicken to the vegetable soup recipe, no harm was done to the cells. Evidently the chicken counteracted the toxic effects of the vegetables. The cells' movement was still slowed, so Rennard assumed that in a human body the slowing down may reduce the number of enzymes at the site of infection, and probably reduce the inflammation and some of the discomfort. Interestingly, the slowed movement did not seem to affect the cells' infection-fighting abilities. Also, this bit of research showed that although a remedy might be traditional, that doesn't mean there isn't a scientific basis for it.

Discover, November 1993.

Magic Numbers

Here's a number puzzle that's bound to make your friends think you are either a mind reader or a magician. Ask your friends to write down any two different numbers from 1 through 9 without letting you see them. Now tell them to reverse the two numbers. They now have two, two-digit numbers. Tell them to subtract the smaller number from the larger one.

Now they should take the number that resulted from the subtraction, reverse the digits, and add that number to the one they got when they subtracted. When they are finished you can tell them the answer is 99. They can do this with any combination of numbers with two different digits from 1 through 9, and you will always be able to tell them the answer, because it will always be 99.

Any time this five-step process is followed with two-digit numbers from 1 to 9, the result will be 99. For example, suppose you choose 8 and 6 as your two digits. Eighty-six reversed is 68; 86 minus 68 is 18; 18 reversed is 81; and 81 plus 18 is 99.

Incidentally, a practical application of this phenomenon is that if your checkbook doesn't balance, and the difference between your balance and the bank's is evenly divisible by 9, there are probably two transposed numbers somewhere.

Note: This same procedure can be followed with three-digit numbers; the answer then is 1,089.

Where Are the Poles?

Here's what seems like an easy test of your knowledge of geography. Stand facing west, and simultaneously point to the north and south poles with your right and left arms. Now, are your arms pointing straight out from your body in opposite directions? If they are, they are not pointing toward the poles, but to outer space. It's the roundness of earth that causes your pointing straight out from your body to the poles to be wrong. In order to point at the poles, your arms must point not only northward and southward, but downward.

To see this clearly, draw a circle on a piece of paper; the circle represents the earth. Make marks at the top and bottom of the circle to indicate the north and south poles. Draw a stick-figure person without arms on the circumference of the circle anywhere but at the poles. Now draw the arms pointing straight out from the body to the right and left, and you can easily see that they are not pointing at the poles, and that to point to the poles they need to be angled downward.

If you draw the arm lines on your stick figure so that they point to the poles, you'll see that a 90-degree angle is formed where the arm lines meet the body. This is the way it is in real life, too, and there's a principle of geometry that explains how this works. Applied to this situation, it basically says that if you could point directly at the north and south poles, and draw imaginary lines from them that come up your extended arms and meet at about your neck, the lines would form a 90-degree angle.

As a matter of fact, no matter where on earth you are, your arms will form a right angle when you point to the poles—except for two places. Do you know where those two places are?

Evans, Barry. *Everyday Wonders: Encounters with the Astonishing World around Us.* Chicago: Contemporary Books, 1993.

Dark Water Spots

When we splash water on our clothes or get caught in the rain, the places where the water hits appear darker than the rest of the cloth. Does the cloth really change color when it gets wet? No, it doesn't, but something does happen to the white light striking the cloth that makes it seem as if there is a color change.

White light, such as sunlight, is made up of a mixture of light of all colors. So when it lands on a pair of blue jeans, for instance, the jeans look blue because when white light strikes the blue threads, mainly blue light is reflected back to our eyes, while most of the other colors are absorbed by the cloth.

When a spot on the jeans gets wet, that area is coated with a film of water, and water fills spaces around the threads. Light striking the wet spot is bent down among the fibers. There it may reflect off the surface of the water, and bounce off the threads several times before it returns to our eyes.

With each bounce more light is absorbed by the cloth, and more non-blue light is absorbed than blue. Eventually some of the light is reflected back to our eyes, and since more of the non-blue light has been absorbed by the wet cloth, what we see looks bluer than the dry material.

The dry cloth looks lighter because there's no water to bend the light down between the fibers where more of it can be absorbed. So even though there is still more blue light reflected, more of all the colors is reflected to our eyes as well. Since all colors combined make white, it's sort of like mixing white with blue to make a lighter blue.

Spotting Satellites

This is a fun activity that you can do during the first two hours of darkness from May through August.

There are thousands of satellites and other pieces of large space junk orbiting the earth. A few hundred of them are visible with the naked eye, and a few thousand with binoculars. You can tell a lot about a satellite from ground observation, but first you need to determine if what you're seeing is a satellite. Any dot of light moving across the sky that's not a plane is almost certainly a satellite. Look for points of light that move from west to east or from north to south or vice versa, because satellites always move in those directions.

When you spot a satellite, there are several things you can tell about it, mainly by judging its speed. If it takes about three minutes for the satellite to cross the sky, it is probably a military spy satellite in a low orbit—about 120 to 180 miles high. If it is moving faster than that, it is probably no longer operational, and is close to being pulled back into earth's atmosphere, where it will burn up.

A slower-moving satellite might be a weather satellite in a higher orbit, especially if it moves from north to south, or vice versa, in what is called a polar orbit. And again, a faster-moving one in a polar orbit might be a spy satellite. Polar orbits are preferred for weather and military observations because the satellite can scan the whole earth in one day.

Incidentally, the satellites that backyard dishes are pointed at can't be seen from earth because they are 22,300 miles out in space.

Ahrens, C. Donald. *Meteorology Today: An Introduction to the Weather, Climate, and the Environment.* St. Paul: West Publishing Company, 1991.
Berman, Bob. "Satellite Season." *Discover,* May 1991.

Two-Point Threshold

Here's a fun experiment that tells you something about your nervous system. You can do it on yourself, but it works best if you do it on someone else, and vice versa. All you need is two pointed objects, such as pencils.

Have your friend close her eyes, and tell her you're going to touch the inside of her forearm with the two pencil points simultaneously about eight inches apart. Then you're going to lift the points and bring them down again and again, each time moving the points closer together. She's to tell you when you're touching her with only one pencil. It's surprising that when she *thinks* she's being touched by only one point, *both* are still touching her arm, and they are one to two inches apart!

Now do the same thing on the pad at the end of her index finger, but start with the points about an inch apart. This time when she thinks she feels only one point, the two will be about an eighth of an inch apart.

Why does she feel only one point when she's being touched by two? And why are the points as much as two inches apart on the forearm when one point is felt, but only an eighth of an inch apart on the fingertip? It's because some areas of the body, such as the fingertips, have more nerves going to them. And the areas of the brain which receive information from these sensitive areas of the body have a greater density of nerves. So since more nerves are present to detect sensations, these areas are more discriminating.

122 This is an interesting experiment, but there is a useful side to the information. This psychological phenomenon is known as the two-point threshold, and it can be used to test for nerve damage. Also, Braille dots were designed so that they are farther apart than the two-point threshold.

Geldard, Frank A. *Fundamentals of Psychology.* New York: John Wiley and Sons, 1962.
Schiffman, Harvey R. *Sensation and Perception: An Integrated Approach.* 2nd ed. New York: John Wiley and Sons, 1982.

Some Like It Hot

Most of us have jumped into a swimming pool and felt the shock of the cold water, only to have it feel just fine after a minute or so. Or we've stepped into a nice warm shower and after a minute reached over and turned up the heat a little because it was not feeling warm enough. Those who like hot showers might turn up the heat a couple of times before it suits them. This ability of the body to adjust to temperatures is called thermal adaptation. When you adapt to a temperature, it means it doesn't feel cold or hot, but neutral.

A simple experiment can clearly demonstrate thermal adaptation. Get three bowls large enough to put your hands in. Put cold water in one; you might add a few ice cubes to make the water cold. In the second put water that is hot, but not too hot to put your hands in. And in the third bowl put water that is warm, about 90 degrees.

Put one hand in the bowl with the cold water and the other in the hot water for about a minute. Now put both hands in the bowl of warm water. The warm water will feel very cool to the hand that originally was in the hot water, and warm to the hand that was in the cold water.

Fortunately thermal adaptation has its limits, because otherwise we might get burned or frozen if at some point the warning sensation of extreme heat or cold didn't override adaptation. Scientists do not completely understand the process of thermal adaptation, but they've known about it for a long time. The first report of the experiment with the three bowls of water was given by the philosopher John Locke in 1690.

Geldard, Frank A. *Fundamentals of Psychology.* New York: John Wiley and Sons, 1962.
Schiffman, Harvey R. *Sensation and Perception: An Integrated Approach.* 2nd ed. New York: John Wiley and Sons, 1982.

When You Eat an Egg, Are You Eating a Baby Chick?

Don Hirose of Honolulu, Hawaii, and a friend had a friendly argument. Don's friend was sure that when you eat an egg you're eating a baby chick, but Don didn't think so. They made a bet and came to *A Moment of Science* to have it settled.

Before we tell you who has to pay up, let's examine the two situations we're dealing with. The first, and less common, scenario involves eggs that are bought from small farmers—so-called free-range eggs.

These often are fertilized eggs, and can develop into baby chicks. But usually the development process is halted before this happens. When the egg first forms, it's only one cell, and is fertilized as it moves down the oviduct to be laid. During the first 24 hours after fertilization, the single egg cell divides a few times, forming a little mass of cells. At this point it's technically an embryo (though it doesn't look like a baby chick), but the cells still have not separated into the ones that make eyes, feet, feathers, etc.

After the egg is laid, the embryo stays in a kind of suspended animation until the hen sits on it to incubate it. If the egg is not incubated within a few weeks, the embryo will die. This is how things work with a fertilized egg, the kind one might get directly from a small farmer.

The second scenario involves the eggs we buy at the local supermarket, which come from what are called "egg factories." The egg factories rely on a peculiarity of hens: they lay eggs whether or not they're fertilized. The egg factories do not have roosters in residence to fertilize the eggs, and these eggs will not develop into baby chicks.

So the eggs that most people eat do not have embryos, and even the egg cells in the "free-range" eggs probably have not developed enough to be at the stage where one would be eating a baby chick. Therefore, Mr. Hirose wins the bet, and maybe he'll want to buy an omelet with his winnings.

Alcoholism

Young men often brag about how they can "hold their liquor." In fact, many young men do have a high tolerance for alcohol. Unfortunately, this might be a bad omen.

Some young men can drink as many as three to five alcoholic drinks with few, if any, intoxicating effects. However, research by Dr. Marc Schuckit of the VA Hospital and University of California, San Diego Medical School indicates that this trait increases the chances that a man will become an alcoholic by age 30. There is an even greater chance if the man's father was an alcoholic, but the chances are also enhanced for men with non-alcoholic fathers, although to a lesser degree.

The primary factor, though, is a low sensitivity to moderate amounts of alcohol. This means that the man has to drink more to feel intoxicated, and his alcohol tolerance might lack the warning signs that tell him to stop drinking. He might feel little or no effect from three to five drinks, but then become drunk rapidly after reaching a threshold level of imbibing.

Even if a man does not set out to get drunk, the fact that he needs to drink more and more to feel even moderate effects can create a problem. The increasingly greater intake of alcohol can lead to physical and psychological dependence on the drug.

The research does not indicate that low sensitivity to alcohol is a specific cause of alcoholism. However, it does give strong evidence that this trait increases the chances of developing alcohol dependence. It can be inferred from these studies that young men with a high tolerance for alcohol should exercise caution with their drinking habits.

Peterson, Ivars. "Alcoholism Exposes Its 'Insensitive' Side." *Science News,* February 19, 1994.

Schuckit, Marc. "Low Level of Response to Alcohol as a Predictor of Future Alcoholism." *American Journal of Psychiatry,* February 1994.

Soap vs. Detergent

Soap has been used for cleaning for thousands of years, but it was not until modern chemists began to understand its molecular structure that anyone knew *how* soap worked its magic. The long soap molecule has one end that is attracted to fats and oils; the other end is attracted to water. When soap is added to the wash water, one end of its molecule attaches to the oily dirt and pulls it away from the fabric or your skin. The other end stays attached to the water, and when the water is washed down the drain, the dirt attached to the other end of the molecule follows.

The problem with soap is that it doesn't work well in hard water. Hard water contains a lot of calcium, and before soap begins to clean you or your clothes, it separates the calcium from the water. This is what makes the scum of the bathtub ring. After the soap has removed all the calcium in the water, it starts to clean. That's why it takes more soap to clean in hard water—the first soap gets rid of the calcium, then more is needed to get rid of the oily dirt.

After World War II, washing machines became very popular, resulting in large demands for soap. However, the public wasn't satisfied with the grungy film left on clothes. When chemists began working on a cleaner that wouldn't leave a film, they knew they needed to keep the basic structure of soap, that is, a molecule with one end that was attracted to oil and the other attracted to water. To eliminate the film, they developed a substance whose water-attractive end would not have an affinity for calcium. These detergents did not separate the calcium which formed the ring, but left it in to be washed away with the dirt. And these are the detergents we use today.

Collier's Encyclopedia. New York: Macmillan Educational Company, 1991.
Van Nostrand's Scientific Encyclopedia. 7th ed. Edited by Douglas M. Considine. New York: Van Nostrand Reinhold, 1989.

Once upon a Time There Was Air Pollution

126   If this were a fairy tale, it might begin, "Once upon a time there was air pollution"—not because there is no longer air pollution, but because we usually think of industrial air pollution as being a fairly recent problem, beginning perhaps a couple of hundred years ago with the Industrial Revolution. However, some recent research indicates that widespread industrial air pollution goes at least as far back as the ancient Greeks and Romans.

Environmental scientist Ingemar Renberg of the University of Umeå in Sweden sampled sediments from beneath 19 Swedish lakes. He discovered that naturally occurring lead concentrations remained fairly constant for many centuries after the lakes were formed by receding glaciers about 10,000 years ago.

Then about 2,600 years ago, the lead levels in the lakes began to rise. This was when the Greeks began minting silver coins. The silver for the coins was extracted from ore that also contained lead, and the smelting process released some lead into the air.

The ancient contamination recorded in the lake sediments increased again about 2,000 years ago, when the Romans were smelting lead throughout south and central Europe, releasing even more lead into the air. As the Roman Empire declined, so did the lead levels in the Swedish lakes.

Then about A.D. 1000 the lead levels in the lakes began to rise again. At this time the Germans had begun to mine silver and lead. By the beginning of the nineteenth century, the lead measured in the lakes was as much as three and a half times what it had been during Roman times.

Apparently some of the lead that escaped into the air during these ancient times reached Sweden, since the levels of lead in the lakes correspond with the lead-processing activities in south and central Europe. While industrial air pollution is certainly not good, Renberg's research has shown that it's far from new.

"Dumping on the Swedes." *Discover,* July 1994.

Why 5,280 Feet?

Our word "mile" comes from the Latin "mille," which referred to the Roman mile. The Roman mile had military origins, since it was the equivalent of 1,000 double paces of marching soldiers. The soldiers' double paces were about 5 feet, so the Roman mile was about 5,000 feet.

Since we got our measurement system of inches, feet, yards, and miles from the British, what does the Roman mile have to do with our mile? Well, Britain was part of the Roman Empire from the first to the fifth centuries A.D., so when the British began to standardize their measuring system, there was a Roman influence.

Even before the British started keeping written records of landholdings, the farmers laid out their fields in plowed furrows that were consistently the equivalent of a modern 660 feet long. This distance became a standard part of their measurements. Over time, by slurring the words, this "furrow-long" distance became "furlong," a unit that is now used almost exclusively in horse racing.

The British eventually used the Roman mile as a model in their measurement system, but they didn't want to give up their furlong. The Roman mile was about 7.5 furlongs, and when the British adopted it, they lengthened the Roman mile to 8 furlongs, which equals 5,280 feet.

Feldman, David. *Imponderables: The Solution to the Mysteries of Everyday Life.* New York: Quill, 1987.

Are We There Yet?

We're driving to a place we haven't been before. It might be just across town, but it seems like it takes a long time to get there. Then, on the return trip home, even though we travel the same route, it doesn't seem to take nearly as long. Scientists have studied this common phenomenon, and have concluded that our perception of how time passes is sometimes based on the amount of information we're processing. The more information we're getting, the more slowly time passes.

Let's apply this theory to our trip. On the way to the strange place, we're bombarded with unfamiliar sights, and perhaps even sounds and smells. We're not sure where we're going, we're not familiar with the traffic patterns, we're looking carefully for road signs or landmarks, a passenger is reading directions to us, and, of course, the kids are whining, "Are we there yet?" We're constantly having to process and evaluate all kinds of information.

On the return trip home, we're at least somewhat familiar with the territory, so much of the information is not new to us. We now process the information more efficiently. We're able to ignore a lot of it because we remember that it does not require action on our part.

Our mental processes might be compared to one of those little flip-page picture books where you let the pages slip from your thumb and the images seem to move. As you smoothly flip the pages, you get a glimpse of each page, and the images move fairly slowly. If you let the pages slip by in bunches so that you don't see each one, the cartoon action is much faster. In a sense time speeds up. It's much the same with our brains: On the way to the new place we see things in great detail, and time seems to move slowly. On the return trip we're not paying as much attention to detail, so time passes faster.

Friedman, William. *About Time: Inventing the Fourth Dimension.* Cambridge, Mass.: The MIT Press, 1990.

Ornstein, Robert E. *On the Experience of Time.* Baltimore: Penguin Books, 1969.

The Versatile Fruit

If you want to make a jelled salad with pineapple, you'd better not use fresh pineapple, or you'll end up with a soupy mess. On the other hand, only fresh pineapple will work as a meat tenderizer. Five hundred years ago, Christopher Columbus found Indians in the Caribbean using pineapple juice to soften their skin, clean their wounds, remove body hair, and cure upset stomach. The secret of the pineapple is an enzyme called bromelain, which is similar to the enzymes that our own digestive system uses to break down protein.

When you marinate meat in fresh pineapple juice, the bromelain begins breaking down the proteins so that by the time the meat gets to your mouth, the digestion is already begun. Pineapple juice works as a skin conditioner because the bromelain breaks down dead and damaged outer layers of skin, exposing the softer skin underneath. Putting pineapple juice on an open wound might be painful, but it can also break down damaged tissue and kill bacteria.

But one place fresh pineapple does not work is in jelled salads, because gelatin is a form of protein, and so is broken down by bromelain, leaving you with a very sloppy salad. But don't despair; since bromelain is broken down by heat, you can still make a gelatin mold with cooked or canned pineapple—only you won't be able to use the cooked pineapple to tenderize meat, soften your skin, or disinfect wounds.

Bickerstaff, Gordon. "Hidden Powers of Pineapple." *New Scientist,* June 2, 1988.
McGee, Harold. *On Food and Cooking: The Science and Lore of the Kitchen.* New York: Scribner, 1984.

Flipping the Switch for Digestion

The human body is capable of digesting a very wide range of foods, including sugars, fats, and proteins. But the trick to such a varied diet is in the body's ability to stop digesting when the food's all gone so that it doesn't start in on itself.

One of the ways the stomach avoids digesting itself involves the body's careful handling of the strong chemical called protease. Protease is a group of enzymes that break down protein. But since the body itself is made of protein, it's important that those enzymes don't go to work on our own bodies.

The body produces protease in the pancreas, but the pancreas doesn't produce protease in a working condition. Instead, the protease produced in the pancreas has to be activated by another enzyme found in the intestine. Only after it is activated by the other enzyme can the protease go to work breaking down protein. The second, activating enzyme in turn does its job only when food enters the stomach.

At night when there's no food in your stomach, the protease is deactivated so it stops working. Unfortunately, disease, alcohol, and some drugs can override the enzyme that is supposed to be controlling the protease. When that happens, the protease begins to digest the stomach wall and ulcers develop.

So, in a healthy person, the body builds its digestive enzymes with what amounts to an on/off switch and then builds a second enzyme especially designed to operate the switch. The digestive system also protects itself by being one of the fast-growing tissues in the body, constantly discarding old cells and reproducing new ones. So some of it does get digested, but there's always more to take its place.

Bickerstaff, Gordon. "Hidden Powers of Pineapple." *New Scientist,* June 2, 1988.

Creaking Snow

"Probably all, or nearly all, who have experienced a cold winter, are familiar with the cheery cry of the snow as it is pressed against a hard surface by the steel tire of a wagon, for instance, or even onto a pavement by the heels of one's boots." Those words were written many decades ago by the physicist W. J. Humphreys in a book called *Physics of the Air.* Humphreys went on to suggest that creaking of snow is connected with very cold temperatures.

Humphreys said that when the temperature is just below freezing and snow is easily packed into snowballs, footsteps and rolling wheels won't create much sound. His reasoning is based on the fact that applying pressure to ice lowers its melting temperature. If ice is so warm that it's about to melt anyway—say, at a temperature of 30 or 31 degrees Fahrenheit—then a little pressure will be all that is necessary to melt it. Snowflakes are small ice crystals. Snowflakes near their melting temperature can, through hand pressure, be made to fuse into a snowball by a process of melting and refreezing. The snow yields to pressure "gently and progressively" and doesn't make sound.

On the other hand, if the snow is very cold, far below its melting temperature, even the pressure of a boot heel or a wagon wheel won't melt it. The snow is powdery and won't form snowballs. Instead, pressure just makes the ice crystals crush and slip over each other as dry particles. That "abrupt and jerky" motion of the dry ice crystals causes vibration and sound, according to Humphreys's book.

So W. J. Humphreys claimed that snow creaks when the weather is very cold, but not when the weather is only moderately cold. Does that claim jibe with your experience?

Humphreys, W. J. *Physics of the Air.* Reprint of 1940 edition. New York: Dover Publications, 1964.

Now You See It, Now You Don't

In the mid-1990s a new kind of art, called a stereogram, was popular, especially on cards, calendars, and posters. At first these pictures looked like abstract patterns, with wavy lines and bright colors jumbled together at random. Once you relaxed your eyes, however, and stared at the picture in a certain way, you were delighted to see a vivid three-dimensional image suddenly appear. This might have seemed like magic at first, but it had more to do with the way your brain processes visual information.

We see in three dimensions because we have two eyes. Although both of our eyes point in the same direction, they give us slightly different views of the world. You can test this by holding a finger, upright, about a foot in front of your face. Close first one eye, then the other. You will notice that the finger seems to change position as you look at it through different eyes. Your brain takes these slightly different pictures and puts them together, forming a single three-dimensional image. This ability to form a three-dimensional image from two slightly different pictures is the key to how these illusions work.

If you can find one, study it carefully. As you scan from left to right, you will notice that the pattern is quite repetitive. Many features repeat, changing slightly as they recur across the picture. Now relax your focus and try to stare through the picture as though it were a window. The picture will get blurry, then each eye will eventually focus on neighboring features in the pattern. Your brain, seeing slightly different pictures from each eye, will put the images together into a coherent three-dimensional picture. That's when the magic moment occurs, and the colorful, abstract blur resolves into a clear picture. It takes practice to relax your eyes this way, but keep trying. The delightful sensation as your brain switches from two to three dimensions is well worth the wait.

Grimes, William. "Thing; Sleight of Eye." *New York Times*, March 6, 1994.

Rheingold, Harold. *Stereogram*. San Francisco: Cadence, 1994.

Tyler, Christopher, Smith-Kettlewell Eye Research Institute of San Francisco (Dr. Tyler invented stereograms).

Icy Fingers of Frost

After your next hot shower, you might find that your bathroom mirror is covered with a uniform white blur. This is because water vapor from your shower condenses evenly on the surface of the mirror. When water vapor gathers as frost, however, a very different thing happens. Look at the frost on a car window the next cold winter morning, and you could find it organized into intricate and beautiful patterns. Why does water condense evenly on a fogged-up bathroom mirror, but in complex patterns as frost?

It's because there's a difference between the ways water molecules organize themselves as liquid and as ice. The fog that gathers on your bathroom mirror after a shower is composed of minute droplets of liquid water. The molecules in liquid water are free to jostle against each other and shift position. Because of this, liquid water molecules are never very organized. Like grains of sand scattered haphazardly on a beach, this microscopic jumble appears uniform when seen from our perspective.

The molecules in frozen water behave very differently. When water freezes, the molecules are no longer so haphazard. They cling to each other in organized hexagonal patterns.

Frost forms when water vapor condenses out of the air onto surfaces that are below freezing. The first water molecules that stick to the glass freeze in this hexagonal pattern. As more water vapor freezes onto the glass, it attaches itself to the ice that's already there, but only as another hexagonal pattern. Even as it bends and twists along the surface of the glass, frost is always built from these basic six-sided building blocks. When the tempera- ture is right, this rigid organization at the microscopic level leads to the beautiful frost patterns we see. If ice molecules weren't arranged so precisely, frost would always be as uniform as fog on the bathroom mirror.

"Frost" and "Ice." In *New Britannica*, 15th ed. Chicago, 1991.

Healing Elbows and Eyeballs

A scratch to the surface of your eye heals quite rapidly, often in a matter of minutes. But a surface scratch on your elbow takes days rather than minutes to heal. The reason for these different rates of healing is directly linked to the kinds of cells that exist on the outermost layers of your skin and your eyeball. When your elbow or your eyeball is scratched, a layer of cells is actually scraped away from the surface. The healing of a scratch happens when new cells take the place of the ones lost to the minor injury.

When the outer layer of cells on an eyeball is scratched, cellular replacement happens quickly because the surface of an eyeball consists of living cells. These living cells have the ability to rearrange themselves and migrate to where the cells are missing.

The outer layers of skin, however, consist of non-living cells, sometimes layered three or four cells deep. These dead cells create a surface that protects the underlying, more tender, living cells. Because they are dead, the cells that make up the outer layer of your skin can't move like the living cells of an eyeball. In order for new skin cells to replace old ones—in other words, in order for healing to occur—live cells, several layers below the surface, must work their way up to the outermost layer of the skin. When compared to the quick healing that the surface cells of an eyeball can accomplish, the healing of an elbow, which must begin several cell layers below the surface, can take a long time.

Quicksand

It's been a staple of adventure movies and fiction for generations. Our hero is traipsing through a swamp, fighting off all manner of alligators, giant snakes, and whatnot, when—suddenly!—he discovers he's stepped into a pit of quicksand. Can he get free, or will he be drawn to certain death, leaving only his hat, bobbing on the surface, to advertise his fate? If this were real life, not the movies, and if he didn't panic, our hero would have no trouble freeing himself from this peril.

Aside from Hollywood studios, quicksand is usually found near the mouths of large rivers or along beaches and streams where pools of water can become partly filled by sand. It's often formed by a flow of groundwater that passes upward through sand.

Quicksand is a mixture of two things: sand and water. The reason you don't sink into ordinary sand is that the sand grains rest against each other in an interlocking pattern. This mutual contact helps them distribute your weight and hold you up. However, if there's enough water between the grains of sand to keep them out of contact, the sand can no longer bear your weight. The sand and water mixture functions like a liquid, and you start to sink.

Unlike in the movies, quicksand will not suck you under. The mixture of sand and water is denser than water alone, so it's actually more buoyant. You float better in quicksand than in water. The only reason some people have drowned in quicksand is that they've panicked.

Don't ever play in quicksand, but in the unlikely event you're accidentally caught, stay calm, float on your back, and call for help. If no one's around, gently squirm on your back to firmer ground.

Cazeau, Charles J. *Science Trivia from Anteaters to Zeppelins.* New York: Berkley Books, 1986.

Marvels and Mysteries of the World around Us. Pleasantville, N.Y.: Reader's Digest Press, 1972.

"Quicksand." In *New Britannica,* 15th ed. Chicago, 1991.

Why Popcorn Pops

Popcorn, like all grains, contains water. About 13.5 to 14 percent of each kernel is made up of water. So when a popcorn kernel is heated above the boiling point of 212 degrees Fahrenheit, this water turns to steam. The steam creates pressure within the kernel, causing the kernel to explode and turn itself inside out. But if the water inside a piece of popcorn is what makes it pop, why don't other grains pop as well? Wheat and rice contain water, so why don't we sit down to watch a movie with a bucket of popped rice or popped wheat?

The answer lies in the differences between the outer coverings, called hulls, of popcorn and other grains. Unlike rice and wheat, and unlike even regular corn, popcorn has a non-porous hull that traps steam. With the porous hulls of other grains, steam easily passes through, so no significant pressure is produced. These grains may parch, but they will not pop.

But even popcorn, with its special hull, doesn't always pop. Popcorn must have two important properties to pop well. First, the amount of moisture in the kernel must be very close to 13.5 percent. Too little moisture, and not enough steam will build up to pop the kernel. Too much moisture, and the kernels pop into dense spheres, rather than the light, fluffy stuff popcorn fanciers love.

Second, the kernels must not be cracked or damaged in any way. Even a small crack will let steam escape, keeping the necessary pressure from building. Popcorn kernels with the right amount of moisture and unblemished hulls pop into the snack that just about everyone enjoys.

Language Production and Speech Errors

Cognitive psychologists believe that our language construction is the result of a two-step word-retrieval process. The first step is the search for a word's meaning, and the second step is the search for the actual sound of a word. Different speech errors occur when you get stuck at different stages of this two-step retrieval process.

When you incorrectly substitute one word for another, calling a cat a "dog," for instance, your brain has erred in the first step by choosing an incorrect word for the concept of "small domesticated furry pet."

When you have a word or a name on the tip of your tongue, you've gotten stuck in the middle of the retrieval process. You've correctly retrieved the meaning of the word but have been unable to retrieve the sound of the word. Because you've successfully completed one of these two steps, you can probably give the word's definition but can't actually say the word. Going through the alphabet one letter at a time might help you remember it. When you come to the initial letter of the word, your memory might be jogged enough to help you complete the two-step process and remember the sound of the word you're looking for.

When you use an incorrect word that sounds similar to the word you mean to say, your brain has erred in the second step, when you were looking for the actual sound of the word. So, for instance, if you said "Moment of Silence" instead of "Moment of Science" when you were talking about this book or the radio show, your brain would have successfully completed the conceptual stage of the word-retrieval process but then would have made a slip during the second stage by choosing another, similar-sounding word that was more familiar than the word you needed.

Interrupted Vision

Have you ever noticed that you can't see your eyes move when you look in a mirror? Put your face close to the bathroom mirror and look yourself in the eye. Notice the appearance of your eyes. Now, without blinking, look down at your nose, but continue to notice your eyes. Your eyes look different. They've moved, but the movement itself was invisible—to you.

If you have someone else do the same thing while you watch, you'll easily see the other person's eyes move. To make the comparison as fair as possible, you should put your face beside the other person's and look at the other person's nose in the mirror. You've just witnessed a mysterious process that shuts off our vision, at least partly, whenever our eyeballs move rapidly.

The kind of quick eye motion we're talking about is called a saccade, from a French word meaning to twitch or jerk. During the fraction of a second that a saccade takes, images sweep over our retinas at high speed. Yet we don't get a feeling of motion, because our brain suppresses visual perception during saccades. Otherwise, the world might look to us like a bad home video where the photographer held the "record" button down while swinging the camera around the room.

An odd thing about this suppression is that it's not complete. Get in the car and have someone drive you past a roadside fence. Without moving your head, glance quickly from front to back; you can make the fenceposts seem to freeze for an instant. Why, in this case, is vision not suppressed?

A team of visual scientists published a study of this question in the journal *Nature*. They found that what gets suppressed during a saccade are large areas of light and dark. Those are the perceptions that seem to contribute the most to a sense of motion. Finer details, like fenceposts, are not suppressed, maybe because there's no need to suppress them—rapid eye motions usually turn them into a blur anyway.

Burr, David C.; M. Concetta Morrone; and John Ross. "Selective Suppression of the Magnocellular Visual Pathway during Saccadic Eye Movements," and accompanying "News and Views" article by Michael J. Morgan. *Nature*, October 6, 1994.

Why Teflon® Is Slippery

Teflon is the trademark name for PTFE, a type of plastic. If you own any non-stick cookware, then you probably use PTFE on a daily basis. You might not realize, as you fry your morning eggs, that PTFE is one of the most slippery materials that can be manufactured. It's about as slippery as wet ice. What makes Teflon so slippery?

Teflon is chemically similar to another, more common plastic: polyethylene, the material used to make plastic bags and other plastic containers. Chemically, polyethylene is made from long chains of carbon atoms with hydrogen atoms bonded to the sides of the chains. To make Teflon, the hydrogen atoms of polyethylene are replaced by fluorine atoms.

It's the fluorine atoms that give Teflon its slipperiness. Fluorine atoms are physically bigger than hydrogen atoms. Their large size makes them huddle around the central carbon chains in a much tighter formation. This tight formation works like a kind of chemical armor, protecting the carbon atoms which in turn hold the molecule together. This chemical teamwork between carbon and fluorine makes Teflon extremely chemically stable, and it's this chemical stability that makes Teflon so slippery. Foreign substances, like a frying egg, can find no chemical foothold on the fluorine armor, so they simply slide away.

Getting this slippery substance to stick to a frying pan is a bit of a trick. Teflon is broken into a fine powder and suspended in water. The pan is then thoroughly cleaned, then roughened by sandblasting. The Teflon is sprayed onto the pan and baked, causing it to fuse together and lock onto the roughened surface of the pan. As long as you don't scratch this protective coating, years' worth of fried eggs, melted cheese, burned milk—even toffee—will slide away effortlessly.

How in the World? Pleasantville, N.Y.: Reader's Digest Association, 1990.

The New Illustrated Science and Invention Encyclopedia. Westport, Conn.: Stuttman, 1987.

Vergara, William C. *Science in Everyday Life.* New York: Harper and Row, 1980.

Your Genetic Cookbook

To stay healthy, your cells must continuously perform a wide variety of chemical tasks. Your DNA genes, in the nucleus of every cell, help orchestrate this activity. A cell uses its genes as a kind of biochemical cookbook: whenever it has to do anything, a cell looks up the recipe in its DNA. It then uses this recipe to cook up whatever proteins it needs to get the job done.

Your cells are hard at work right now, creating thousands of tailor-made proteins for thousands of different biochemical jobs. Sometimes, however, things can go wrong. When a virus attacks, it injects its own DNA into one of your cells. Like your own genes, the viral DNA contains recipes. Unfortunately, these recipes are good only for making new viruses. No matter what your cell was doing before, it will stop its healthy functioning and make only viruses, following the viral recipe until it runs out of raw materials. Then your once-healthy cell bursts open, releasing new viruses to infect more cells.

Cancer is another problem that can develop through a cell's recipe-reading process. Each cell contains dozens of genes that regulate its healthy growth and reproduction. If these genes become damaged or altered, the results can be dangerous. Instead of growing in a healthy fashion, the cell grows and divides at an alarming rate. A cancerous tumor is made up of cells like these, cells whose growth and reproduction genes are altered.

So viral infections are caused when alien recipes are added to a cell's genetic cookbook, and cancer is caused by errors within your own genetic recipes.

Cohen, Jack S., and Michael E. Hogan. "The New Genetic Medicines." *Scientific American*, December 1994.

Shroyer, Jo Ann. *Quarks, Critters and Chaos*. New York: Prentice Hall, 1993.

What Is Jell-O®?

It's pretty easy to guess what most of your food is made of. The meat in your hamburger probably came from a cow, the bun was made from grain, the ketchup from tomatoes, and so on. There is one kind of food, however, that might have you guessing animal, vegetable, or mineral for the whole meal. But no more, because here's the scoop on Jell-O.

Jell-O is a trademark name for gelatin, a food that people have enjoyed for generations. To answer the question animal, vegetable, or mineral: Gelatin is an animal product. It is prepared by soaking the bones, skin, or connective tissue from pigs or cows in a bath of mild hydrochloric acid solution. After this, the animal products are heated in distilled water for many hours, and finally boiled. The fluid that collects from this process is drawn off. What's left is dried and ground into a fine, pale yellow powder. This is unflavored gelatin, the basis of all gelatin salads, desserts, and drinks. Gelatin is valuable as a food because it is pure protein and it is easy to digest. A gelatin made from vegetable protein, called agar-agar, is made for vegetarians.

When powdered gelatin is stirred into hot water and then chilled, it forms the jiggly, gelled product that we are most familiar with. This gelled product is not strictly a solid or a liquid. Technically it's a colloid: a liquid suspended in a solid framework. As the hot mixture cools off, the long strands of animal protein lock together into a solid framework, trapping tiny droplets of liquid water in the process. It's these droplets of water, trapped in a mesh of animal protein, that hold all the coloring and flavoring in your favorite gelatin dessert.

"Gelatin." In *McGraw-Hill Encyclopedia of Science and Technology*, 6th ed. New York, 1987.

"Gelatin." In *World Book Encyclopedia*. Chicago, 1994.

McGee, Harold. *On Food and Cooking: The Science and Lore of the Kitchen*. New York: Scribner, 1984.

Palm-Reading Scientists

In fairy tales and other stories, people curious about their fate could consult a palm reader who, as the story goes, would tell their fortune by looking at the lines on their palm. While there's no scientific evidence linking the lines on your palm to your fate or fortune, scientists have learned that your palm and fingerprints do have a story to tell. The medical study of palm and fingerprints is called dermatoglyphics.

The ridges on your hands, fingers, feet, and toes formed while you were still in the womb, five or six months before you were born. They are the result of stress patterns that formed as your hands and feet developed. Because the growth pattern of every fetus is slightly different, your finger and palm prints are absolutely unique. Even identical twins have slightly different patterns.

Differences in fingerprints have always been useful to police detectives, but what can a doctor tell from looking at your prints? Actually, quite a bit. Many genetic diseases affect the way that the fetus develops. This results in characteristic irregularities in the palm prints. Scientists have statistically linked dozens of genetic diseases to unusual palm prints.

Sometimes even viral diseases can leave telltale traces on an infant's palms. For example, women who caught German measles early in pregnancy during the 1960s sometimes passed birth defects along to their children. A study in 1966 found that such children had characteristic palm and fingerprints as well. Studies have linked irregular palm prints to such diseases as schizophrenia, fetal alcohol syndrome, and even allergies. While they can't tell you how long you'll live or how many children you'll have, the lines on your palm can tell you something.

"Integumentary Patterns." In *McGraw-Hill Encyclopedia of Science and Technology*, 6th ed. New York, 1987.

"Integumentary Systems." In *New Britannica*, 15th ed. Chicago, 1991.

Smith, Antony. *The Body*. New York: Viking, 1986.

Various *Medline Express* abstracts, including "Dermatoglyphic Asymmetry in Fetal Alcohol Syndrome," "Genetic Loadings in Schizophrenia: A Dermatoglyphic Study," and "Dermatoglyphics in Nasobronchial Allergic Disorders."

Our Biological Clocks

Each of us has an internal clock that, among other things, dictates when we get sleepy and hungry. Scientists call our biological clocks "circadian clocks." The word "circadian" comes from two Latin words: *circa,* "about," and *dies,* "day." Our internal clocks are almost parallel to the twenty-four-hour cycle of a day, but not quite.

Research has shown that most people's circadian clocks, left on their own, work on an approximately twenty-five-hour cycle. Without any external stimulus, our internal clocks would usually gain about an hour each day and would be synchronized with the earth's time only one day out of every twenty-four. In effect, our biological clocks must reset themselves each day to become attuned to the twenty-four-hour clock we all live by. Scientists are not exactly sure how the resetting of our clocks happens, but they are fairly confident that our brains utilize sunlight to fine-tune our internal clocks.

Our biological clocks influence practically all of our bodily functions. Our temperatures rise and fall according to these clocks. And because our bodies are set to a daily rhythm, we react to chemical and physical stimulus differently at various times of the day. For instance, studies have shown that our livers process alcohol more efficiently in the evenings than in the mornings, and that we are more likely to have allergic reactions in the middle of the night than in the afternoon.

But what would happen if we were isolated from the influences of the sun, clocks, or any other devices that would mark time for us? In an experiment by researcher Rutger Wever, human subjects were placed in isolated rooms for a month. With no windows, clocks, or television sets, these people, each in a separate room, had no way of knowing what time it was.

Wever found that these subjects extended their sleeping and waking cycles each day, without any knowledge of doing so. Some would sleep as long as seventeen hours at once, and then stay awake for as long as thirty hours. Though the sleeping and waking cycles of the subjects extended far beyond the standard twenty-four-hour period, the biorhythms of the subjects' bodies kept approximately a twenty-five-hour internal clock. The subjects' temperatures were routinely monitored, and the rising and falling of these temperatures never varied much from their twenty-five-hour clock. These results showed Wever that the rising and falling of a subject's temperature is dictated by an internal clock and not by sleeping and waking patterns.

At the end of the experiment, subjects often would be astonished to find that the month was over because, according to their own calculations, based on their sleep cycles, they had been in isolation for only two or three weeks. They were convinced that thirty days had passed only after being shown newspapers that appeared to be from their future.

Winfree, Arthur T. *The Timing of Biological Clocks.* New York: Scientific American Books, 1987.

Déjà Vu

"Have you really been there before?"

Many people at one time or another have experienced déjà vu. French for "already seen," déjà vu is a sudden strong feeling that a moment identical to the present one has occurred at some earlier time.

143

To a cognitive psychologist, déjà vu is proof of the immense amount of knowledge and experience we store in our brains. When we experience déjà vu, what actually happens is that, in a fraction of a second, we retrieve bits of many different memory fragments and piece them together, producing what seems to be a complete memory. So, if you experience déjà vu in a mall restaurant while waiting for a pepperoni pizza with your best friend, your mind has taken perhaps hundreds of stored memories of various experiences, and put together fragments from those memories to give you the sensation of having been there before, even though you haven't been there before at all.

Cognitive psychologists who study how we use language are not surprised at the brain's ability to create déjà vu. Actually, language comprehension and déjà vu have many parallels. When you hear someone speak, you usually understand her even though you've probably never heard her words presented in exactly the same way. You understand these sentences because your brain is able to remember the individual meanings of words, based on hundreds of past experiences with those words. Your brain takes the meanings of individual words and splices them together to comprehend their meaning as a whole. As with déjà vu, this entire process happens in a split second.

Fresh Fruit in January

Ripe fruit spoils fast, and since freezing ruins most fruit, storing and shipping fruit has always been a problem. Not long ago, fresh fruit in the grocery store had to be locally grown—and still in season.

In a book entitled *On Food and Cooking,* Harold McGee offers this history of how supermarkets came to offer fresh fruit in January:

144

"In the Caribbean islands, around 1910, it was reported that bananas stored near some oranges had ripened earlier than the other bunches. In 1912, California citrus growers noticed that green fruit kept near a kerosene stove changed color faster than the rest. What secret ripening agent did the stove and the fruit have in common? The answer came two decades later: a simple compound of carbon and hydrogen called 'ethylene,' which is produced naturally by most fruits—and, incidentally, by burning kerosene. The naturally produced ethylene stimulates the processes that we know as ripening: namely, a softening, a sweetening, and a change in color."

With a knowledge of ethylene, the fruit companies could now pick unripe fruit for packing and shipping. The firm, unripe fruit is less likely to spoil or bruise than ripe fruit. When it arrives at the supermarket, the crates of unripe fruit are then gassed with ethylene to prepare them for your kitchen. Ethylene also helps us get fruits that are out of season, since unripe fruit can be stored a lot longer than ripe fruit. Months later, a dose of ethylene restarts the ripening process.

Ethylene doesn't completely duplicate nature, and most fruits still taste best when they're allowed to ripen on the tree. But as long as there's a market for exotic fruits, the fruit industry can use ethylene to satisfy our out-of-season tastes.

McGee, Harold. *On Food and Cooking: The Science and Lore of the Kitchen.* New York: Scribner, 1984.
Ray, Peter. *Botany.* Philadelphia: Saunders College Publishing, 1983.

Why Honey Turns Hard

If a little honey on a piece of homemade toast or in a cup of tea is how you like to start the day, you're not alone. Cave paintings show people a thousand years ago enjoying honey. One drawback to honey, though, is that after sitting too long on the shelf it crystallizes, and that soft, amber liquid turns to a hard, gooey mass.

Actually, though, only part of the honey is crystallizing. Honey is made mostly of two kinds of sugar: glucose and fructose. What crystallizes is the glucose, so the more glucose there is in comparison to fructose, the more likely it is to crystallize. Some honeys, like those made from the nectar of tupelo, locust, or sage, contain slightly more fructose than glucose and so they crystallize more slowly.

But before honey can crystallize, it needs what's called a "seed" for the crystals to grow on. The seed might be a grain of pollen, a speck of dust, or even a scratch on the inside of the jar. But the best seed of all is a bit of honey that has already crystallized. Most of the honey in a supermarket has been heated and filtered to remove virtually all the possible seeds. That slows the crystallization, but the heating process also drives off some of the honey's distinctive flavor. When honey does crystallize, you can soften it again in a microwave or a pan of warm water, but as it cools, the crystallization will begin again—faster even than before.

Honey crystallizes faster the second time because heat alone can't remove all the seeds. Dust, crumbs, and other tiny particles that have accumulated since you first opened the jar will remain as seeds to start the process all over again.

McGee, Harold. *On Food and Cooking: The Science and Lore of the Kitchen.* New York: Scribner, 1984.

Food and Mood

When we think about a pill that helps an overweight person take off the pounds, we usually think of an appetite suppressant. But suppressing your appetite will help you lose weight only if the reason you eat is that you are hungry. Some people eat because they are depressed rather than because they're hungry. When these people want to lose weight, doctors may prescribe not traditional diet pills, but antidepressants.

These antidepressants have helped many overweight people stop craving high-calorie carbohydrates. Depressed people often crave carbohydrates because eating carbohydrate-rich food lifts their mood. As a side effect, they gain weight. Though scientists are not exactly sure how carbohydrate intake influences mood, they do know that it has to do with the chemical messengers, called neurotransmitters, that allow two areas of the brain to communicate: the area responsible for appetite and the area responsible for mood.

More specifically, an intake of carbohydrates increases the levels of the neurotransmitter responsible for mood, called serotonin. Though only a small percentage of the brain's neurotransmitters are made up of serotonin, if this small amount is even minutely tinkered with, a patient can experience fairly drastic mood shifts.

A patient taking antidepressants may stop craving carbohydrates because these drugs function like carbohydrates. They alter the serotonin that communicates messages between the mood and appetite centers of the brain. Once an antidepressant drug begins to work, the abnormal craving for carbohydrates is interrupted and the patient can start losing weight.

Number Crunching at the Electronic Feast

Bits, bytes, kilobytes, megabytes: Such terminology might have you wondering whether you're in a computer store or a fast-food restaurant. Maybe this Moment of Science will make computer bytes a little easier to digest.

Bits and bytes measure the amount of information that a computer's memory or disk drive can hold. Bits are the smallest of these. Computers can process information only as ones and zeros, and a single bit holds one of these—a one or a zero—nothing else. It's like a light switch, either on or off.

A byte is eight computer bits grouped together. You can think of it as a set of eight light switches in a row. While a single switch can have only two positions, on or off, a set of eight switches can be turned on or off in a variety of patterns. As it turns out, there are 256 unique ways that eight switches can be set. Therefore, although it's made of only ones and zeros, a byte can hold any number from 1 to 256.

Grouping bits into bytes makes it possible for computers to handle non-numeric information such as text. Most computers have a built-in table that assigns each of the 256 values a byte can hold to a unique letter, numeral, punctuation mark, or graphic symbol. Working from this table, the computer can use one byte of its memory to store each character in a text document.

A kilobyte is roughly a thousand bytes, and a megabyte is roughly a million. The newest measure—a gigabyte—is a billion bytes' worth of information. A modern one-gigabyte hard drive can hold more text than all the volumes of an encyclopedia. Our number-crunching appetite keeps growing, though: You need four gigabytes to hold all the sound and video from a Hollywood movie.

Measuring Earthquakes

You feel the earth move under your feet: You're in an earthquake. If you were a seismologist, you might be thinking about the best way to measure this unruly natural phenomenon. That was the feeling of Charles Richter, who in 1935 devised a new method for measuring the strength of earthquakes that plagued his native Southern California. Unlike previous scales, which just estimated earthquake damage, his used measurements from a specific type of seismograph. This was one of the first scales to attempt to measure an earthquake's actual intensity.

Although you're likely to hear the term "Richter scale" still used in current news stories, most modern seismologists have replaced the original Richter scale with more sophisticated refinements. We've come to realize that not all earthquakes shake in quite the same way. While the original Richter scale may have worked well for a Southern California–type quake, it doesn't let us compare them to other kinds of quakes.

Today's seismologists look at many different factors of an earthquake, using separate scales to measure different types of seismic waves. Some seismic waves ripple along the surface of the earth, causing the ground to rise and fall much like ripples spreading out on a pond. To measure this type of wave, seismologists use a "surface-wave" magnitude scale.

Deep earthquakes don't make many surface waves, however, but send their energy like a giant shock wave through the earth's interior. A "body-wave" magnitude scale measures these quakes. Even the surface-wave and body-wave scales fail to account for all the energy released by the largest quakes. For this the "moment magnitude" scale is used. Because there are many ways to measure earthquakes, you will sometimes see different amounts reported for the magnitude of the same quake.

But regardless of the scale that is being used to measure the quake, what do the numbers mean? Perhaps there was a magnitude 5 quake, or a magnitude 6 or 7. We can see that the higher the number, the more damaging the earthquake was, but unless you were standing right there, it might be hard to picture what these numbers actually mean. Earthquake strengths vary enormously: The smallest measurable quake releases no more energy than a falling stone, while the largest ones are more powerful than many nuclear bombs. This tremendous range makes it difficult to deal with earthquake numbers directly, so seismologists use a logarithmic scale instead. In a logarithmic scale, each number represents 10 times the amount of the number below it. This means that a magnitude 5 quake has seismic waves that are 10 times larger than those of a magnitude 4. Magnitude 6 waves are a hundred times bigger than magnitude 4 waves.

What's more, the destructive energy released by an earthquake increases in even larger jumps than the wave sizes. For each step you climb on the scale, the amount of energy increases more than 30 times. Thus, although the waves are a hundred times larger between a magnitude 4 and a magnitude 6 quake, a thousand times more energy is released.

Just how much energy are we talking about, anyway? A magnitude 2 quake, which you probably wouldn't even feel, releases the energy of an average lightning bolt. A magnitude 6 quake, which could destroy some buildings, has the same energy as the atomic bomb dropped on Hiroshima. An 8.3 quake, like the one that rocked San Francisco in 1906, was stronger than more than a thousand of those bombs. It released more energy than the Mount St. Helens eruption of 1980.

The Handy Science Answer Book: The Carnegie Library of Pittsburgh. Detroit: Visible Ink Press, 1994.

Monastersky, Richard. "Abandoning Richter." *Science News,* October 15, 1994.

Vergara, William C. *Science in Everyday Life.* New York: Harper and Row, 1980.

Money Changers

Ever wonder how a money-changer machine knows if you've given it a one-, a five-, or a ten-dollar bill? When a bill is inserted into a money-changer machine, it disrupts a light beam from within the machine. This action triggers the motor to pull the bill into the money changer. The machine then begins a procedure by which it first makes sure that the bill is actual currency, and then determines the denomination of the bill.

With a computer chip and measuring devices, the money changer checks the length, width, and thickness of the bill. If the bill is not the exact length and thickness it should be, the changer will reject it and refuse to give you any change. The sensors that evaluate the bill are so sensitive that even an old, wrinkled bill usually will not pass this authenticity test because it will not measure precisely the same as a crisp, new bill.

After the machine measures the bill's width, length, and thickness, it optically scans the bill to determine if it is a one-, five-, or ten-dollar bill. The machine makes this decision by "reading" how much ink is in different places on the bill. The U.S. Treasury Department uses specially manufactured ink that has unique magnetic properties. The machine's optical scanner measures this magnetic ink. And because a one-dollar bill has a different ink pattern than a five- or ten-dollar bill, the computer inside the machine is able to differentiate between these denominations with a quick scan.

Hot and Cold Chirping Crickets

Imagine that you're camping deep in the woods on a summer night. The sun sinks below the horizon and the temperature begins to fall. You shiver, and as you pull your jacket around your shoulders, you wonder just how cold it really is. Here's a clever way you can find out. All you'll need is a wristwatch, your ears, and a little patience.

Start by listening for a chirping cricket. Male crickets around the world make this characteristic sound by rubbing their wings together. The edge of a male cricket's right wing is covered with little ridges, like a file or a washboard. As he rubs his left wing cover across the uneven right wing, he produces a love song that female crickets find irresistible. Female crickets use this amorous chirping to find their perfect mate, listening with a pair of special ears located below the knees. You can use these same serenades to calculate the temperature.

Most insects tend to be more active when it's hot, and more sluggish in cooler weather. Crickets are no exception to this rule. In cold weather, a cricket will do everything more slowly, and as the temperature drops, so does the tempo of his love song. By measuring how quickly he chirps, you can find out approximately how cold it is.

It's easy to do: Simply count the number of chirps a single cricket makes in a 15-second period, then add 37. Although individual species might be a little faster or slower, this should give a fair approximation of the temperature in degrees Fahrenheit. Even if the chirping keeps you awake all night, at least you'll know the temperature.

Hanson, Jeanne K., and Deane Morrison. *Of Kinkajous, Capybaras, Horned Beetles, Seladangs, and the Oddest and Most Wonderful Mammals, Insects, Birds, and Plants of Our World.* New York: Harper Collins, 1991.

When a Boy's Voice Changes

For adolescent boys, a changing voice that cracks in the middle of a sentence can be a great embarrassment. Though embarrassing, a cracking voice is a natural part of adolescent development. As a boy goes through adolescence, his secondary sex characteristics develop. One of these characteristics is the rapid growth of the larynx and vocal cords. A boy's voice deepens as his larynx develops because the bigger the vocal cords, the deeper the voice.

In fact, vocal cords are similar to other musical instruments in this regard. The longer the harp string, for instance, the lower the note it plays. Similarly, if you are blowing into a bottle to create a certain pitch, the larger the bottle, the lower the pitch. When it comes to voices, the bigger the vocal cords, the lower they resonate, and the deeper the voice will be.

But why does a boy's changing voice break and crack? For the same reason growing adolescents are often gangly and awkward—because the brain is becoming accustomed to working with bigger body parts. Even for an adult, a consistent and even voice depends on the brain's ability to constantly monitor the sounds that come from the voice. The brain can do this quite easily under normal circumstances. But when a boy's vocal cords enlarge, the brain must relearn how to monitor and control the voice. A cracking voice is proof that an adolescent boy's brain hasn't become completely proficient at coordinating its careful monitoring of the sounds coming from the vocal cords.

How Dogs Eat

If you've ever watched a dog eat, you've probably marveled at how quickly it gulps down its food. You might even wonder why, no matter how hungry a dog is, it will often eat as much food as you put in front of it.

Dog owners may be concerned about this behavior, but it poses no problems for the dog. People chew their food and try to teach their children to eat slowly because digestion for humans begins in the mouth. Our saliva mixes with food and prepares that food to be broken down into its primary nutrients once it enters the stomach. A dog's digestion, on the other hand, doesn't begin until the food reaches the stomach, so dogs do not need to take time chewing their dinners.

Most dogs probably eat so quickly because in the days before they were domesticated, they had to survive by eating their prey before another dog or scavenger animal stole it. The evolutionary programming of dogs dictates that they eat and keep moving. As a species in the wild, they didn't have the luxury of hanging around and eating at their leisure.

Even their teeth aren't designed for them to savor their food. While most of the teeth in a human's mouth are flat and designed to facilitate chewing, most of the teeth in a dog's mouth are pointed and designed to allow the dog to grab its food and swallow it whole.

Hundreds of years of domestication hasn't changed most dogs' eating habits very much. Even if a dog has been given regular, dependable meals every day, it will still gulp those meals down in a flash, ensuring that no scavenger will take its food away.

Johnson, Norman H. *The Complete Puppy and Dog Book.* New York: Atheneum, 1977.

Morning Breath

Morning breath is a topic of many jokes, and a real boon to the mouthwash and toothpaste industries. But what exactly causes the foul taste and odor in your mouth when you wake up in the mornings?

The most basic answer to this question is gravity. If you've eaten fewer than three hours before you go to sleep, your stomach hasn't had time to digest all of your food. When you lie down, gravity causes the gastric juices that are busy digesting your food to come up into your throat.

Because your airway and food pipe are side by side, they share an adjoining wall. Those gastric juices that have backed up in your food pipe actually permeate that wall and enter into your air pipe. These juices can irritate your larynx, and cause your voice to be hoarse and your breath to turn foul. In addition, gastric juices are acidic enough to burn the mucous membranes in your throat, resulting in a sore throat that occurs in the mornings but lessens throughout the day.

Morning mouth tends to worsen with age, because as you get older, the top of your esophagus, the thin tube that leads from the mouth to the stomach, loosens. With the softening of the top of this tube, gastric juices can more easily escape from the esophagus into the air pipe.

Another contributing factor to morning breath is infrequent swallowing during sleep. Swallowing allows us to keep our mouth relatively free from odor-producing bacteria. But when we're asleep, these bacteria can thrive, contributing to the bad taste in our mouths when we wake up.

Lowering the Thermostat

When you lower your thermostat at night, are you really saving energy? Or does it take *more* energy to *reheat* a cold house? This Moment of Science will tell you why turning *down* your thermostat will never *raise* your heating bills.

To see why, it may help to think of the house as a bucket with a hole in the bottom, and heat as water being poured into the bucket. The pressure of the water in the bucket forces water out the hole—the more water there is in the bucket, the greater the pressure, and the faster the water will leak out. But as the water level drops, the pressure will drop too, and the leak will slow down. So it would take more water to keep the bucket full than it would to let some or even all of the water leak out and then refill it.

When it's cold outside and warm inside, that temperature difference acts like the water pressure in the bucket, forcing heat out through the walls. Heat leaks more slowly out of a cooler house because there is less heat trying to get out. It may take a lot of energy to heat a cold house, but not nearly as much energy as would have been saved by letting the temperature drop.

Some houses with what's called a high "thermal mass" keep a steadier temperature by absorbing heat during the day and giving it off slowly at night. In these houses a lower thermostat won't save as much energy, but it'll still save some. That's because thermal mass is like a sponge in the bottom of the bucket: It may slow the leak, but it can't reverse the process.

Turning the heat down too far could get uncomfortable or even cause the pipes to freeze. But it won't raise your heating bill.

Learning to Catch

It's a line drive headed straight for your glove. All you have to do is close your hand at the right moment. It takes only about fourteen one-hundredths of a second to close your hand around a baseball, but in that time a baseball going 90 miles an hour travels more than 18 feet. Closing your hand a little late or a little early could turn the final out into a home run.

But how do we know when the ball is exactly fourteen one-hundredths of a second away? We could use two variables—the ball's speed and its distance—to calculate when it would arrive. But our subconscious mind does it without calculating and with only one variable. That variable is the rate at which the image of the ball is expanding in relation to the size of the image at that moment.

Here's how it works: A ball thrown from a distance grows gradually from a tiny speck until it reaches us. The speck grows slowly at first, but the closer it gets, the faster it grows. A big ball far away may look the same size as a small ball up close, but if they're traveling at the same speed, the closer ball grows faster.

Knowing how big the speck is and how fast it's growing, you could calculate how long it will take to reach you, but our subconscious mind does it in a single glance. By interpreting a single variable—that is, how fast the ball appears to be growing relative to how big it appears at that moment—our mind knows just how long it will be before that speck turns into a baseball in our hand.

Savelsbergh, G. J. P.; H. T. A. Whiting; and R. J. Bootsma. "Grasping Tau." *Journal of Experimental Psychology: Human Perception and Performance* 17, no. 2 (1991).

Biodiversity and Genetic Engineering

If you want a single yardstick to measure the overall health of Planet Earth, most biologists would say that this yardstick is biodiversity. Biodiversity is a measure of the number of different species that exist. For example, a small forest with 50 different kinds of trees has more biodiversity than a large plantation with only 1. Why is biodiversity so crucial to the health of earth's ecosystem?

The more species earth has, the better able it is to survive—and stabilize—a changing climate. You can think of earth's ecosystem as a large building, supported by many beams and pillars. As different species become extinct, it's like knocking out a beam here, a pillar there. The building might not collapse at once, but the next change of wind could spell disaster.

You might think that genetic engineering, which develops new strains of plant and animal species, would help to increase biodiversity. It can, but unfortunately there are also ways that genetic engineering might reduce biodiversity rather than aid it.

One way genetic engineering might harm biodiversity is by encouraging irresponsible farming techniques. For example, if scientists developed a strain of corn that's cheaper and easier to grow, farmers might plant this variety only, letting others fall by the wayside. This is called monocultural farming, and it's extremely risky. If a plant disease came along that attacked this strain of corn, we wouldn't have others to fall back on. This happened on a small scale in 1970, when a blight wiped out 15 percent of the U.S. corn crop. If genetic engineering encourages more monocultural farming, then the 1970 blight could be just the tip of the iceberg. We can only hope that genetic engineering will make us more sensitive to the value of our planet's biodiversity. Our future depends on it.

Doyle, Jack. *Altered Harvest.* New York: Viking Press, 1985.

Fox, Michael W. *Superpigs and Wondercorn.* New York: Lyons and Burford, 1992.

"Genetic Engineering." In *Opposing Viewpoints Sources: Science and Technology.* San Diego: Greenhaven Press, 1990.

Leary, Warren E. "F.D.A. Approves Altered Tomato That Will Remain Fresh Longer." *New York Times,* May 19, 1994.

The Secret Life of Hiccups

We've all experienced them at one time or another, often right after a big meal. A normal bout of hiccups usually lasts only a few minutes and may contain up to 70 individual "hics." Unlike coughing or sneezing, which can help clear your airways, hiccups seem to serve no beneficial function in the human body. What's the story behind these strange convulsions?

Two separate things happen to your body when you hiccup. The muscles in your diaphragm, which normally control your breathing, contract with a sudden jerk. This causes a sharp intake of breath. At the same time, your vocal cords contract to stop this breath, resulting in a loud "hic."

This is all caused by a misfire in the nerves that control your diaphragm. These nerves run from your neck to your chest, and any unusual pressure or irritation along this length can cause a misfire. Thus, hiccups are often triggered by overeating, gulping your food too quickly, or eating something too hot or too cold. Stress can also cause hiccups.

There are many folk remedies for hiccups, but none seems to work for everyone. Such remedies include holding your breath, breathing into a paper bag, or drinking a glass of water without breathing. It's possible that by depriving the diaphragm muscles of oxygen, these remedies force them to resume a more normal breathing pattern.

Other remedies include pulling your tongue, sucking a lemon, or having a friend startle you. What these remedies have in common is that they trick your nervous system with a diversion, perhaps shocking the nerves that control the diaphragm into normal behavior. No one knows exactly why these remedies sometimes work.

It's extremely rare, but severe cases of hiccups do occur. If you have persistent hiccups that simply refuse to go away, you should probably consult a physician.

"Curing Hiccups." University of California, Berkeley Wellness Center, October 1985.
"Hiccups." In *ABC's of the Human Body,* ed. Alma Guinness. New York: Reader's Digest Press, 1987.

"Hiccups." In *Mayo Clinic Family Health Book,* ed. David E. Larson. New York: Morrow, 1990.

"Hiccups." In *Prevention's Giant Book of Health Facts,* ed. John Feltmann. Emmaus, Pa.: Rodale Press, 1991.

Noise from the Upstairs Neighbors

Are you annoyed by thuds and thumps when your upstairs neighbors walk around? And if so, what can you do about it? A surprisingly discouraging answer to that question appeared in the *Journal of the Acoustical Society of America.* After investigating the question, a private consultant and a California state noise-control officer report that "in multifamily, wood-frame residential construction . . . at present, there is no economically practical method of avoiding the perception of 'thuds' and 'thumps' in rooms beneath the walking surface."

The occasion for this study was a lawsuit. Homeowners on the lower floors of a Northern California condominium complex sued the builder for $80 million because of thumps, booming, and other "feelable" structural vibration as upstairs neighbors walked around. The $750,000 condos had been marketed as having "luxury" acoustical privacy.

In a quiet empty warehouse, the researchers built a full-size mock-up of a pair of stacked rooms like those in the condo in question. Then they studied the sounds in the lower room caused by a standard tapping machine and a real person walking on the upper floor.

They found that resilient mats, carpeting, and the use of sneakers or bare feet upstairs would eliminate high-frequency noises such as clicks and scrapes. But the low-frequency sounds— the thuds and thumps—were caused by the floor vibrating like a giant drumhead. Track shoes actually made those sounds worse. And resilient mats upstairs seemed to encourage the walker to move with a springier gait, making the booms below louder still. In short, these two researchers found no feasible way to make the upstairs neighbors inaudible in a wooden residential building.

Note: The suit was settled out of court in favor of the plaintiffs—but for a lot less than $80 million.

Blazier, Warren E., Jr., and Russell B. DuPree. "Investigation of Low-Frequency Footfall Noise in Wood-Frame, Multifamily Building Construction." *Journal of the Acoustical Society of America,* September 1994.

Bright Light Can Help You Sleep

Most people's sleep schedule follows day and night cycles. We are awake during the day when it's light, and asleep during the night when it's dark. This cycle is controlled by an internal biological clock that tells our bodies when to get sleepy and when to wake up. Research has shown that this internal clock works even if a person is put in a cave that never receives any light. So, exposure to the sun's light doesn't establish our internal clocks, but it does help fine-tune them. In fact, light plays a very important role in helping us sleep. Exposure to light during the day reinforces our internal clocks by making us feel more sleepy at night and less sleepy in the day.

This happens because retinal fibers in our eyes are connected to the part of our brain that controls our internal clock. When those fibers sense bright light at midday, they send a message to the brain that it should get sleepy later in the day. In theory, the more exposure to bright sun you get during the day, the stronger this message will be and the better you will sleep at night.

This works well for those who work during the day and sleep at night, but what about night workers? If you are up at night and asleep during the day, you are fighting the influence of light on your biological clock. However, you can work with light to make things easier by tricking your body into believing that night is day and day is night. To do this, increase the brightness of the lights you work around and make the room you sleep in as dark as possible. By tricking your internal clock, you will be more likely to stay awake at work and then go home to get a good day's sleep.

Kelly, Dennis D. "Sleep and Dreaming." In *Principles of Neural Science,* 3rd ed. New York: Elsevier, 1991.
"Setting the Body's Clock for Sleep." *Consumer Reports on Health,* March 1994.

Why Ice Is Not Slippery

Try telling someone who has just fallen on a patch of ice that ice is not slippery and they'll think you're crazy. But, in fact, ice itself isn't slippery because it is a solid. One quality of solids is that when two solids are together, there is friction between them that will keep them from slipping.

So how can your shoe slip on ice? The answer lies in two peculiar properties of ice. The first is that as water freezes, its molecules move farther apart. The molecules of most substances move closer together as they freeze, making them shrink at lower temperatures. But water molecules move farther apart at temperatures below 39 degrees, making water expand as it freezes. That is why frozen water pipes burst, and a tray of ice cubes will freeze over its top if you fill it too full.

The second peculiar property of ice is directly linked to its first peculiarity. When subjected to pressure, ice melts. Remember that the molecules in ice are farther apart than the molecules in water; therefore ice molecules are vulnerable to pressure which pushes them closer together, causing the ice to change into water.

159

So when you step on a patch of ice, you exert pressure on the ice, which causes its molecules to move closer together. That makes them revert to their more dense state, which is water. If you slip on a patch of ice, then, you in fact are slipping on a thin layer of water that the pressure from your weight has created. And unlike solid ice, water as a liquid is quite slippery.

Cazeau, Charles C. *Science Trivia: From Anteaters to Zeppelins.* New York: Plenum Press, 1986.

Flatow, Ira. *Rainbows, Curve Balls and Other Wonders of the Natural World Explained.* New York: William Morrow and Company, 1988.

McGee, Harold. *On Food and Cooking: The Science and Lore of the Kitchen.* New York: Scribner, 1984.

How Fruits and Vegetables Help Prevent Cancer

Everyone has heard that fruits and vegetables are good for you, but scientist Gladys Block has proven it as a fact. Block took the results of 156 separate scientific studies and determined that, except for quitting smoking, the best way a person can help prevent cancer is to eat more fruits and vegetables. According to these studies, people who eat the most fruits and vegetables have half the cancer risk of those who eat the least.

One of the major reasons fruits and vegetables are such great cancer fighters is that they help combat the ill effects of oxygen circulating through our bloodstreams. Of course, oxygen helps keep us alive, but it also takes a toll in the process. As oxygen travels through your bloodstream, some oxygen molecules lose an electron. Because electrons usually travel in pairs, these unpaired electrons, called free radicals, are chemically unstable. To make themselves stable again, free radicals take electrons from other molecules in the body, which damages these molecules. Over time, the damage caused by this electron thievery can alter a cell's DNA and can eventually lead to cancer.

In order to combat the ill effects of unstable oxygen molecules, you can eat fruits and vegetables high in vitamins A and C. These vitamins donate electrons to the free radicals and, in the process, stabilize them and keep them from needing to steal electrons from molecules in the body. In the long run, this can keep the body's cells cancer-free.

As a rule of thumb, when choosing fruits and vegetables, go for those that have the brightest colors. Spinach, carrots, and other brightly colored vegetables usually have lots of vitamins A and C. These foods are so good at stabilizing free radicals that the National Cancer Institute recommends that we eat at least five servings of them a day.

Castleman, Michael. "Mother Knew Best." *Sierra*, December 1994.

Honey from Honeydew

We've all heard that bees make honey, and for the most part that is where honey comes from: The bees extract nectar from flowers, which they take back to their hives, to be made into honey. But in areas without flowers or in times when flowers are scarce, another insect joins the honey-making process. Aphids suck the sap out of the stems of plants, eating some, but letting a lot more drip onto the plant or the ground.

If you've ever parked your car under a tree filled with aphids, you may have come out to find it covered with tiny sticky spots. Those spots are the sap sucked out of the tree and dropped by the aphids. That sap is called "honeydew" because it looks like a sweet dew. Honeydew makes a mess of your car, but for hungry bees, it's a reasonable substitute for nectar. Bees collect it, just as they collect nectar from flowers, and bring it back to the hive to be made into honey.

Honey made largely from honeydew doesn't taste as good as honey made from nectar because it contains a large number of bad-tasting and undigestible proteins. Even bees restricted to a diet of honeydew honey may sicken and die. But when there's no nectar to be had, honeydew—extracted by aphids from the stems of plants—may provide at least a temporary substitute and a way to supplement a hive's supply of honey.

In fact, bees will convert anything with a high enough sugar content to honey. Urban beekeepers even report that after a large outdoor concert in a nearby park, bees that have been feasting on the dregs of soft-drink containers produce honey with a similar flavor.

McGee, Harold. *On Food and Cooking: The Science and Lore of the Kitchen.* New York: Scribner, 1984.

Measuring the Pressure in Your Eyeball

Often when you go to an optometrist to have your eyes checked, you have to sit in front of an instrument that shoots a puff of air into your eye. The purpose of that puff of air is to measure the pressure in your eyeball.

Your eyeball has pressure that can be measured because it is filled with fluid, just like a water balloon. The more water in a balloon, the more pressure there will be on the wall of the balloon, and the more potential there is that the balloon will be damaged.

The same is true for the eyeball. If fluids build up in an eyeball, pressure will increase on the tissues of the eye. In an unhealthy eyeball, this pressure can increase to the point of damaging the nerve fibers. If nerve fibers are damaged, they cannot get information back to the brain, and vision becomes impaired.

So how does that special instrument measure the pressure in your eyeball? By measuring the shape of the eyeball during the test. When the puff of air hits the eye, it momentarily flattens out a small part of the cornea, the clear, curved surface on the front of the eye. The instrument measures the amount of time it takes for the puff of air to flatten the cornea. An eyeball that has more fluid in it, and therefore has greater pressure, will take longer to flatten out than one that has less fluid.

Think of the water balloon again. If you are holding a water balloon that is as full of water as possible, you won't be able to push on it and change its shape very easily. If the balloon is only half full, any pressure you put on it will change its shape quite quickly.

The information about the pressure in an eyeball can help eye doctors diagnose early stages of eye diseases, especially glaucoma. With regular visits to your eye doctor, this and other eye diseases can be caught early and treated.

Why Tires Have Treads

If you've ever driven on a highway during a heavy rain, you know about the danger of skidding. This "waterskiing" on the road is technically called hydroplaning, and it happens when water comes between the road and your tires, causing you to lose traction and go out of control. Your car is less likely to slide around when the road is dry because there is enough friction between your tires and the road to keep you steady, even at high speeds. But when it rains, a layer of water builds up between your tires and the road. This water interferes with the friction that helps your tires grip the road surface.

This is where the treads on your tires come in. If the road you are driving along is covered with water, the pressure of the tire against the road surface causes the water to be squeezed up into the tire treads. These treads help your tires pump water out from underneath the tire so that the rubber can be in contact with the road, thus creating the friction that will stabilize your car.

The faster you go, the more water your tires have to remove. That's why your car may not hydroplane at 30 miles per hour, but might at 60 miles per hour. In fact, at highway speeds, during hard rains, each tire must pump away about a gallon of water every second. This is hard for tires to do if they are old and have treads that are worn down. When there isn't enough space in the tire's grooves, water can't find a place to go, and so it creates a layer of lubrication, causing you to do the equivalent to waterskiing on the highway.

"Grabbing the Wettest of Roads." *Discover*, October 1992.

Another Kind of Herpes

You might call them cold sores or canker sores or maybe fever blisters. Whatever they're called in your house, if you get them, you're in the company of about 95 million other Americans who suffer from the virus that causes cold sores. The scientific name for this virus is herpes simplex, type one. Although it is a relative of herpes simplex two, more commonly known as genital herpes, its effects are usually less serious.

As soon as this herpes virus begins producing a cold sore, the body's immune system manufactures antibodies and white blood cells to combat the virus. The immune system may be able to win the battle against an individual cold sore, but it can never win the war against the virus that causes the cold sore. Even after the cold sore is completely healed, the virus remains hiding in the body in a resting, or latent, phase. If triggered, this latent virus will begin the cycle again and cause another outbreak.

In fact, recurrence of these painful cold sores is very common because once you have the virus, you never get rid of it. The latent virus can be triggered by many factors. Exposure to wind and sun can cause an outbreak, and so can physical or emotional stress. Many people who have the virus get a blister every time they come down with a cold because their immune systems get over-loaded and can't attend to everything at once.

Some people never get cold sores because they have never been infected with the virus, which you can get through direct contact with the lips or mouth of a person with an active sore. Researchers believe that most people were infected as children when an adult with a cold sore kissed them.

Dorland's Illustrated Medical Dictionary. 27th ed. Philadelphia: Sanders, 1988.
The Merck Manual. 14th ed. Rahway, N.J.: Merck, Sharpe and Dohme Laboratories, 1982.
Stedman's Medical Dictionary. 25th ed. New York: Macmillan, 1990.

Why Kids Can Sleep through Just about Anything

Have you ever been to a party and seen a child sleeping happily on a couch, undisturbed by the adults talking and laughing in the room? How can kids sleep so soundly when exposed to noise and commotion? The answer lies in the difference between how adults sleep and how children sleep.

There are four different stages of sleep, and all sleepers cycle between these stages up to six times each night. The biggest difference between how adults and children sleep occurs in stage-four sleep, which is called slow-wave sleep because in this stage your heart rate and your blood pressure decrease; your brain is less active than at any other time; and your dreams, if you have any, tend to be vague and abstract. Slow-wave sleep is also called deep sleep. Children spend far more time in this stage of sleep than adults.

During deep sleep, you sleep so heavily that you lose control of many of your muscles. Your mouth can drop open and you might drool. You probably won't be awakened by noises and activity around you. For the most part, as people grow older, they spend less and less sleep time in deep sleep. By the age of 60, most people will spend almost no time in this stage of sleep. Children, however, spend most of their sleep time in deep sleep, so those children sacked out on a couch at a party are probably not going to be disturbed, even by a bunch of adults standing around having a good time.

Fighting AIDS, Fighting Evolution

One way our bodies resist disease is by producing a variety of chemicals called "antibodies," which destroy the virus or bacterium causing the disease. Antibodies have to be selective to avoid destroying the wrong cells, so each type of antibody recognizes and attacks only a specific virus or bacterium. And that means that each new disease requires a new type of antibody.

But in fighting disease, evolution sometimes works against us because the faster an organism multiplies, the faster it adapts to changes in its environment. For bacteria, the appearance of a new antibody means a big change in their environment, but unfortunately it's a change the bacteria often adapt to. Since a single bacterium can multiply a thousandfold in three hours, there's a good chance that some of those offspring will vary from the rest in ways that make them unrecognizable to the antibody. Those bacteria will then produce millions more like themselves.

Some viruses, including HIV, which is responsible for AIDS, evolve even faster than bacteria. Unlike bacteria (as well as plants and animals), which carry their genetic information in the form of DNA, these viruses carry their genetic information in a similar molecule called RNA. When RNA is copied to make a new virus, the process is less accurate, and far more mutations occur than when DNA is copied. That means more variety among the offspring and more chances that a few of them will escape the antibodies. In fact, viruses evolve so quickly that the same virus in two individuals often evolves into two different strains. All living organisms adapt to changes in their environment, but RNA viruses, like HIV, adapt much faster because they produce more offspring with more variation.

Losing Your Voice to an Echo

Shout "HELLO" between two cliffs and you'll hear the echoes as the sound waves bounce back and forth. Two things happen as the echoes bounce between the cliffs. First, the echoes get fainter because when the sound hits the cliff, not all of it comes back: some is absorbed by the rock, some bounces off in other directions, and some misses the cliff altogether.

But your voice also gets distorted so that each succeeding echo sounds less like the original sound. Even though your voice contains a wide range of frequencies, what happens to those frequencies depends on the size, position, and material of the objects they come into contact with as they echo between the cliffs. Every situation is slightly different, but inevitably some frequencies are more likely to be reflected while others simply fade away. So after a few echoes, the sound loses the characteristics of your voice and takes on new characteristics unique to the area you're standing in.

Real echoes usually fade away before they become that distorted, but you can see how it works with an artificial echo on two tape recorders. Say "hello" followed by your name into one tape recorder. Then play it back into the microphone of the other one. Play that recording back into the first tape recorder and so on— back and forth about five to ten times. Gradually the two words will sound the same, as they lose their original characteristics and conform to the acoustic characteristics of the room and of the two tape recorders.

Incidentally, this is a problem in concert halls, which have to be specially designed to reflect all the different frequencies accurately.

Sonic Booms

On October 14, 1947, U.S. Air Force pilot Chuck Yeager became the first person to fly a plane faster than the speed of sound. As with every supersonic flight since, Yeager's plane created a loud noise, called a sonic boom, that could be heard on the ground.

When a speedboat moves through water, it creates waves that you can see. Planes create similar waves in the air, which you can hear. As a plane travels, it compresses air molecules in front of it, creating waves that spread in all directions. These waves travel at the speed of sound and are known as sound waves. When a plane itself approaches the speed of sound, which is roughly 750 miles per hour, it begins to move as fast as the sound waves it is creating. When the plane moves faster than its own sound waves, it forces those waves to pile up one on top of another.

This concentration of sound waves becomes what is known as a shock wave. Shock waves are powerful waves that travel in all directions, including toward the ground. At each location where shock waves hit the ground we hear a sonic boom, which is not just a one-time result of breaking the sound barrier. Because the plane is creating shock waves the entire time it flies at supersonic speeds, sonic booms can be heard the entire time as well.

But not all sonic booms are alike. As a general rule, the bigger the aircraft, the larger the shock waves and the longer the duration of the sonic boom. The smallest aircraft capable of traveling faster than the speed of sound generates a boom that lasts one-twentieth of a second. The largest supersonic aircraft creates a boom that lasts ten times longer, or half a second.

However, two aircraft the same size flying at different altitudes will create sonic booms of different intensities. A craft flying higher will create a less intense sonic boom, because the shock waves have farther to travel before hitting the ground, and therefore have more time to dissipate. Although not as intense, the sonic boom created by this high-flying plane will be heard over a larger geographic area than the boom created by a low-flying plane because as the shock waves travel to the ground, they spread out and increase the radius they affect.

Luckily, even the most intense sonic booms can't hurt people, but they have been known to damage plaster walls and break windows.

"Sonic Boom." In *McGraw Hill Encyclopedia of Science and Technology,* 7th ed. New York: McGraw-Hill, 1992.
"Sonic Boom." In *World Book Encyclopedia.* Chicago, 1994.

Spoonerisms

At some point, everyone has transposed the first letters in two words and come up with a nonsense phrase. You might mean to say "barn door," but it comes out "darn boor." These slips of the tongue are called spoonerisms, and cognitive psychologists study them because of what they say about how our brains construct language.

Early twentieth-century psychologists believed that language was produced in our brains one word at a time, that each word acted as a stimulus to produce another word. But cognitive psychologists now believe that we produce language in clumps rather than one word at a time.

The study of spoonerisms has helped scientists formulate these new theories. Spoonerisms may seem like random mistakes, but in fact they follow a regular set of rules. When two sounds are transposed between two words, they are almost always sounds that belong in the same position. For example, the beginning of one word almost never exchanges with the end of another. The close association your brain makes between two words such as "barn" and "door" indicates that your brain chose those words as a unit, rather than one at a time.

We make speech errors like this because as we construct language, our brain builds a frame for what we are going to say before we choose the actual words that will go into that frame. When we get a phrase right, our brains have successfully coordinated this frame with the sound of a word. Spoonerisms happen when this coordination breaks down, often because of the interference of external or internal stimulus.

Viking Tales: Poetic License or Medical History?

In the Icelandic family sagas, composed more than 800 years ago, the intellectual and physical prowess of the Viking poet and warrior named Egil (pron. *Eye*-yihl) stands out as almost beyond belief. According to the saga, Egil's fierce appearance alone was enough to make at least one of his enemies capitulate to the Viking's demands on the spot. And apparently he was as tough as he was fierce: According to the saga, Egil's skull was so strong that after he died, it couldn't be broken even with the full swing of an axe. But if Egil was a thick-skulled warrior, other parts of the saga suggest that he was also a gifted and sensitive poet who suffered from the pain and stigma of disabilities including headaches, blindness, and loss of hearing.

Scholars have often used the axe passage to show how unreliable the Icelandic sagas really are; after all, everyone knows that an axe is tougher than a skull. But a rare disease, named after a nineteenth-century English surgeon, could have made Egil as extraordinary as the sagas claim.

Paget's disease, which produces a thickening and malformation of the bones, also causes blindness, headaches, and loss of balance and hearing—all problems that Egil describes in his own poetry. Even the cold hands and feet Egil describes could have been caused by a loss of circulation associated with Paget's disease. But even with a massively thick skull, Egil could have been a gifted poet, because the bone accumulates only on the outside of the skull, leaving the brain undamaged.

The Icelandic sagas may not be perfect historical records, but the combination of medical and literary evidence suggests that the story of Egil's skull may have been more than a literary device designed to exaggerate the Viking's heroic stature.

Byock, Jesse L. "Egil's Bones." *Scientific American,* January 1995.

Potential Energy

When we think of the concept of energy, we often think of objects in motion: a car rolling down a hill or a jogger running up a hill. This kind of energy-in-motion, called kinetic energy, isn't the only kind of energy. Another type, which motionless objects can have, is called potential energy.

Potential energy is stored energy—that is, energy that can be tapped later. To better understand the concept of potential energy, consider how a crossbow works. If you took a crossbow, pulled its string back, and cocked it so that the arrow remained in place until you decided to shoot it, you would have created energy, energy that can be released by pulling the trigger. You have increased the *potential* energy of the crossbow.

The amount of potential energy in the cocked crossbow is equal to the amount of work you put in it by pulling it back and cocking it. This potential energy becomes kinetic energy when you pull the trigger. With the release of the trigger, the potential energy of the cocked crossbow converts into kinetic energy as the arrow flies through the air. Except for a bit of energy lost to friction, the kinetic energy of the flying arrow is equal to the potential energy that was stored in the cocked crossbow.

Of course, potential energy doesn't exist only in crossbows. Other examples include a boulder on the edge of a cliff and gasoline in the tank of a car. In effect, potential energy is simply kinetic energy waiting to happen.

The Shape of Lightning Bolts

As a thundercloud moves through the air, a strong negative charge gathers near its base. Because opposite charges attract, this negative charge is anxious to combine with the positive charges in the ground. Eventually a lightning bolt forms to neutralize these different charges.

We might think that this bolt would want to jump in a straight line, that the electric charge would try to find the most direct route between thundercloud and ground. Why then are lightning bolts so jagged and irregular?

The answer has to do with the complex way a lightning bolt forms. Although it looks like it forms all at once, a lightning bolt is actually produced in many steps. Instead of jumping right to the ground, the cloud's negative charge begins with a short downward hop. This initial hop is called a leader, and it's no more than a few hundred feet long. From the lower end of this leader, another leader forms, and from the lower end of this, another. In this manner, the negative charge hops downward from leader to leader like a frog jumping from lily pad to lily pad across a pond.

While this is going on, the ground sends up its own chain of shorter, positively charged leaders. It's only when these two chains meet, about a hundred feet off the ground, that we see the lightning bolt's flash.

So lightning is jagged because each leader forms independently of the others. Each place a lightning bolt zigs or zags is where one leader stopped and another one started. Each place a lightning bolt forks is where two separate leaders formed from the bottom end of a single leader above. This whole process takes only a few thousandths of a second, but that's enough time to sculpt beautiful and complex lightning bolts.

Trefil, James S. *Meditations at Sunset: A Scientist Looks at the Sky.* New York: Collier, 1987.

Bugs in Cake Mixes

Those white, wiggly bugs sometimes found in boxes of grain foods go by many names: mealybugs, mealyworms, and, most appropriately, wigglies. These annoying critters aren't precisely bugs or worms, but are the larvae of moths and beetles. Their favorite food is starch, and what better place to find starch than in boxes of flour, sugar, and cake mixes?

Manufacturers of these convenience foods put their products through processes that kill any moth and beetle eggs which might eventually hatch out into the food. So when you find wiggling bug larvae in your pudding mix, you're not looking at the results of a food company's inferior standards.

Most of the time, moth and worm larvae enter a box of food from the outside because they are attracted by the starch in the glue that holds the box together. Once they eat through the box, they find a veritable cafeteria that could feed them for a long, long time.

After eating much of the starch in the foods they have infested, the bug larvae leave the food hard or clumpy, mainly because starch is the part of grain that keeps it from clumping and hardening. Boxes of food that have sat on a shelf for a long time are more likely to have larvae infestations than new food.

The good news about grain larvae is that they are not poisonous in any way. Nutritionists assure us that if most people weren't so squeamish about eating food that moves, they wouldn't need to purge the infested boxes from their shelves. The bad news about these invisible invaders is that if they aren't found early enough, they can ruin an entire pantry of food.

How Time Passes in Dreams

Many people believe that hours' worth of events and activities can be dreamed about in a matter of seconds. Despite this common belief about how we dream, time in dreams actually is not compressed. If you dream of an activity that would take five minutes in waking life, you probably dream about it for a full five minutes.

Dream and sleep researcher William Dement conducted two studies that demonstrated that dream time was similar to real time. Because dreamers' eyes move under their eyelids very rapidly while they are dreaming, Dement was able to monitor sleepers and record the length of their dreams by observing their rapid eye movement.

After recording this information, Dement would wake dreamers and have them write down a description of their most recent dream. He assumed that longer dreams would take more words to describe than shorter ones. When he compared the number of words in each dream report with the number of minutes over which the dream had occurred, he found that the longer the dream, the more words the dreamer used to describe it.

In another related experiment, Dement woke sleepers while they were dreaming and asked them how long they perceived their most recent dream had taken. Eighty-three percent of the time they perceived correctly whether their dreams had been going on for a long time or for a short time. With these experiments, Dement concluded that time in dreams is nearly identical to time in waking life.

So the next time in your dreams you slay a dragon or fly from your house to your workplace, the amount of time it seems to take will probably be just about how long it actually will take to dream it.

Kelly, Dennis D. "Sleep and Dreaming." In *Principles of Neural Science,* 3rd ed. New York: Elsevier, 1991.

The Land of Sweat and Honey

Milk and honey may be emblems of the easy life, but for a bee, making honey is no easy task. In fact, honey making is such hard work that for every pound of honey that goes to market, bees eat eight more pounds just to maintain the activity of the hive.

One bee is so small that it doesn't need much honey to get around: In terms of fuel efficiency, a bee gets about 7 million miles per gallon of honey. But with more than 20,000 bees in a hive, honey consumption adds up fast.

Every day a worker bee makes up to 25 trips between the hive and the flowers to gather nectar, each time returning with a load equal to about half its body weight. But half the body weight of a bee comes to only around two one-thousandths of an ounce. So for all its effort, a bee may work its entire life to make less honey than you stir into a cup of tea.

Back in the hive, the nectar still has to be converted to honey. First, the bees pump the nectar in and out of themselves for 15 to 20 minutes to reduce the water content. At the same time, they mix enzymes into the honey to break the nectar's complex sugar into simpler, more soluble sugars. Next it's spread on the honeycomb, where it evaporates further. To speed the process, the bees continually move the air around by fluttering their wings. In about three weeks, bees pack the finished honey into cells in the honeycomb and seal it with wax.

So relax and enjoy the sweet flavor of fresh honey, but remember that, for the bees, at least, a land of milk and honey would be no easy life.

McGee, Harold. *On Food and Cooking: The Science and Lore of the Kitchen.* New York: Scribner, 1984.

The Muscles in Our Ears

There are muscles in our ears that protect us from loud sounds, including the sound of our own voice. These muscles are in the middle ear. They're attached to the small bones connecting the eardrum to the cochlea, the chamber in the inner ear that contains sound-receptor cells. When these muscles contract, they dampen vibrations in the small bones, in effect muffling the sound before it reaches the inner ear. These muscles are not under voluntary control—they contract in a so-called acoustic reflex either just before a person speaks or just after a person hears a loud noise. Two specialists in hearing, Erik Borg and S. Allen Counter, wrote about the middle-ear muscles in the magazine *Scientific American.*

Apparently the contraction before speech has the function of protecting the speaker from the sound of his or her own voice. Borg and Counter estimate that without the acoustic reflex, the sound of a baby's crying would reach the baby's own ears with about the same intensity as the sound of a nearby passing train.

The contraction of the middle-ear muscles is especially effective at screening out the low-frequency components of the speaker's own voice, preventing high-frequency sounds from being drowned out. Many of the most important sounds in speech have high frequencies, so the acoustic reflex enables a person to understand the speech of others, even while speaking.

The middle-ear muscles also contract one or two tenths of a second after a loud external sound. That's fast enough to protect the inner ear from loud natural sounds such as thunder, but not fast enough to muffle a gunshot. Borg and Counter suggest that soldiers hum just before firing, to stimulate the acoustic reflex and protect their hearing. Another hearing expert once recommended that, for the same purpose, large guns be equipped with devices to generate a loud tone just before firing.

Borg, Erik, and S. Allen Counter. "The Middle-Ear Muscles." *Scientific American,* August 1989.

Rossing, Thomas D. *The Science of Sound.* 2nd ed. Reading, Mass.: Addison-Wesley, 1990.

Picket–Fence Echoes

Stand in front of a picket fence, clap your hands, and listen to the musical quality of the reverberation. The reverberation from a picket fence is made up of individual echoes of your handclap from each of the slats in the fence. The echo from each slat reaches your ears a tiny fraction of a second later than the echo from a neighboring slat a few inches closer to you. That's because the sound's round-trip travel time—from your hands, to a slat in the fence, and back to your ears—is shorter for slats nearer to you than for slats farther away.

If the slats are evenly spaced, as they usually are in picket fences, then the echoes reach your ears at regular intervals and you perceive the train of echoes as a musical tone. Notice that the pitch of this tone depends on the spacing between slats in the fence, not on the quality of your handclapping.

But we need to refine this story by pointing out that the musical tone you hear will not have a constant pitch. The tone will start out high in pitch and quickly sweep down to a low pitch. The high-pitched sounds come from the slats nearest you, which are all at just about the same distance from you. So echoes from those slats reach your ears very close together, giving you the impression of a high musical pitch.

The low-pitched part of the reverberation comes from the slats at the far ends of the fence. Each of those faraway slats is at a quite different distance from you than its neighbors. So echoes from those slats are separated by bigger time intervals, and you hear a lower pitch.

You might recognize this as being another example of the Doppler effect. Incidentally, you may hear the same "picket fence" effect by clapping near a long staircase or a corrugated wall.

Humphreys, W. J. *Physics of the Air.* New York: Dover Publications, 1964.

Heating Your Kitchen with the Refrigerator

Turn on your oven, and you'll warm up the kitchen. With the oven door open, the kitchen warms up even faster. That much is obvious since the purpose of an oven is to make things hot. But the opposite is not true of your refrigerator. Running the refrigerator makes the room warmer, and if you leave the door open, the kitchen warms up even faster. The first rush of cold air may cool things down a little, but in the long run the room will get warmer.

To see why, we need to think of heat as energy and cold as a lack of energy. The stove produces heat, but the refrigerator can't actually produce cold. All the refrigerator does is move heat, or energy, from one place to another. As the food inside the refrigerator loses its heat—or, in other words, gets colder—that heat ends up in the kitchen. Physicists call this kind of system a "heat pump."

But like any motor, the heat pump in your refrigerator needs energy just to run. So while it's busy moving energy out of the fridge and into the kitchen, it's also drawing in more energy in the form of electricity or gas. Since some of that energy is released as heat, you end up with more heat in the kitchen than you started with.

Air conditioners can cool your house because part of the unit is outside. That way the air conditioner can pump the heat out of your house and release it to the outdoors. So just as your refrigerator heats your kitchen while cooling the food, air conditioners heat the outdoors while cooling your house.

Listening Underwater

If you've ever been underwater at a pool when someone jumped in near you, you know that the sound of the splash is clearly audible. But telling where the splash came from is another matter. Even though water does a much better job than air of conducting sound waves, that extra conductivity makes it harder, not easier, to tell where a sound comes from.

Above the surface of the water, we can tell whether a sound comes from the left or the right because it strikes one ear a little sooner and a little more loudly. The more distant ear gets a smaller dose of the sound a little bit later because it's farther away from the source and also because it's shielded by the head. Even though we don't notice the difference consciously, it's enough for the brain to decide which direction the sound came from. But sound travels five times faster in water than it does in air. Traveling that fast, the sound is detected by both ears at almost exactly the same moment. That's one reason that underwater a sound seems to come from all directions at once.

The other reason is that underwater sound waves pass directly into your head, bypassing your ears altogether. That's because body tissues contain such a large amount of water. Try plugging your ears underwater and listening for another splash of someone jumping in. It will be just as loud as the last splash when your ears were not plugged. With sounds coming into every part of your head at almost exactly the same time, it's no wonder the brain has trouble deciding what direction the splash came from.

While you're in the pool, try this next demonstration with your friends. Duck your head underwater and listen to the conversation. If they talk loudly enough, you'll hear the vowels—*a, e, i, o,* and *u*—but no consonants. So the words won't make sense.

Sound travels very well underwater, but some sounds have more trouble than others getting from the air into the water.

But why the vowels and not the consonants? Every spoken sound is actually a combination of different sounds, some low, some high. Even though we don't notice the different sounds, the way they're combined is what gives each spoken sound its own character. In general, consonants contain a lot more high-pitch sounds than vowels. Those are sounds made of faster, smaller sound waves. Compared to consonants, vowels are mostly made of low pitches, in other words of larger, slower sound waves.

When the small sound waves hit the uneven surface of the water, they get scattered in all directions like ping-pong balls landing on a rough road. The much larger, lower-pitch waves aren't affected as much by the little water-waves because they hit a much wider area on the water's surface. If we think of a small sound wave as a little ping-pong ball on a rough surface, a larger sound wave is more like a big basketball, which is less affected by little bumps on the road. Unlike balls bouncing on a road, sound waves pass through the water, but like the basketball, the large waves come through with less distortion. That's one reason why when you listen underwater to someone up above, you won't hear the consonants with their high-pitched sounds and short sound waves.

Miller, Mary K. "Science in the Bathtub." *Exploring,* Winter 1993.
Schiffman, Harvey Richard. *Sensation and Perception: An Integrated Approach.* 2nd ed. New York: John Wiley and Sons, 1982.

A Major League Balancing Act

Try balancing a baseball bat straight up and down on the palm of your hand. When you let go with the other hand, the bat starts to fall. But if you're quick, you can move your hand in the same direction to keep it upright for a little longer. With some experimenting, you'll find that the bat stays up longer if you put the heavy end up. That's because in that position it falls a little more slowly, which gives you more time to respond before it falls off your hand.

But why does it fall more slowly with the heavy end up? After all, if you drop a light ball and a heavy ball, they should fall at about the same speed. The difference is that as the bat starts to fall, the bottom of the bat stays still on your hand while the top of the bat moves in an arc, both down and to the side. So gravity has to pull the bat down *and* get it moving horizontally at the same time. Even though a light object and a heavy object will *fall* at the same speed, it takes longer to get the heavy object moving horizontally. That's why pushing a VW is easier than pushing a Cadillac. Next time you're at the circus, watch the balancing acts. You'll see that whenever possible, the objects they're balancing will be weighted at the top.

178 *Cross-eyed Cats*

Have you ever noticed that Siamese cats are cross-eyed? In fact, that's the only way a Siamese cat can see straight. Unlike the eyes of some animals such as rabbits, a cat's eyes both point forward— just like ours—so most of what it sees it sees with both eyes. In order to see clearly, however, the brain has to coordinate the signals it gets from a group of nerve endings called the retina on the back of each eye.

For every spot on the retina of one eye, there's a spot on the retina of the other eye that has to see the same thing. Let's say, for example, that those spots are focused on a mouse. For the brain to interpret what it sees as one mouse instead of two, the nerves that detect the mouse in one eye have to go to the same part of the brain as the nerves in the other eye that detect the same mouse. If the eyes send the mouse images to two different parts of the brain, the cat sees two mice instead of one.

And that's what's wrong with the eyes of a Siamese cat. Instead of being lined up in the back of the eye, the center of the left retina is shifted to the right, and the center of the right retina is shifted to the left. So if a Siamese cat's eyes were pointed straight ahead, its retinas would be looking in different directions, sending a very confused message to the brain. By turning its eyes in, a Siamese cat looks cross-eyed, but its retinas are now lined up like a normal cat's, sending the brain a clearer picture.

Stent, G. C. "Explicit and Implicit Semantic Content of the Genetic Information." In *Foundational Problems in the Special Sciences,* ed. Robert E. Butts and Jaakko Hintikka. Dordrecht, Netherlands: Reidel Publishing Company, 1977.

Stent, G. C. "Strength and Weakness of the Genetic Approach to the Development of the Nervous System." *Annual Review of Neuroscience,* 1981.

Becoming Part of the Music

If you get close enough to the speakers at a loud concert, you can actually feel the low notes vibrating in your body. The higher notes may be just as loud, but you don't feel those.

Unlike waves on a lake, sound waves don't travel up and down. Instead they're more like layers of high and low pressure traveling outward in all directions. Each wave consists of a layer of high pressure followed by a layer of low pressure. The bigger the difference between the high pressure and the low pressure, the louder the sound.

But sound waves don't just travel in air: except for a vacuum, they travel in whatever they encounter, including your body. So when you listen to loud music, your whole body alternates between high and low pressure just like the air around it.

The reason high and low pitches feel different has to do with the length—or thickness—of the wave. High-pitch sounds produce thousands of very short waves—maybe 8 to 10 inches thick—each second. A very low note might generate only about 65 waves per second, but they could be nearly 17 feet thick.

That difference affects the way you *feel* the music because with a low note, your body spends a relatively long time actually inside the layers of low and high pressure. The waves of a high note travel through your body as well, but they oscillate so quickly between high pressure and low pressure that on the average you don't feel any real pressure change. So next time you're at a concert and you feel those low notes going through you, remember that you are a *part* of the music.

179

Why It's Hard to Burn One Log

Imagine a cheerful fire, with several wood logs piled up in the fireplace. Separate one of those logs from the others, and it will usually stop burning. Separate all the logs from each other, and the flames soon die away.

Scientists who have studied the burning of wood in detail have found why it's hard to keep one log burning. The flames that envelop a burning log are fed not so much by the solid wood near the surface but mostly by flammable gases coming from inside the log. Those fuel gases, in turn, are released when molecules making up the solid wood are broken down by heat from the fire. A log won't burn unless layers of wood below its surface are kept hot enough to continue producing those flammable gases.

One log, burning by itself, cannot generally send enough heat into its own interior to continue producing those gases. Most of the heat from a burning log travels away from the log, either in the form of hot gases and glowing soot particles, or as infrared light which is sometimes called radiant heat energy. So one way to keep a single log burning would be to put a concave metal mirror near it. The mirror would provide a reflecting surface to return some of the heat that would otherwise escape from the log.

Of course, a mirror near a burning log is likely to be blackened by soot. A more practical way to keep one log burning is to put another burning log next to it. Then each log captures radiant heat energy from its neighbor. The interior of each log is heated not only by the flames on its own surface but by heat captured from the neighboring log. That extra heat keeps the interior of each log hot enough to continue producing fuel gases, and the fire can continue to burn.

Lyons, John W. *Fire.* New York: Scientific American Library, 1985.

Mushrooms and Rocket Fuel

Perhaps the most popular wild edible mushrooms are a group called the morels. A similar group, known as false morels, also contains some edible species, but just how edible false morels really are is something of a tricky question.

What once puzzled both scientists and mushroom hunters was the way people reacted to these mushrooms. According to popular wisdom, the cook was much more likely to get sick than the guests. And when the guests did get sick, it was usually only one or two, while the rest felt fine. One theory held that it was simply an allergic reaction.

The explanation came with the development of the space program, when someone noticed that workers exposed to rocket fuel showed the same symptoms as people poisoned by false morels. The culprit turned out to be a group of chemicals called hydrazines, which are both a major component of rocket fuel *and* one of the poisons found in false morels.

The way hydrazines affect the body, there's a fine line between a poisonous dose and a harmless dose. So if one person eats just a little more than someone else, he or she could become terribly sick while the other wouldn't feel a thing. Also, hydrazines evaporate very easily. So cooked mushrooms contain much less toxin than raw mushrooms. And the cook, who breathes the vapors, is more likely to get sick than the guests who eat the mushrooms after the hydrazines have been boiled out.

Other mushrooms, including the ones in the grocery store, contain hydrazines, but in even smaller amounts than the false morels. And if you cook your mushrooms, even those small amounts will evaporate.

Ames, Bruce, and Lois Swirsky Gold. "Dietary Pesticides (99.99% All Natural)." *Proceedings of the National Academy of Sciences* 87 (October 1990).

Lincoff, Gary. *The Audubon Society Field Guide to the North American Mushrooms.* New York: Alfred A. Knopf, 1981.

Lincoff, Gary, and D. H. Mitchel. *Toxic and Hallucinogenic Mushroom Poisoning: A Handbook for Physicians and Mushroom Hunters.* New York: Van Nostrand Reinhold Company, 1977.

*Lest you get the impression
that all science is based on
incontrovertible facts resulting from extensive investigation, these next three pieces
should let you know that
sometimes more research is
necessary. And since some of
this research is unique, we are
always careful to air reports
on it on the appropriate day
in the spring of the year.
After all, timing is
everything.*

Where Do Bulbs Go in the Winter?

If you actually enjoy planting flowers, you probably prefer flowers such as pansies, nasturtiums, and marigolds that have to be planted every year. If you like flowers but prefer to keep your knees out of the mud, you may find bulbs more to your liking. Plant a batch of daffodils, crocuses, or day lilies, and they come back year after year.

But where do the bulbs go when they're not in bloom? Every spring the crocuses appear, followed by daffodils, then tulips and hyacinths. But soon each one disappears until the following year. Older theories speculated that the bulbs simply stayed put, but that doesn't make sense since they wouldn't have anything to do and would get so bored they'd probably die.

In fact, the truth wasn't revealed until 1979, when a major earthquake opened the ground in Central America to reveal thousands of migrating hyacinth bulbs. Since then, botanists have determined that between nine and eleven days after pulling in their leaves, bulbs gather in large flocks. Huddled together for protection against predators, the bulbs begin a long migration to their communal spawning grounds in the South American rain forests.

As spring arrives, newly hatched bulbs leave their dying parents behind and head for the northern climates. Crocus bulbs, being the smallest, travel fastest through the ground, and that's why they appear first.

How bulbs navigate the long and arduous journey to a destination many have never seen is still a source of wonder. According to one theory, they communicate telepathically with high-flying ducks. Of course there's no good reason for this theory, but if it's scientific, who needs reasons?

A Taste for the Musical

Have you ever noticed that you, your children, and your parents all like different music? Of course you have, but you may not realize the biological basis for these differences.

As it turns out, a patch of taste buds located on the inner ear is controlled throughout an individual's life by various chemicals released in the pituitary gland. During puberty, the pituitary gland releases large quantities of an enzyme known as Zepellinase. As Zepellinase is released by the pituitary gland, it travels to the inner ear, where it binds to heavy metal receptors located on the cell walls. Zepellinase somewhat blocks the effectiveness of the taste buds, causing a need for excessive volume and preventing the reception of more than one or two chords during any given piece.

As the body's chemical systems settle into a middle-aged routine, Zepellinase is replaced by the hormone Vivalderone, causing the inner ear to crave large doses of baroque fugues. A debilitating though lamentably common hereditary condition causes the pituitary gland to release an excess of Vivalderone, producing a craving for harpsichord inventions—the more parts the better.

Sometime into senescence, the taste buds fall off altogether, at which time the ear loses all basis for filtering, screening, or otherwise discriminating. A frequent result of this late condition is a desire for the recordings of Lawrence Welk and Barry Manilow. Fortunately, however, a group of scientists led by Dr. Karl Haas are already investigating the use of dietary supplements as a means of reversing these traumatic effects.

Where Do the Socks Go?

This Moment of Science is going to deal with one of the most perplexing mysteries to confront modern societies: the disappearance of socks in a clothes dryer. It doesn't seem possible that you can put five pairs of socks in the dryer, and have only four and a half pairs left at the end of the drying cycle. Scientists do not yet fully understand this phenomenon, but here is a report on a recent promising theory.

As the socks tumble in the dryer, water molecules are shaken from them into the warm air in the dryer. An exhaust fan draws the warm, moist air to the outside. Eventually all the water molecules leave the socks and are exhausted to the outside.

Scientists now theorize that on occasion there are chemical changes that take place which affect a whole sock, not just the water molecules. There is evidence that in about every fourth to sixth load, the agitated environment in the dryer creates an atmosphere with abnormal concentrations of dimethyl terphthalate, ethylene glycol, and ozone. The first two chemicals are essential raw materials in the manufacture of polyester fibers, and ozone is, well, the stuff with the big hole in it. The compound that results has been named hozone.

For reasons not fully understood, when the dryer has such a high concentration of hozone, one sock in the load is converted into these component chemicals and shunted off into an as yet undiscovered area called the hozone layer.

To date this is the most plausible explanation for the missing socks, but it has also raised another concern: Scientists are investigating the possibility that the heat-absorbing qualities of the billions of socks in the hozone layer might be having some effect on the environment, although they don't yet know if the mysterious layer is contributing to global warming or cooling.

DON GLASS has worked in public radio for thirty years. He has a number of national productions to his credit, and has been associated with the radio series *A Moment of Science* since its inception in 1988. His producing and writing of the radio programs has allowed him to combine his professional radio career with his lifelong interest in science. He also edited this book's predecessor, *Why You Can Never Get to the End of the Rainbow, and Other Moments of Science.*

Stephen Fentress is on the staff of the Strasenburgh Planetarium of the Rochester Museum and Science Center in Rochester, New York, where he writes and produces planetarium shows. *Barbara Bolz, Eric Sonstroem,* and *Don Ulin* are doctoral candidates in the English Department at Indiana University. Their writing skills have allowed them to share with a large audience their fascination with the world around them, first through the radio programs and now through this book.